BEEKEEPING STUDY NOTES for the BBKA EXAMINATIONS

Volume 1 (Modules 1, 2, 3 and 4)

Prepared by:
J.D. YATES B.Sc. (Hons), C.Eng., FIEE.
and
B.D. YATES SRN, SCM.

BEE BOOKS NEW AND OLD

BBNO
The Weaven
Little Dewchurch
Herefordshire HR2 6PP

First published 1996

COPYRIGHT © J.D. & B.D. Yates
ISBN 0 905652 - 33 - 9

Printed and bound in Great Britain by
Butler & Tanner Ltd. Frome and London

PREFACE

The modular examination system aims to give beekeepers who have passed the Basic Examination the opportunity to study the craft of apiculture further with the goals of obtaining an Intermediate Certificate for passing modules 1 to 4 inclusive and an Advanced Certificate for passing modules 1 to 3 and 5 to 8. Certificates are awarded for each module passed, the pass mark being 60% for all modules (credit 70% and distinction 80%). In order to qualify for either an Intermediate Certificate or an Advanced Certificate the necessary modules must be passed within a time period of 8 years.

The modules are a re-hash of the old Intermediate and Senior Part 2 syllabi arranged so that nothing is repeated at a higher level as was the case in the old system. Our notes for the new examinations have been taken from those which we prepared for the two old examinations and brought up to date where required. Our objective has been to provide again under one cover all the detail required in the syllabus of each module for examination purposes in order to minimise the cost of purchasing the many books required to seek out the necessary information. This volume covers modules 1 to 4 for the Intermediate Certificate. A companion volume will be prepared for modules 5 to 8 leading to the Advanced Certificate.

The BBKA Examinations Board prepare and regularly update a list of recommended books to be read for all the BBKA examinations, ranging from the Basic through to the Practical and the Microscopy. It is free and available from the Secretary to the Board. We suggest that prospective Candidates obtain the list for guidance in their reading. The list is exhaustive and its length is likely to be 'off putting' to someone who has just passed the Basic and is wishing to start on the modules. Don't be discouraged; it is because of the large number of books involved that these notes have been prepared, the preparation of which has required an undue amount of reading!

It is hoped that Candidates will come forward for examination in greater numbers and proceed eventually to the Advanced level, finally becoming Master Beekeepers by completing the Practical Examination (the old Senior Part 1). Most of the CBIs are now extinct and the two or three still remaining may be expected to go in the fullness of time. This, coupled with the severe reduction in services provided by MAFF, means that beekeeping education in the future must rest in the hands of those who attain the Master Beekeeper status.

If these notes help to achieve this objective, both of us will be well pleased.

JD & BD Yates,
Newton Ferrers,
Devon. 1996.

CONTENTS

MODULE 1: HONEYBEE MANAGEMENT

The Candidate shall be able to give a detailed account of:

1.30   how colonies are prepared for the winter period and give the principles underlying this preparation;

1.31   the effects of honeybee stings and recommended first aid treatment.

MODULE 2: HONEYBEE PRODUCTS AND FORAGE

The Candidate shall be able to give detailed accounts of:

2.1   the main requirements of the current statutory regulations affecting the handling, preparation for sale, composition, labelling and weight of packs of honey;

2.2   how worker honeybees collect nectar and process it into honey;

2.3   the methods used to decap honeycombs, and of separating the cappings from honey;

2.4   the extraction of honey from combs and the types of extractor used;

2.5   the straining and settling of honey after extraction;

2.6   the storage of honey including the underlying principles of storage;

2.7   the preparation and bottling of liquid honey, including ling heather honey;

2.8   the preparation and bottling of naturally granulated, soft set and seeded honey;

2.9   the preparation of section, cut-comb and chunk honey for sale;

2.10   the constituents expressed in percentage terms of a typical sample of U.K. honey and an outline of the normal range of variation of its main constituents;

2.11   methods of determining the moisture content of honey;

2.12   the spoilage of honey particularly by fermentation (including the effect of water content, storage temperature and the presence of yeast);

2.13   the physical properties of honey including specific gravity, viscosity, hygroscopicity and reaction to heat;

2.14   the main constituents and physical properties of beeswax;

2.15   methods of recovering saleable beeswax from used comb and cappings;

2.16   the range of uses for, and preparation of, beeswax;

2.17   the uses of other bee products such as pollen, royal jelly, venom and propolis;

2.18   the preparation of bee products for the show bench;

The candidate shall also be able to give:-

2.19   a list of 10 major nectar and/or pollen producing plants of the U.K. and their flowering periods together with detailed knowledge of those in his/her own locality;

2.20   illustrated descriptions of the floral structure of apple, oil-seed rape, heather, lime, dandelion, white clover and salvia (bee pollinated species) including plant family names;

2.21   an account of the processes of pollination and fertilisation in a typical flowering plant;

2.22   the genetic and evolutionary importance of cross-pollination and the methods used by plants to favour cross-pollination;

2.23   an illustrated description of the extra-floral nectaries of broad bean, cherry laurel, cherry and plum;

2.24   an account of the composition of nectar and its variations;

2.25   a list of floral sources of undesirable nectar in the UK with a brief description of the effects of these nectars;

2.26   an account of the factors affecting nectar secretion and the variations in the composition of nectar in different flower species and differing weather conditions;

2.27   an account of the origins and typical composition of honeydew with a brief description of the characteristics of honeydew honey

MODULE 3: HONEYBEE DISEASES, PESTS AND POISONING

The Candidate shall be able to give:-

3.1   a detailed account of the field diagnosis of American foul brood (A.F.B.) and European foul brood (E.F.B.) and a detailed account of the signs of these two diseases;

3.2   an account of the life cycle of the causative organisms of AFB and EFB and their development within the larvae;

3.3   a detailed account of the development of AFB and EFB within the colony;

3.4   a detailed account of the ways in which AFB and EFB are spread from one colony to another;

3.5   a detailed account of the treatment of colonies infected with AFB and EFB including methods of destruction of colonies and the sterilisation of equipment;

3.6   a detailed account of the statutory requirements relating to foul brood, Varroosis and the importation of honeybees and the implementation of these requirements in the United Kingdom;

3.7   a description of the life cycle and natural history of *Varroa jacobsoni* including its development within the honeybee colony and its spread to other colonies;

3.8   a detailed account of the signs of Varroosis describing methods of detection and ways of monitoring the presence of the Varroa mite in honeybee colonies;

3.9   a detailed account of methods of treatment and control of Varroosis and a knowledge of which are currently available in the United Kingdom;

3.10 a detailed account of the cause, signs and recommended treatment (if any) of the following brood diseases and conditions:- Chalk brood, Sacbrood, Chilled brood, Bald brood, Neglected drone brood and Stone brood;

3.11 a detailed account of the cause, signs and treatment (if any) of adult bee diseases currently found in the UK; these diseases to include Nosema, Dysentery, Acarine, Amoeba and Chronic Bee Paralysis Virus (both syndromes);

3.12 an outline account of the life cycle of the causative organisms of adult honeybee diseases;

3.13 a detailed account of the treatments for adult bee diseases;

3.14 a detailed account of the laboratory methods of diagnosis of Acarine, Nosema and Amoeba disease in worker honeybees;

3.15 a detailed description of the fumigation of comb using acetic acid (ethanoic acid), including safety precautions to be taken;

3.16 a description of the effects of Acute Bee Paralysis Virus and an elementary account of other viruses affecting honeybees including their association with other bee diseases where applicable;

3.17 the scientific names of the causative organisms associated with diseases of honeybees;

3.18 an outline account of the life cycle of *Braula coeca* and a description of the differences between adult *Braula coeca* and *Varroa jacobsoni*;

3.19 an outline account of the signs of poisoning by natural substances, pesticides, herbicides and other chemicals to which honeybees may be exposed;

3.20 a list of crops most likely to be sprayed with chemicals harmful to honeybees and the sprays most likely to be hazardous to honeybees;

3.21 an outline description of methods of application of pesticides, herbicides and fungicides;

3.22 a detailed description of the action to take, and practical measures possible, when prior notification of application of toxic chemicals to crops is given;

3.23   an outline description of a spray liaison scheme operated by a beekeeping association;

3.24   an account of the action to be taken when spray damage is suspected;

3.25   a description of the damage caused to colonies and equipment by mice, woodpeckers and other pests and ways of preventing this;

3.26   a detailed account of wax moth damage and the life cycle of both the Lesser and Greater wax moth *(Achroia grisella and Galleria Mellonella)*;

3.27   a detailed account of methods of treating or storing comb with particular reference to preventing wax moth damage.

MODULE 4: INTERMEDIATE HONEYBEE BIOLOGY

The Candidate shall be able to give simple accounts of:

4.1   the structure and function of the alimentary system;

4.2   the excretory, circulatory, respiratory and nervous systems including the sense organs;

4.3   the exocrine glands and their secretions including the hypopharyngeal, mandibular, Nasonov, sting and wax glands;

4.4   the storage of metabolites in the fat body;

4.5   metamorphosis in the honeybee including the duration of the stages of development of larva and pupa;

4.6   caste differentiation in female honeybees particularly with respect to feeding;

4.7   laying workers and drone laying queens and the conditions leading to their development;

4.8   the external structure of queen, worker and drone and the differences between them;

4.9   the structure and function of mouthparts, legs, antennae, sting and wings of the adult honeybee;

4.10   the functions and behaviour of the worker honeybee throughout its life, including foraging behaviour and orientation;

4.11   the mating behaviour of the honeybee queen and drone;

4.12   parthenogenesis in the honeybee;

4.13   the seasonal variation in the population size of a honeybee colony including the effects of external factors and the egg laying behaviour of the queen;

4.14   the differences between summer and winter worker honeybees;

4.15   the organisation of a honeybee colony including the importance of pheromones, particularly queen substance, Nasonov pheromone and the two alarm pheromones;

4.16   methods of communication used by the honeybee including food sharing, dancing and scenting;

4.17   the collection of nectar and water and their use by the colony;

4.18   the conversion of nectar to honey and the inter-relationships of nectar, honey and water in the honeybee colony;

4.19   the processes of swarming and supersedure and the distinguishing features of swarm, supersedure and emergency queen cells;

4.20   one method of rearing queens suitable for use in an apiary of five to ten colonies;

4.21   methods of queen introduction itemising necessary precautions;

4.22   the signs of queenlessness and a method of confirming the condition;

4.23   the methods of marking and clipping queens and the advantages and disadvantages of these practices.

APPENDICES

1. Frames (an article from Beekeeping Quarterly - Autumn 1994).
2. Calculation of the angle of tilt for a solar wax extractor.
3. BBKA Standard for bees, colonies and nuclei.
4. Colony inspections (timing).
5. Queen substance and swarming.
6. Consumption of stores during winter.
7. Average colony population cycle.
8. The size of the colony for winter.
9. Bailey frame change.
10. Semiochemicals.
11. Migration and evolution of the honeybee.
12. Preparations using products of the hive.
13. Measurements and conversions - Imperial to Metric.
14. Wagtail dances.
15. The plant kingdom.
16. Useful information.

FOREWORD

The BBKA examinations for Proficiency in Apiculture have now been reorganised on a system of modules, of which 1, 2, 3 and 4 are replacing the old Intermediate Examination. The relative syllabus is extensive, and the list of recommended books for study may seem somewhat forbidding to beekeepers who are considering studying for the examination. A distinctly discouraging aspect in this connection is the cost of purchasing recommended reference books, coupled with the fact that Association branches frequently have a very inadequate library. It is, therefore, helpful to find that John and Dawn Yates have prepared very extensive Notes covering every item of the very extensive syllabus. In doing so they are giving their readers the full benefit of their personal experiences and expertise, trusting that students will find the Notes helpful.

It is certainly not expected that students should ignore entirely the recommended books, nor would they be wise if they did so. A sensible approach would be to use the Study Notes in conjunction with a limited number of carefully chosen books from the recommended list for full enjoyment of study and for success in the examination. This is my personal opinion on how the Notes could well be used. Quite apart from the examination aspect there is no doubt that any beekeeper, whether experienced or not, will find the Notes clearly explanatory and informative.

Past students have frequently expressed appreciation of the help given them by earlier BBKA Examination notes prepared by John and Dawn Yates. No doubt their present efforts are likely to be equally helpful. Any beekeeper can usefully have a copy on the bookshelf. Existing and potential students will know that the full number of modules leading to the Master Beekeeper's Certificate is eight, and it is hoped that the authors of this present publication will proceed to the next four modules in due course.

Frank Alston
Newlands,
Knowle Road,
Budleigh Salterton.

MODULE 1: HONEYBEE MANAGEMENT

The Candidate shall be able to give a detailed account of:

1.1 The types of hive and frame used by beekeepers in the UK.

1.1.1 General.

Frame and hive size. The size of the frame and the brood chamber are irrevocably connected one with the other. In general, the size is dimensioned by the fecundity of the queen and strain of bee aiming to operate with a single brood chamber with 10 to 12 frames. The British Standard (BS) frame and national hive were based on the performance of the Old English Bee which at best could produce only 8 frames of brood leaving 2 or 3 for brood chamber stores during the season. Such low fecundity does not exist with present day bees whether they be mongrels or of a purer line. The demise of the native bee occurred about 1920 when new strains were introduced into UK; it is therefore surprising that hives using the BS frame have continued to be so popular in this country.

Double walled hives. The principle involved here is that the two walls provide better weather protection which cannot be denied. It increases the cost which also cannot be denied and are unsuitable for migratory beekeeping. However it should be noted that one or two commercial beekeepers have used them for migratory purposes in the past; no doubt when labour was relatively cheap.

Single walled hives. The principle of the single walled hive is its constructional simplicity compared with the double walled types. All except the Modified National are of very simple construction involving only four pieces of wood to form the sides and all utilise frames with short lugs to allow this simplicity of construction. In the case of the Modified National extra timbers (4 in all) have to be used to form the rebate. Being simple makes them more suitable for migratory beekeeping.

Square versus oblong horizontal section. The square section is said to facilitate stacking hives when moving them from one crop to another on lorries or other vehicles. We doubt the validity of this and cannot think that a square could be more advantageous than a rectangle.

Top or bottom bee space. The principle is the same no matter whether it above or below – personal preference is a major factor when selection is made. The little experience that we have had with top bee space suggests that it minimises squashing bees when replacing supers but makes the removal of a frame with short lugs more difficult. Bottom bee space seems to be the most popular in UK.

Long hives. One of the principles with this hive is that it not necessary to lift heavy supers at difficult heights and its low profile keeps it out of sight (neighbours and vandals) and sustains less wind pressure in winter gales.

Measurements. As all the hives discussed in this section were designed on the Imperial

System of measurements (feet, inches and fractions of an inch), we have used Imperial measure first followed by the metric (millimeters) measure where appropriate. It should be noted that the conversions from Imperial to Metric are to the nearest mm.

It is unlikely that any list of hives will be complete as there will always be someone somewhere using either a hive of very old design or one which is not considered popular. However, the list should include the following:

Those using BS frames

The Modified National (probably the most widely used).
WBC (with plinthless outside lifts).
The Smith Hive (frames with short lugs still popular in Scotland).

Those using other frame sizes:

The Modified Commercial.
The Langstroth.
The Dadant.

We believe that it essential for anyone contemplating this module of the examinations to actually see each of the above hives take them to pieces and make their own notes about them. Below we give a brief description of each and the BS frame, emphasising the important points only.

1.1.2 The Modified National hive.

This developed from the old British National which had finger tip lifting recesses, two single walls and two double walls which itself had developed from the Simplicity hive (1920). The distinctive rebates on the ends of the hive provide the accommodation for the long lugs and also make it into a truly single walled hive which is very easy to lift, the rebates providing a good hand hold. It was incorporated into BS1300 in 1946 and revised in 1960 but which has since lapsed. The salient points are as follows:

- Outside dimensions $18\frac{1}{8}$in x $18\frac{1}{8}$in x $8\frac{7}{8}$in (460mm × 460mm × 225mm)
- Inside dimensions $14\frac{5}{8}$in x $16\frac{5}{8}$in (371mm × 422mm)
- Normally constructed with bottom bee space but can be made with top bee space if required.
- Supers are constructed in an identical manner but with a depth of $5\frac{13}{16}$in (148mm)
- The floorboard 2in (51mm) deep with the actual floor $\frac{7}{8}$in (22mm) from the top edge to allow an entrance block $\frac{7}{8}$in x $\frac{7}{8}$in x $16\frac{5}{8}$in (22mm × 22mm × 422mm)

1.1.3 The WBC hive.

The fore runner of this hive was the Woodbury hive in 1860 the first double walled hive in Britain. William Broughton Carr designed his hive in 1890 which had lifts with parallel sides and plinths to locate one on top of the other. In 1899 James Lee & Son modified the design to the one we know today with sloping sides to the lifts and without locating plinths. The design has remained unchanged to this day and is still to be seen in the appliance manufacturers' catalogues. The salient features are as follows:

- The floorboard is of a special sloping design and stands on four legs splayed out at each corner.
- Slides are incorporated in the first lift for closing the entrance to the hive beneath an entrance canopy.
- All other lifts are identical and symmetrical.
- The roof is gabled with two sloping areas and the front and rear gables were traditionally fitted with a conical bee escape.
- The brood chamber and supers inside are constructed of very light weight timbers and each holds ten BS frames. There is no room for a dummy board in these boxes.
- Generally more expensive than the single walled equivalent.

We have not given the outer dimensions of the inner boxes as they tend to vary slightly from maker to maker depending on the weight of timber used. The inside dimensions are 15in x $16^5/_8$in x $8^7/_8$in (381mm × 422mm × 225mm).

1.1.4 The Smith hive.

This hive was designed by W. Smith in Scotland based on a single walled hive used in America and with top bee space using BS frames with shortened lugs $^3/_4$in (19mm). The construction is similar to a British National and again has finger tip lifting recesses. It is constructed with timber of thickness $^7/_8$in (22mm). The salient features are as follows:

- Outside dimensions $18^1/_4$in x $16^3/_8$in x $8^7/_8$in (464mm × 416mm × 225mm).
- Inside dimensions $16^1/_2$in x $15^5/_8$in (419mm × 397mm).
- Supers are constructed in the same way but have a depth of $5^{13}/_{16}$in (148mm) compared with $8^7/_8$in (225mm) for the brood box.
- Floors, crown boards, roofs, etc. are all dimensioned to fit on a similar basis to the Modified National.
- The hive is still very popular in Scotland.

1.1.5 The Modified Commercial hive.

The hive was designed by Simmins (date unknown) but mention is made of it in his book 'The Modern Bee Farm' published in 1914 so the hive must have existed at a date earlier than the date of publication of his book. Simmins held strong views about the inadequacy of the size of the BS frame and the hives designed around it. The Commercial hive sometimes called British Commercial and more often Modified Commercial uses Simmins frames 16in x 10in in size. We have not been able to trace whether the original hive was modified at any time as its name would suggest. Like the Smith hive it uses finger tip lifting recesses and it is not easy lifting a well filled brood chamber of this size by this means. The Commercial frames have short lugs in order to allow the hive to be square in cross section. The salient features are as follows:

- Outside dimensions $18^5/_{16}$in x $18^5/_{16}$in (465mm × 465mm).
- Inside dimensions $16^9/_{16}$in x $17^5/_{16}$in (421mm × 440mm).
- Supers are constructed the same way with a depth of $6^3/_8$in (162mm) compared with $10^1/_2$in (267mm) for the brood chamber.

- As the outside dimensions are only $^3/_{16}$in (5mm) greater than the British National hive it is possible to use National floorboards, supers, roofs crown boards and queen excluders with a Commercial brood box.
- Normally constructed for bottom bee space use.

There is only one point about this hive which is detrimental and that is the continual use of the bent metal runners which were designed for the National hive where long lugs on the frames are the order of the day. As the rebate in the Commercial hive is only just large enough to accomodate the runners ($^3/_8$in wide and $^{11}/_{16}$in deep) and they taper down into the corner of the recess, the taper being less than a bee space, all strains of bee are encouraged to propolise this area making manipuluation difficult. The problem is easily solved by using runners of flat strip metal $^1/_{16}$in thick, $16^9/_{16}$in long by 1in deep attached with number 6 stainless steel pan head screws which then leaves a $^3/_8$in slot behind each runner which is the maximum dimension for a bee space. This space is not propolised. This is a good example of the equipment suppliers continuing to provide unsatisfactory equipment.

1.1.6 The Langstroth hive.

This hive must be the most used hive in the world and predominates in the major honey producing countries such as USA, Australia and New Zealand. In this country it is not used widely. The hive is a single walled hive with either top or bottom bee space using a frame $17^5/_8$in x $9^1/_8$in (448mm × 232mm) of comparative area to the Commercial frame. It can be designed to house either 10 or 11 frames. The salient features are as follows:

- Outside dimensions 20in x $16^1/_4$in (508mm × 413mm).
- Inside dimensions $19^1/_8$in x $14^1/_2$in (486mm × 425mm).
- Supers made the same way with a depth of $5^3/_4$in (146mm) compared with $9^7/_{16}$in (243mm) for the brood chamber.

There are variations of this hive perhaps the best known is the Langstroth Jumbo which has a depth of $11^3/_4$in (298mm) and uses Modified Dadant frames which have the same length as the normal Langstroth frame. Sparsholt College has used them since the 1960s with crown boards with 4 ventilation holes $1^1/_8$in (29mm) diameter 3in (76mm) in from each corner.

1.1.7 The Modified Dadant hive.

The modification of this hive from the original one designed by Charles Dadant is well documented and is a mixture of ideas from Langstroth [length of frame $17^5/_8$in (448mm) and Quinby depth of frame $11^1/_4$in (286mm)]. It is single walled and uses top bee space. The salient features are:

- Outside dimensions 20in x $18^1/_2$in (508mm × 470mm).
- Inside dimensions $19^1/_8$in x $16^3/_4$in (486mm × 425mm).
- Depth $11^3/_4$in (298mm) and $6^5/_8$in (168mm) for brood chamber and super respectively.
- It is capable of holding 12 frames with $1^3/_8$in (35mm) spacing or more usually 11 frames and a dummy board.

The best known variation of this hive is the Buckfast Dadant designed by Bro.Adam which is square in cross section and can accommodate 12 frames plus a dummy board.

1.1.8 Other hives.

There are many other hives being used in the UK and for completeness we include a brief description of some of them:

The Catenary hive. The basis is the catenary curve (the shape of the bottom edge of the comb built naturally by the bees in the wild). It was designed by Bill Bielby in 1968 when he was the CBI for Yorkshire based in Wakefield. It was found that top bars with wax starters were all that was necessary for the bees to build comb which they did not attach to the side of the brood chamber. National supers were used and the entrance was through a disc with the frames orientated the 'warm way'.

The British Deep hive. This hive is identical with the Modified National but $3\frac{1}{2}$in (89mm) deeper and takes a frame called a British Deep, similar to a BS frame but $3\frac{1}{2}$in (89mm) deeper. Appliance manufacturers make the frames and the hives. National supers are used.

The Dartington Long hive. This hive was designed by Robin Dartington in the early 1980s and is based on the British Deep frame. The length of the hive is such that it can accommodate 21 frames plus dummy boards and queen excluders. Provision is made for supers on top if required but normally honey is stored to the sides of the brood nest.

The Burgess Perfection hive. Not now manufactured but was made originally by Burgess of Exeter at the beginning of the century. It is a double walled hive with the outer lifts fitting one inside the other for wintering and then reversing them to provide space for supers in the summer. We have seen some still in use in Devon.

In addition to the various hives for full colonies, there are also many kinds of different nucleus boxes that have been designed for queen rearing and mating using full frames, half frames, mini and micro frames. Ingenious ideas have developed for uniting adjacent nuclei and methods of overwintering them have been evolved. They are too numerous to discuss here and are outside the scope of the syllabus.

1.1.9 A description and measurements of various types of frame used in the UK.

(Note: section 1.2 deals with frame spacing. It is very important and is addressed in this section also because of self spacing frames.)

It is important to thoroughly understand the concept of bee space before considering the pros and cons of various frames available commercially for use in different types of hive (see section 1.2). Nominal bee space = $\frac{5}{16}$in (8mm). It should be noted that as all initial work undertaken in UK and USA on frames and bee space was done in imperial units we have given them preference.

To understand the various types of frame available it is vital to actually see the different types and preferably to handle them; it is an unbelievable jungle and difficult to understand why so many variations are still available for purchase, particularly when many have so little to offer in the way of advantages.

1.1.9.1 Frames general: they have a top bar, two side bars and two bottom bars. They can have long or short lugs to suit the hive type and they are jointed to allow assembly without glue using only thin nails (gimp pins). They are better assembled using glue and copper pins giving a more robust construction with an infinitely longer life. There are two types of top bar; wedge type and slotted with a saw cut. Both are for fixing wax foundation onto the top bar without recourse to melting wax. The slotted type is a haven for the wax moth to pupate in. Side bars come in two types; parallel sided or with shoulders to provide self spacing (eg. Hoffman), both types usually have a shallow slot as a guide for wax foundation on the inner surface. Bottom bars also come in two types; wide and narrow, the wide type being more robust and discourages the building of brace comb below the frame. All types of frame use wood $^3/_8$in (10mm) thick for the top and side bars.

1.1.9.2 Brood frames: top bars are available in two widths namely $1^1/_{16}$in (27mm) or $^7/_8$in (22mm) and similarly the side bars; it is possible to mix these with wide top bars and narrow side bars. Spacing of brood frames can be either $1^3/_8$in (35mm) or $1^1/_2$in (28mm) nominal [$1^9/_{20}$in (37mm) = the width of a metal end]. When metal or plastic ends are used then the ends of the top bar must be $^7/_8$in (22mm) wide. Self spacing is generally achieved with Hoffman frames which gives a space of $1^3/_8$in (35mm) between the centre line of each frame. It should be noted that a feral colony building its own comb from scratch, will have a spacing of $1^3/_8$in (38mm) between the centre line of each adjacent comb. If the bees build this way when left to their own devices, one may ask, why use spacers of $1^9/_{20}$in (37mm) and end up with $1^1/_2$in (38mm), give or take a bit of propolis.

Consider now the spaces between top bars and side bars when the two brood chamber spacings are used with the two top and side bar widths.

Using $1^3/_8$in (35mm) spacing:
with $1^1/_{16}$in (27mm) frames, the distance between adjacent frames = $^5/_{16}$in (8mm)
with $^7/_8$in (22mm) frames, ... = $^1/_2$in (13mm)

Using $1^1/_2$in (35mm) spacing:
with $1^1/_{16}$in (27mm) frames, the distance between adjacent frames = $^7/_{16}$in (11mm)
with $^7/_8$in (22mm) frames, ... = $^5/_8$in (16mm)

Only the first combination meets the criterion of bee space; ie. between $^1/_4$in (6mm) and $^3/_8$in (10mm). Using this combination will minimise the building of brace comb between the woodwork of the frames.

1.1.9.3 Super frames: are usually spaced at $1^1/_2$in (38mm) and $1^7/_8$in (48mm) using metal or plastic ends or $1^5/_8$in (41mm) using Manley self spacing frames. If the wide ends are used they can be staggered to reduce the spacing initially to $1^3/_8$in (35mm) if foundation has to be pulled out. Manley discovered (by experiment) that a spacing of $1^5/_8$in (41mm) was the maximum that can be tolerated for foundation to be drawn satisfactorily and produce thick combs of honey. The Manley frame has the further advantage of the top and two bottom bars being the same width, $1^1/_{16}$in (27mm), thereby providing a guide for uncapping and, of course, there are no ends to remove before extracting. Supers generally require a frame spacing wider than the brood chamber. During a honey flow 'wax builders' are in much evidence and, in the author's experience, unless the bee space concept is observed much brace comb will be built in the supers. If $1^7/_8$in (48mm) spacing is used with $^7/_8$in (22mm) and $1^1/_{16}$in (27mm) wide top bars, then the distance between adjacent frames becomes 1in (25mm) and $^{13}/_{16}$in (21mm) respectively; very much larger than a bee space! This simple arithmetic shows how little attention has been paid to the bee space concept in the design of frames and their spacing within the hive.

1.1.9.4 Other frames: are available but are not in general use, for example:

- made of plastic instead of wood. They are generally split in two halves in order to equip them with wax foundation.
- specially made frames for catenary hives. It was expensive to manufacture these to match the catenary of the brood chamber and most users just use a top bar; the bees do not attach comb to the walls of the hive catenary, a most interesting phenomenon.
- more recently an arrangement of specially manufactured plastic corners to accommodate the wooden bars without recourse to additional fixing nails or glue (trading under the name of 'Easy Beesy'). We have never tried them but in general we have an aversion to all plastic equipment for a variety of reasons,

1.1.10 Other types of spacers: are available but not very popular, for example:

- Plastic Hoffman adapters for converting frames with $\frac{7}{8}$in (22mm) side bars with metal or plastic spacers to self spacing Hoffman.
- Yorkshire spacers which also attach to $\frac{7}{8}$in (22mm) side bars.
- Screws or studs in the side bars.
- Castellated spacers; usually 9, 10 or 11 slots for say a National and should only be used in supers, never in the brood chamber They save removing metal ends before extracting.

1.1.11 The British standard frame.

As this frame is the most widely used in the UK, all Candidates for this module must be familiar with it including its dimensions. We believe that for examination purposes the dimensions of other frames need not be committed to memory but a general knowledge of the rough comb area is adequate with a knowledge of where to look up the exact details. It is wrong now to call this frame a British Standard because BS1300 has been allowed to lapse and has not been replaced. The salient features of the frame are as follows:

- The top bar can be either $\frac{7}{8}$in (22mm) or $1\frac{1}{16}$in (27mm) wide, the latter being preferable because with $1\frac{3}{8}$in (35mm) frame spacing, the distance between top bars then equals one bee space of $\frac{5}{16}$in (8mm) and reduces the brace comb building between adjacent top bars. Those top bars $1\frac{1}{16}$in (27mm) wide still have their lugs cut to a width of $\frac{7}{8}$in (22mm) in order to take a metal or plastic end spacer. Practically all top bars have wedges for fixing foundation (slotted top bars are not in much evidence these days).
- The side bars are normally $\frac{7}{8}$in (22mm) wide but can include the Hoffman shoulders to provide self spacing without recourse to additional spacers. All side bars are slotted on the inside to provide a guide for the wax foundation.
- The two bottom bars are $\frac{7}{32}$in (5 or 6mm) wide and when fitted provide a slot $\frac{1}{8}$in (3mm) wide for inserting the wax foundation This slot is inadequate and makes it difficult to re-wax the frame without removing one of the bottom bars.
- The thickness of timber throughout is $\frac{3}{8}$in (10mm) except for the bottom bars which are $\frac{1}{4}$in (6mm).
- The overall size is 14in x $8\frac{1}{2}$in (356mm × 216mm) with a 17in (432mm) top bar giving lugs of $1\frac{1}{2}$in (38mm) at each end. The comb area of one side = 107 sq.in (69030 sq.mm) approx.

We believe that the design of the frame could be radically improved particularly in respect of the bottom bars. Our own design uses bottom bars $^5/_{16}$in (8mm) square thereby allowing a slot of $^1/_4$in (6mm) making the frames more robust and, easier to assemble and also easier to re-wax later. Additionally the design can be improved by replacing the Hoffman knife edge with a simple round or pan head screw in order to minimise the build up of propolis.

1.2 The principles which govern the design of hives and frames, including the concept of bee space, and the main features in their construction.

In order to address this part of the syllabus we must first consider the needs of the bees and the needs of the beekeeper in order to derive the principle of the design of hives and frames. Once the principles have been established then the necessary features of their construction can readily be enunciated.

1.2.1 The basic needs of the bee.

If the bee in its feral state is considered, then its needs are very simple. It requires the following:

> 1. Adequate space for a full sized colony - about 30 to 40 litres in the range 20 to 80 litres. The size of the cavity depends on the race and strain of the bee.
> 2. A relatively small entrance 4 to 5 metres above the ground for ease of defence. This does not vary with the strain of the bee to any large extent.

That is the end of the story as far as the bees are concerned. They have the ability to adapt to their surroundings. If the nest site happens to be too draughty the bees will seal it up to their liking with propolis and at the same time waterproof it as well. If there is any debris, they have the ability to remove it bit by bit.

1.2.2 The needs of the beekeeper.

The needs of the beekeeper are very much more extensive and include the following:

> 1. The hive will be used in a variety of environmental conditions from very hot to very cold and from very wet to very dry.
> 2. The hives may be required for migratory beekeeping.
> 3. The colonies will require to be inspected and checked for swarming, disease, adequate stores, etc.
> 4. The brood will require to be separated from the surplus honey which must also be easy to remove.
> 5. The physical ability of the beekeeper is an important factor as there is a fair amount of lifting and carrying in bee husbandry so the hive weight should be minimised.
> 6. Finally, the beekeeper will not want an entrance 4 to 5 metres from the ground. This is really the only item which directly conflicts with the needs of the bees other than keeping many stocks at close quarters in one apiary. This never happens in the case of feral colonies; such colonies are generally well separated geographically.

1.2.3 The principles which govern the design of hives and frames.

From the foregoing needs it is now possible state the design principles.

1.2.3.1 Hives.

1. The frames must be readily and easily removable for inspection at all times. In order to satisfy this then the principle of 'bee space' must be rigorously observed.
2. The hive must be weatherproof under all conditions.
3. Provision must be made for adequate ventilation for drying and cooling the interior.
4. The size must be compatible with the race and strain of bee.
5. Provision must be made for the separation of brood and surplus honey in order to harvest the crop by providing a queen excluder.
6. The cost of the hive must be generally acceptable, both the initial capital cost and the subsequent maintenance costs.
7. The hive must be capable of disinfection.
8. It must be stable under all conditions with a minimum of expansion and contraction.

1.2.3.2 Frames.

1. The first is identical with the hive principles, ie. the frame must be readily removable.
2. It must be capable of having wax foundation fitted quickly and easily.
3. The frame must be strong enough to withstand the loads imposed on it without distortion. A British standard brood frame holds 5lb of honey when full and should be capable of being oriented in any direction.
4. The frame must be simple to construct.
5. It must be capable of being disinfected.
6. It must be stable and not warp or skew under its normal working conditions.

The most important principle of the above is, of course, the 'bee space' and this is so important that it must be addressed in some detail.

1.2.3.3 Definition and description of the concept of 'bee space'.

The Rev. L.L.Langstroth of Philadelphia USA is credited with 'inventing' the bee space in 1851/2. He showed that with a bee space of $^1/_2$in (13mm) between parts of the inside of the hive, the bees would make little attempt to construct brace and burr comb. He found that by observing this bee space, parts of the hive could be made moveable and interchangeable. This was the turning point from skep beekeeping to modern day beekeeping with the moveable frame hive. The salient points relating to bee space in the moveable frame hive are as follows:

- Bees will propolise a space less than $^1/_4$in (6mm) and will build brace (horizontal) or burr (vertical) comb in a space greater than $^3/_8$in (10mm).
- Bee space is now considered to be $^5/_{16}$in (8mm) thereby allowing $^1/_{16}$in (2mm) tolerance above and below this figure to cater for expansion and contraction of the woodwork while the parts are in use.
- The bee space in a modern hive includes the space between boxes of frames and between the frames and the crown board, the space between the wall of the hive and the side bars of the frames, the space between the walls and the end combs and lastly the space between adjacent top bars and side bars of the frames. All these should be $^5/_{16}$in (8mm).
- There is one exception in most hives and that is between the bottoms of the frames in

the brood chamber and the floorboard which is of the order of 1in (25mm). The reasons for this are a bit obscure; in practice the authors have found that during rapid colony build up in the spring much drone comb is built in this area by extending downwards the comb in the brood frames. It also provides a 'parking space' for bees in a large colony in bad weather.

- If a frame spacing of $1\frac{3}{8}$in (35mm) is used the space between comb faces becomes $\frac{1}{2}$in (13mm) [ie. two bee spaces of $\frac{1}{4}$in (6mm)] allowing the bees to work the two comb faces back to back. If the frame spacing is $1\frac{1}{2}$in (38mm) then the inter comb space increases to $\frac{5}{8}$in (16mm), ie. two bee spaces of $\frac{5}{16}$in (8mm).
- In the brood chamber the only combination of frame and frame spacing dimensions that fully meets the bee space criterion is frames with top and side bars = $1\frac{1}{16}$in (27mm) with $1\frac{3}{8}$in (35mm) spacing between frames.
- In supers with $\frac{7}{8}$in (22mm) frames and $1\frac{7}{8}$in (48mm) spacing between frames, the space becomes 1in (25mm) between adjacent frames which is much greater than a bee space.

1.2.4 The main features in the construction of hives and frames.

From the foregoing the main features for the construction of hives and frames can be deduced

1.2.4.1 The construction of hives.

The following notes are concerned primarily with the construction of hives in wood the traditional building material for bee hives.

1. A decision has to be made whether to opt for top or bottom bee space which must be observed throughout the hive and throughout the hives in the apiary to allow inter-changeability one with another. The most common arrangement in the UK is bottom bee space which is curious when it is argued that with top bee space there is less likelihood of squashing bees during a manipulation.

2. Because the interchangeability requirement, construction must be to a high standard with manufacturing tolerances of not greater than $\pm\frac{1}{32}$in (1mm). Very few manufacturers achieve this standard.

3. For long life and minimum maintenance all joints in wooden hives should be dovetailed, glued and fastened with nonferrous nails and screws. Failure to observe this will lead to nail corrosion and subsequent rot of the woodwork. Nail sickness, as it is called, is very common and can be seen in most apiaries.

4. Material for hive building is traditionally in wood which should be well seasoned (less than 15% water content). Red cedar is the lightest timber in weight with durable qualities but it is the most expensive in this day and age. Soft woods (deal and pine) are cheaper and quite satisfactory giving a long life but they require more maintenance than cedar. The main drawback is the proliferation of knots in soft wood. To prevent rot in soft timber it is very often pressure treated with a fungicide such as 'tanalith'. This is a trade name for an arsenic based fungicide which is toxic to bees and care should be taken to avoid it for construction purposes. In our opinion creosote is the most cost effective preservative for timber.

5. It is important that the construction is square and that there is no skew, a very common fault in home assembled equipment which can easily be obviated by ensuring that all construction work is done on a large flat surface.

6. The runners in supers and brood chambers are another critical part of the construction. When fitted they must provide a bee space below the lugs of the top bars. Most metal

runners from the manufacturers require adjustment to obtain the correct $^5/_{16}$in (8mm). Metal runners are really the only acceptable material because of the requirement for disinfection by scorching with a blow lamp. Plastic runners are now appearing to cut down on costs; false economy in our opinion.

7. Roofs are very often provided by certain manufacturers too large for the hive and thus are easily blown off in a gale of wind in winter. The clearance between the inside of the roof and the outside of the boxes should be about $^5/_{16}$in (8mm). All corners should be dovetailed, glued and fastened with non ferrous nails. Additionally, copper strengthening plates should be fitted at each corner on the lower edges to prevent distortion when under load with heavy supers during a summer inspection. Manufacturers used to fit these years ago but again they have disappeared as a cost cutting exercise. All our own hive roofs have them but they have been added to standard equipment. Metal covering for the roofs in galvanised steel is essential and should have a layer of sheet polystyrene on the underside of the metal to minimise the temperature at the top of the hive in summer. The metal should be fixed with screws and not galvanised tacks. The roof ventilators require gauze (about 12 mesh per inch) on both the inside and the outside to prevent silent robbing. We have not yet come across a manufacturer who does this and most provide a mesh far too small thus restricting a ready flow of air. Most roofs have an inadequate spacer around the inside thereby not providing a large enough volume above the crown board. We keep our entrance block/mouse guard in the roof space of the hive and if the space is inadequate it will not fit in. Most of our roofs have been modified because of this requirement.

8. Floorboards should be made of a weatherproof plywood rather than the old fashioned planked type to obviate cracks and joints in the floor where debris collects.

The main features in the construction of wooden hives has been described. Wood is the accepted material which, of course, was selected by the bees themselves many millions of years ago. Other materials have been tried for hives as follows:

Concrete reinforced with chicken wire (rather on the same construction principle as concrete boat hulls) for use in termite infested areas, eg. Africa. Termites can very quickly destroy a wooden hive and the log hive in Africa is normally hoisted by a rope into the branches of a tree to avoid termite damage. It is lowered by the same rope when it is required to inspect it or collect the honey crop.

High Density Polystyrene. This has been tried on account of its low thermal conductivity providing better insulation than most other materials. Impossible to disinfect with a blow lamp!

Other plastics. Many other types of plastic have been tried such as synthetic resins (reinforced with fibre glass) and polymeric substances. Most of these suffer from condensation problems and have insufficient porosity.

Metals. In the West Indies and Africa hives have been made from old oil drums.

No material seems to have surpassed wood for general use and cedar was the preferred timber as it was durable and light in weight compared with other hard woods of comparable durability. It is expensive these days and the soft woods and laminated shuttering are now in vogue. Both are perfectly suitable providing they are scorched regularly with a blow lamp and treated with a wood preservative. We always maintain ours every two years and always use creosote. The blow lamp treatment not only kills the bee disease pathogens but those that cause wet and dry rot in timber. If laminates are used it is essential to ensure that the glues used for laminating are waterproof (take a test piece and boil it for half an hour in water – if delamination occurs then don't use it).

It goes with out saying that bee space is observed in the construction of all the hives discussed. We regard bee space to be $^5/_{16}$in (8mm) to allow a tolerance of plus or minus $^1/_{16}$in (2mm) for expansion or contraction when the hive is in use. This means that the bee space can vary between $^1/_4$in (6mm) and $^3/_8$in (10mm) which is within the limits for use by the bee without propolising or building brace comb.

It will be clear from the above that there is a lot wrong with hive equipment from the bee appliance manufacturers which can only be corrected by the beekeeper demanding higher standards.

1.2.4.2 The construction of frames.

The main features in the construction of (perhaps assembly for most beekeepers) frames may be summarised as follows:

> 1. It is important that each frame be assembled so that it is square and free from skew otherwise it will upset the bee space when the frames are used in the hive either one frame to its neighbour or the frame with respect to the side walls of its box.
> 2. For long life all joints must be glued (eg. Cascamite) and fastened with copper nails. Copper nails do tend to be rather thick and pre-drilling is advisable to prevent the timber from splitting. Compare frames a few years old assembled without glue and fastened with steel gimp pins with those assembled as described. The joints will be slack and there will be evidence of nail sickness in the surrounding wood. An old frame should be quite rigid before it is re-waxed with new foundation. A reasonable pressure on opposite corners trying to force the frame into a parallelogram will be a satisfactory test.
> 3. In general the nails fastening the joints should be in a direction at right angles to the direction the joint is put together. The wedge top bar fixing the foundation should be pinned horizontally; so many times one sees frames where the pins have been put in vertically from below and the points protruding from the upper surface of the top bar precluding scraping with a hive tool.

1.2.5 Other points of interest.

> 1. We consider that there is a case to be made for the re-design of the frames that are used in the hives used in the UK as most of those available have design faults. See appendix 1.
> 2. The following leaflets are worth seeking out and studying:

>> a) BBKA Advisory Leaflet 'The preservation of beehives and their ancillary equipment'.
>> b) MAFF Leaflets which are exceptionally good but unfortunately all are out of date and unlikely to be reprinted. Many of the older beekeepers have copies and some may be found in association libraries. The following should be sought:

>> #144 – Beehives
>> #367 – The British National Hive 1979/1982
>> #445 – The Smith Hive 1960/1981
>> #468 – The Modified Commercial Hive 1982
>> #549 – The Langstroth and Modified Dadant (MD) Hives 1980

3. The Encyclopedia Beekeeping by Morse and Hooper has good sections on hives and frames together with good photographs. A Case of Hives by Heath is also worth reading for this part of the syllabus.

1.3 The use of wax foundation and how it can be made on a small scale.

On a small scale perhaps needs definition before exploring this part of the syllabus. Our own definition of small scale is beeswax recovered from 1 to 20 hives. Up to 50 could be classed as medium and greater than 50 moving into the large scale or commercial class of operation.

1.3.1 The purpose of wax foundation in the moveable frame hive.

The purpose of wax foundation is to induce the bees to build straight comb in wooden frames thereby allowing:

a) easy inspection of both sides of the comb and facilitating inspection of every cell on the comb face,
b) easy extraction of honey,
c) easy manipulation of the colony,
d) re-use of the wooden frames,
e) either worker or drone comb to be constructed as required by the beekeeper,
f) minimising the amount of wax that has to be produced by the bees (the bees use the extra wax contained in the extra thickness of foundation compared with natural comb).

The types of wax foundation available are as follows:

a) thick foundation, wired in brood chambers and wired or unwired for use in supers,
b) thin foundation to be used for cut comb, sections or Cabanas,
c) all foundation may be either worker or drone cells,
d) sheets are available to fit most types of frame for most types of hive used in the UK.

The wired foundation is in different styles depending on the manufacturer or supplier as follows:

a) the wire can be either straight or crimped,
b) the positioning of the wire in the sheet can be either horizontal, vertical or diagonal formation (the terminology is a bit misleading – actually a series of V's from top to bottom),
c) the material varies from tinned iron, stainless steel to monel metal.

Historical: Mehring in Germany produced the first wax foundation in 1857, not long after Langstroth invented the first moveable comb hive. Weed in the USA produced the first machine to roll foundation in quantity on a commercial basis. Many beekeepers these days make their own foundation as a DIY activity using a simple press or a die between rollers. Foundation for BS brood frames has about 8 sheets per lb of wax and for Commercial frames about 5 sheets.

1.3.2 Small scale recovery of beeswax from combs and cappings.

1.3.2.1 Types of wax collected: during the season there are cappings during extraction, brace and burr comb collected during inspection and manipulations and finally old combs which are being discarded.

a) The cappings are of high quality and need very little treatment to clean them up for use. They should be used solely for show wax, making cosmetics (eg. cold cream) and for high quality blocks for sale.

b) Quite a considerable amount of brace and burr comb is collected during colony manipulations and should be lumped in with the old combs for rendering. Since these two sources contain wax contaminated with propolis (which cannot be removed) it is only suitable after home rendering and cleaning for making foundation, candles, etc. There is no way of cleaning wax at home comparable with large scale commercial operations with heated pumps and filters.

1.3.2.2 Processing cappings.

a) The cappings will be initially separated in a decapping tray or similar device with a mesh basket to allow the honey to drain off.

b) The cappings can be given back to the bees to clean up or washed to make mead with the washings.

c) Finally the cappings are melted and filtered through lint as a final cleaning process. The wax should not be heated above 150°F (65°C) to prevent discolouration. To save the natural colour of the wax, metal containers should be avoided.

1.3.2.3 Processing old comb.

a) After the wax has melted it adheres to the old larval skins and except by pressing or centrifuging at high temperatures some wax will inevitably be lost. These two methods are generally unsuitable for home operation.

b) There are two suitable methods for home use, these are the solar wax extractor and the steam boiler.

c) The steam wax extractor is a boiler with a mesh cage suspended inside with a drain at the bottom for the wax to run off. The device has a water reservoir which is converted to steam which melts the comb and wax inside. It can be driven by gas or electricity.

d) The solar wax extractor is probably the best device, it costs nothing to run and can be made for a few £s. They are expensive to buy from the equipment suppliers. Most of the doubling glazing merchants have lots of old panels available which they are only too glad to sell and produce a better job than the commercial models available.

e) A second melting in a saucepan of soft water leaving it to cool and float on the water. Any dross ('slumgum') can be scraped off the bottom and it is ready for use. Further cleaning by filter if required.

1.3.2.4 The solar wax extractor. As this method is by far the most suitable and there is little meaningful information in the general literature, a few points of interest on the device are:

a) When it is normal (at right angles) to the sun on a cloudless day the energy collected is approx. 1 kW per metre square (compare this with the heat from a 1 kW electric fire).

b) The correct angle to the horizontal (α) is given by the formula: $\alpha = \text{Lat} - \text{Dec}$ where

Lat = latitude and Dec = sun's declination. The sun's declination varies from 0° in March to +23° in June to 0° again in September. It goes on to −23° in December (the winter solstice) and then to 0° again the following March. The average value for the summer months March to September = c.13°. On the South Coast of UK with a latitude of say 50°, then $\alpha = 37°$. See appendix 2 for details.

c) Black bodies absorb the most radiation so the inside should be black or as dark as possible, and not white, for the greatest efficiency.

d) The glazing should be double and preferably a sealed unit and very good insulation (fibreglass for lofts) is also necessary for efficiency.

e) Take care not to burn yourself on the metal inside, the temperature is well over the boiling point of water on a good day.

f) Because the temperatures are so high it acts as a steriliser and will kill most pathogens. It is therefore a good idea to make the extractor large enough to take one or two whole brood frames complete with comb. To ensure that foundation wax is free from AFB and EFB pathogens, the wax should be maintained at 100°C for 30 to 60 minutes and this should be done as a separate operation outside the solar wax extractor if there is any doubt, particularly if colonies have been treated with antibiotics for EFB.

g) Keep the glass clean for maximum efficiency. The inner surface is the most difficult to clean as it develops a thin film of vaporised wax and propolis; methylated spirit will clean it off.

1.3.2.5 Other points of interest.

a) One very old type of extractor (the M & G extractor) is still to be found and works well with care and controlled heating. It is a metal drum and old comb is put inside and filled up with water and a filter is tied across the open top. Around the out side and as part of the device there is a large rim to catch the contents as they are pushed through the filter. The rim has a spouted outlet for the wax. The wax is forced out by hydraulic pressure when water is poured into the high spout, the bottom end of which is connected into the lower part of the drum. If care is not used it is claimed that the ceiling is likely to receive a wax treatment.

b) Physical properties of beeswax are:
    Specific gravity = 0.95.
    Melting point   = 147.9 ± 1°F (64.4 ± 0.5°C).
    Solidifying point = 146.3 ± 0.9°F (63.5 ± 0.5°C).
    Insoluble in water.
    Soluble in chloroform, ether, benzene, etc.
    When stored cold for some time it develops a surface bloom which is not a mould or a mildew – its cause is not well understood.

c) Most appliance suppliers will purchase rendered beeswax or exchange it for equipment.

1.3.3 A method of preparing home made foundation.

1.3.3.1 General.

There are two methods suitable for making foundation at home. These are by 'press' or by 'Herring' methods (both are described below).

• Foundation is required in two thicknesses, one for wiring (thick) and the other for cut comb (thin) which requires to be very refined as it will eventually be consumed. We do not believe that it is possible to make thin foundation of sufficient quality at home for two reasons:

> a) without recourse to a mill with rollers the thickness is too variable and more often than not out of limits.
> b) without special pumps and filters it is not possible to clean the wax sufficiently unless, of course, only capping wax is being used.

- It is not easy to measure the thickness of foundation and a good guide is to check the number of sheets to the lb. BS brood frames for wiring have about 8 sheets to the lb and Commercial about 5 sheets.
- Historical – Mehring is credited with making the first wax foundation in Germany in 1857 not long after the discovery of bee space. Weed, in the USA, made the first automatic mill for producing foundation on a large scale.

1.3.3.2 The foundation press method.

- The equipment consists of a bottom tray with a tinned copper platen soldered inside. The lid, with a similar matching platen, fits inside the tray and is hinged to one of the longer sides. They are expensive to purchase.
- In use, molten wax is poured into the tray and over the lower platen and the lid quickly closed. As soon as the lid is closed the excess molten wax is poured off. When cooled (a matter of seconds) the moulded foundation is removed from the press; this should remove easily if the dies have been treated before moulding with a suitable release agent (washing up liquid or similar).
- The sheet of foundation needs to be trimmed accurately to size; this is usually done with a trimming board, which is the exact size required, and a sharp knife or roller cutter.
- The principle is simple but there is a fair degree of skill required in getting the right working temperature for the wax, the right amount of detergent in the water for the release agent and the speed of working with the right amount of wax being poured into the press.

1.3.3.3 The Herring method.

- This method, due to Mr. Herring, is probably the best for use at home. It has not been written up in the general literature and Herring himself has not been given sufficient credit for producing, at low cost (about 10% of the cost of a press), a simple and efficient device.
- The Herring die consists of two flexible moulds, made of rigid polythene, and joined on one of the shorter sides, the whole being an inch or two larger than the foundation size being produced.
- To produce a sheet of foundation, a flat sheet of wax is placed in the die and the whole rolled through the mangle of a washing machine (albeit an old one).
- There are two methods of producing the flat sheet of wax (In both cases the boards are well soaked in water to allow the wax sheet to come away from the board), either by:

> a) Dipping a board once or twice in a container of molten wax (to control the thickness) which produces two sheets one on each side of the board, or
> b) by pouring onto a flat board with edging all round except for a small opening to run off the excess wax.

- The wax sheet needs to be warm, about 95°F (35°C), and malleable to be rolled and impressed. The die needs to be soaked in a release agent as for the press method.

- A trimming board is used to finally trim the sheets to size in the same way as for the press method.
- Other points on the method;

  a) Old wringers are becoming hard to come by these days.

  b) We have found a thermostatically controlled reservoir, for warming the die and the wax sheets for pressing, makes the operation easier. The reservoir is filled with water and the release agent (a few drops of washing up liquid).

  c) It takes us about half a day to make approximately 100 sheets of foundation (15 to 20lb. of wax) using the pouring method.

  d) After the sheets are dry they are stored flat between pieces of newspaper.

  e) Take care to position the wax sheet in the die squarely otherwise the final foundation will be incorrectly orientated in the frame.

1.3.4 Other points of interest.

- The publication Bee Craft has published a design of wax press by John Hamer. It has fibre glass platens and the design is very similar to the commercial one described above in section 1.3.3.2.
- Mr. Herring is now deceased and his family no longer continue to market the Herring die despite the demand for the device. A French manufactured equivalent is available through the bee suppliers in the UK made in a black plastic rather than the clear high density polythene of the Herring version. The price is about £90 compared with c.£20 for the Herring when it was available. Understandably the sales of the French 'job' are not very brisk. We consider that a Herring type die could be made in glass resin by moulding the two sheets from good wax foundation on a large flat piece of glass or mirror and then joining them along one edge. Another gadget to try when time permits.
- Tony Curnow, a member of our own branch in Plymouth and a great exponent of using the press method, advocates the following release agent rather than washing up liquid:- dissolve a dessertspoonful of honey in 500 milli-litres of warm water and the add and stir in 60 milli-litres of methylated spirit.
- In both methods of making foundation it should be remembered that in general the hotter the wax the thinner the foundation but there is a critical temperature for easy release with the release agent that is used.
- As a guide to the amount of wax collected from an apiary during the course of a year from all sources it would be reasonably safe to work on 1lb per hive average. During 1995, a good year for honey, we produced 39lb of wax from 20 hives. The figures quoted are after the wax has been cleaned and strained ready for using for wax foundation.

1.4 Methods of fitting frames with wax foundation including wiring and embedding.

Wax foundation can be fitted into frames with or without supporting wire embedded in the wax foundation. If the frames are wired then thick foundation is necessary in order to satisfactorily embed the wire. Whether the wax foundation is wired or unwired there is a right and a wrong way to fit it into the frame.

1.4.1 Fitting frames with foundation.

This is so fundamental that it is curious to find it in the syllabus but the following points should be observed:

- The orientation of the foundation must be as the bees build their comb naturally with the point of the hexagon uppermost.
- Most frames use a wedge top bar (an odd name because the bar of wood bears no resemblance to a wedge!) which fits in the shaped top bar. It should be nailed in to hold the foundation with the nails horizontal with the frame in its normal position hanging vertically.
- With most commercially manufactured frames the slot between the bottom bars is too narrow to slide the foundation into the frame easily and without damaging it. Fit the foundation with only one bar assembled and then finally fit the second bottom bar. If all other joints are glued this one may be left unglued for future removal when the frame is re-waxed.
- Use copper nails and pre drill the wedge for the fixing nails. Three are required ensuring that the heads are just below the surface of the top bar if they are super frame so that the uncapping knife does not foul them.

1.4.2 Two methods of wiring frames and embedding wire into foundation.

1.4.2.1 General.

- Providing wire embedded into the wax foundation gives the finished comb a more stable fixing in the frame rather than relying solely on the adhesion of the comb to the wooden frame. A Commercial brood frame holds c. 7lb. of honey when it is full and a BS frame for a Smith or National hive holds c. 5lb With plenty of stores in these frames on a warm day (particularly if the comb is relatively new) it is easy for the comb and adhering bees to part company with the frame and fall to the ground during manipulation if there is no network of supporting wire. It is good beekeeping practice to wire all large size frames ie. those for use in the brood chamber. It is essential to have supers wired if tangential extraction is to be used; if a radial extractor is used, then it is possible to dispense with the wiring but the occasional comb breakage does occur during extraction. The authors never wire supers and always use thin foundation so that the best frames can always be selected for cut comb. Those not up to cut comb standard can be extracted.
- The wire can be embedded into the foundation and then the wired foundation inserted into the frame. Alternatively the frame is wired and the wax foundation fitted and finally the wire embedded into the wax. All materials expand and contract with a change in temperature and the wire in wax foundation is no exception. In wired foundation the foundation is bent into a slight curve if the temperature is above or below the temperature when it was made. If the frame is wired no change in shape takes place and the foundation and frame remain in the same plane; only the tension in the wire changes providing the frame remains rigid (the timber sizes are adequate for this to be so). The authors preference is for the latter but it is more labour intensive and time consuming than using wired foundation.
- Modern wiring is always crimped before it is embedded to minimise movement along the wires and to provide the maximum surface area in contact with the foundation. The size of the wire used is not critical, but it is usual to use SWG 28 to 30. If any part of the wire is exposed at the bottom of a cell, the cell will not be used for brood rearing. It is best to use stainless steel or monel metal wire to minimise corrosion.

1.4.2.2 Two methods of wiring frames.

1) The old method uses 4 small hooks attached to the inside surfaces of the side bars about

1in (25mm) from the top bar and the same distance from the bottom bars. Call these A and B on one side bar and C and D on the other: A and C being nearest to the top bar. The wire is then made off at A the start point and threaded as follows: AC taught, CA slack, AB, BD slack and looped through CA, DB pulling the whole mesh taught before making off finally at B.

2) The modern method uses wires parallel to the top and bottom bars. The number of parallel wires depends on the size of the frame, however a distance of about 2in (50mm) between wires is about right. Holes are drilled in the side bars and small brass eyelets are inserted on the outside faces of them in order to prevent the wire cutting into the woodwork when tensioned. The wire is threaded through the holes and terminated with small copper tacks after tensioning. The wire is then crimped with a crimping tool (usually two coarse knurled wheels) before the foundation is fitted and the wire embedded.

1.4.2.3 Method of wiring foundation and embedding wire.

- This can only be done satisfactorily with a specially constructed wiring board. The sheet of foundation is placed on the board and the wire is then fitted over the foundation by threading it round strategically placed pins to give the required pattern or mesh configuration. Usually half the pins can be levered apart from their opposite numbers to tension the wire before passing a current, for a few of seconds, through the wire to heat it and therefore embed it in the wax foundation. When cool and the wire embedded, the tension is released and the piece of wired foundation removed from the board. The current is usually DC, from a battery charger or 12V battery, of 3 to 5 amps for a few seconds. The timing is by trial and error but dependent on the resistance of the wire which in turn is related to the diameter, length and the material from which it is made.
- A similar method is used for embedding the wires of a wired frame into the foundation when it is fitted. Current is passed through the wire to heat it and the foundation is gently pressed on to the warm wires. There is a certain amount of skill required to get the embedding just right but it is easily acquired with a little practice.
- A slower method which can be used in both cases is to use a special embedding tool with a spur wheel. This is heated and rolled over the wire on top of the foundation warming both the wire and the wax foundation and pressing it into the foundation at the same time. Again, a certain skill is required for good results.

1.5 The methods of spacing frames in hives, the usual measurements used and the advantages and disadvantages of varying the spacing.

1.5.1 General.

To become familiar with the various types of spacing it is essential to see and handle the bits of equipment involved. There are two major methods of spacing frames. Firstly, self spacing where the dimensions of the frames automatically provide the correct distance between the frames when they are placed in the hive. Secondly, frames can be spaced by attaching specially designed spacers to the frames. Both methods are widely used in the UK.

It is important when manipulating a colony to always ensure that the frames are levered up tight to one side of the brood chamber when closing the colony down. Failure to do this each time, will result in a build up of propolis on the spacing surfaces and the spacing between frames gradually becoming too large. Also it prevents, to some extent, the building of uneven combs which are thick at the top with an arch of honey and are consequently difficult to move to a different position in the brood chamber (note that wide top bars and $1\frac{3}{8}$in (35mm) spacing obviates this trouble). It is easier to do the levering with the hive tool between the dummy board and the hive wall. Generally it is the beekeepers who do not use a dummy board that experience this problem; it often gets to the stage where the first frame has to be levered out and forcibly pushed back which is very difficult to do without damaging some of the bees.

1.5.2 Self spacing frames are used in both the brood chamber and in supers. There is one type for the brood chamber, the Hoffman frame, where the side bars have specially shaped 'shoulders' with a 'V' on one side and a flat on the other. The overall dimension between the 'V' and the flat is $1\frac{3}{8}$in (35mm) giving the same spacing between centres when the frames are placed in the hive. The self spacing frame for supers is the Manley frame which has parallel sided side bars $1\frac{5}{8}$in (41mm) wide. These provide $1\frac{5}{8}$in (41mm) spacing between the centre lines of the comb when placed in the hive.

1.5.3 Spacers for attachment to frames: are listed below with their spacing dimension.

Metal ends
originally $1\frac{9}{20}$in (37mm) but now $1\frac{7}{16}$in (37mm) for brood chamber use, $1\frac{7}{8}$in (48mm) for use in supers.

Plastic ends
$1\frac{7}{16}$in (37mm) for brood frames,
2in (51mm) for use in supers.

Double V plastic ends
$1\frac{7}{16}$in (37mm) for brood frames (min. contact area).

Hoffman adapters
$1\frac{3}{8}$in (35mm) for brood chamber use (2 types available).

Yorkshire spacers
c. $1\frac{1}{2}$in (38mm) for brood chamber use (seldom used these days)

1.5.4 Other spacing methods: include castellated metal strips for use in supers only and screws or studs on the side bar edges. We have found one or two cases where the beekeepers concerned use 'finger' spacing or spacing the frames by eye. This is not recommended except as a temporary measure (nb. it would be very foolish to move a colony without proper spacers).

There is no doubt in our minds that the best spacing is self spacing frames with round or pan head screws to obtain the minimum contact area between frames. It has taken us many years of painful experience to come to this conclusion; the advantages are obvious but seem to be overlooked by the majority no doubt due to the fact that such frames and spacing are not made by the bee supply merchants

1.6 How to begin beekeeping, including the acquisition of bees, sources of equipment, costs and any precautions necessary.

1.6.1 General considerations:

It is essential to obtain some knowledge of bees before actually owning and managing them.

This is best acquired by joining the local beekeeping association, attending their meetings both in the winter and summer and by attending any evening classes which may be available.

Reading suitable books, in the early days, is also necessary as well as having a good book readily available at home for reference when required. Two suitable books could be 'A guide to bees and honey' by Hooper or 'Teach yourself beekeeping' by Vernon; both are relatively inexpensive and readily available. If some of the old MAFF leaflets can be obtained or borrowed, these would also be useful, eg. 283 Advice to intending beekeepers, 412 Feeding bees, 367 The British National hive and 561 Honeybee brood diseases and disorders. There is a further publication 'The Beeway Code' published by DARG which is a must for all prospective beekeepers.

Before acquiring the bees, a prospective beekeeper must obtain some essential items of equipment; these are: protective clothing (say white overalls), bee proof hat and veil, hive tool and smoker, together with protective gloves and footwear if required. He/she is then in a position to attend association demonstrations and to examine any bees likely to be for sale.

It would be ideal if an experienced beekeeper could take a beginner 'under his wing' for a season and personally instruct him/her in his own established apiaries. A year for the beginner without his own bees would make him alert to some of the pitfalls he may likely encounter when setting up on his own. The only danger is that many 'experienced' beekeepers have some very undesirable beekeeping habits which should not be passed on to the uninitiated. There's no fool like an old fool as the saying goes, so choose your old fool carefully if he is to be a mentor for a newcomer.

During this learning process, the prospective beekeeper must make up his own mind on the type of hive and equipment he wants to use. This is a very difficult task for a beginner but it has to be faced and he has to be guided in a non-biassed way. Reading 'A case of hives' by Heath could be a good starting point on this decision making process but most newcomers are likely to be utterly confused by every expert extolling the virtues of every type of hive in the book.

The prospective beekeeper has two other decisions to make before acquiring his bees. These are how is he going to start (with a nuc, a full colony or a swarm when available) and where is he to keep them (see sections 1.6 and 1.7). It is always best for the beginner to start off in a small way with a nuc early in the season and develop it into a full colony during the season. He should be encouraged to maintain a minimum of two colonies as soon as possible to be able to measure one against the other. This will assist in the overall management, should problems arise with one of them.

1.6.2 Acquisition of bees: and possibly the equipment they are delivered or purchased in. The bees can be either a nucleus, a colony or a swarm. A nucleus or a colony can be purchased and acquired at virtually any time of the year except for about three months in the winter, whereas a swarm can only be obtained during the swarming season from say May to August.

The ideal approach must be the acquisition of an overwintered nucleus early in the year (April) after the theoretical learning preparations in the winter. This will allow the new beekeeper to see the nucleus expand and become a colony and to reap a surplus (hopefully) during the first year of beekeeping. The second best method will be the purchase of a full sized colony which is satisfactory if the prospective beekeeper has had some hands on experience. The least attractive is the swarm; stray swarms are a liability mainly because the origin is generally not known and there is often the problem of bad temper as well as possible disease. Swarms are someone else's problem and the beginner should be discouraged from starting with an unknown one.

Bees can be purchased from the following sources:

a) recognised bee suppliers,
b) a member of the local association,
c) from advertisements in the bee press or local press.

Purchasing bees from a recognised supplier provides some guarantee of quality because of the good name the supplier wishes to retain. The age of the queen should be known and they must be guaranteed disease free; it is not unreasonable to ask for a written assurance on these two points.

If bees are purchased from any other sources it is essential to have the bees inspected by a competent beekeeper and samples taken for disease diagnosis before a deal is struck. A prospective purchaser is strongly recommended to consult the BBKA Standard for Bees, Colonies and Nuclei before making any purchase (see appendix 3). It is to be noted that the BBKA define nucleus, colony and stock (colony plus hive). Details can also be found in the 1986 edition of the BBKA year book (A pity the standard is not more readily available either in every edition off the year book or as a leaflet). The competent beekeeper should also advise on the temperament of the bees and whether they are suitable for a beginner. We have seen many times beginners sold bad tempered bees and the beginner after being badly stung has given up beekeeping. Make no mistake the craft has its share of unscrupulous beekeepers.

1.6.3 Acquisition and sources of equipment: can be considered under three categories, namely, new from recognised equipment suppliers, buying second hand and finally making the equipment as a DIY activity.

Purchasing new: is the most expensive but perhaps the most reliable way of acquiring the necessary equipment. It can be done from the catalogues available and preferably done out of season when the rush is not on and discounts may be available. Take advice from experienced beekeepers on what to buy and don't forget to ask why a particular choice is being made (eg. what feeder to purchase and why that particular design).

Purchasing second hand: equipment is always popular but fraught with danger. A very large proportion is rubbish, not constructed to standard size and the newcomer to beekeeping must seek expert assistance in the second hand market. When it has been purchased, treat it like the plague and as if every bit is infected with AFB. Every item must be completely sterilised and not brought near the apiary or bees until this has been done.

Constructing equipment at home: as a DIY activity is fine and extremely educational to the newcomer. It is essential that recognised plans are obtained and that the equipment is constructed to standard designs and measurements. If this is not done trouble will arise in the future due to incompatibility.

1.6.4 Other points for consideration:

a) The cost of new equipment should be obtained from the latest catalogues of the recognised bee equipment suppliers. When buying second hand the new price is of course the yardstick. As a guide, good second hand equipment sells at about a third to a half of the new price.

b) Starting beekeeping is an expensive hobby and the prospective beekeeper is advised to get a little manipulative experience before finally taking the plunge on his own. He must ascertain whether he is allergic to bee stings.

c) Spare equipment is necessary and advice should be sought on what additional gear to have on standby (eg. for swarm control).

d) Finally the newcomers should be encouraged to study for the BBKA Basic Examination.

1.7 The criteria used in the selection of apiaries.

General considerations for siting a home apiary will equally apply to siting colonies in an out apiary. Before the siting of the colonies, consideration should be given first to the site itself and indeed whether it is suitable for keeping bees. Criteria for the site are as follows:

- Is there adequate forage in the surrounding area for the colony to support itself and can it readily obtain water throughout the year?
- There must be no question of danger to humans, particularly children, or animals. One sting can kill an allergic subject if not given expert medical treatment very quickly (often a matter of a few minutes).
- Ideally, the apiary should be in a place where nobody except the beekeeper can be stung. This criterion is nigh impossible to achieve and siting of the colonies in the apiary becomes of vital importance to minimise this risk.
- Under no circumstances should an apiary be established adjacent to a public thoroughfare, even if there is a barrier (eg. hedge or wall) of suitable height between. Bad tempered bees while being manipulated will attack moving human and animal targets up to quite large distances from their hive. The authors know of at least two 'experienced' beekeepers, who should know better, who have apiaries adjacent to a public thoroughfare. We were both stung on the face getting out of our car on the public highway adjacent to one of these apiaries. One shudders to think what would happen to a young mother with her child in a pram in such circumstances. The said beekeeper was, of course, dressed up to the nines in gloves, 'wellies' and space suit.
- The site should not be in a frost pocket and protection from the prevailing winds is most desirable.
- The site should be free from any form of flooding or under trees in or on the edge of a wood. The old beekeeper's saying that bees in a wood ne'er do good is very true. Farmers and landowners like to put the beekeeper out of sight in a wood or copse.
- The site should be accessible by road at all times of the year.
- The site should be surrounded by a stock-proof fence if it is adjacent to pasture where livestock is likely to be grazing.
- The next criterion is a matter of ethics relating to out apiary sites which are often on farmer's land; if another beekeeper has bees close by on the same owner's land, then look elsewhere for another site no matter what the farmer says.

- This takes us back to the first criterion about the forage. It is essential to check the surrounding area for other beekeepers who, for some peculiar reason, like to keep their whereabouts as secret as possible from other beekeepers. Could the reason be the dishonesty of others in the craft? In our own County of Devon bee rustling is more commonplace than one would imagine.
- Dr. Bailey has shown very elegantly elsewhere that if the number of colonies in a given area rises above a certain figure then disease is likely to become a continual problem. He states that 1 colony per 10 square kilometres is critical and should not be exceeded. In the foraging area surrounding the apiary (πr^2, where r = 3 miles or 4.8 kilometres) if there are no other apiaries then the maximum size of the apiary = 7 hives. Check our arithmetic and see if you agree. Therefore, if the area becomes overpopulated with bees then there is insufficient forage and then disease starts to crop up more often than it would otherwise do.
- It cannot be over emphasised that the utmost care must be taken in siting an apiary and the colonies in it. Bees cannot be moved around like other livestock. If there is any doubt about any aspect of siting, expert advice should be sought.

1.8 The factors to be considered in the siting of colonies in home and in out-apiaries.

Detailed considerations for siting colonies in a home apiary implies that there is a dwelling house nearby with other people, children and domestic animals, if not in the in the same grounds then on neighbouring property.

1.8.1 General considerations when siting both home and out apiaries:

- Stocks must be sited so that the flight path of the bees avoids footpaths and areas where there is likely to be any human or animal activity. Stocks can be sited so that bees have to fly up and over hedges and fences thereby getting the bees to a safe height above anyone on the ground. Under normal circumstances such an arrangement is quite workable but aggressive bees must be considered. It is essential to have a 'bolt hole' prepared, over 3 miles away, so that a stock may be moved in an emergency at short notice.
- There must be plenty of space around each stock for colony manipulations and maintaining the site (eg. grass cutting). A distance of 6ft. between colonies would not be out of the way for setting up nucs and doing artificial swarms between the adjacent stocks.
- Space should be allowed at the planning stage for expansion in the future, this aspect is often overlooked.
- The layout of the stocks should be in an irregular fashion in order to minimise drifting.
- Hives should be provided with permanent bases to raise the floorboard off the ground to prevent damp and possible rot starting to occur in the lower woodwork of the hive.
- Concrete bases are undoubtedly the best but try a temporary solution until the site has been tried out for a couple of years. The income from sites quite close together vary very considerably. We have had sites $3/4$ mile apart which have shown great variations in honey yield with the same type of bees.
- The height of the top of the brood chamber to minimise too much bending is very important if large numbers of stocks are involved. Even $1/2$ dozen hives becomes a real pleasure if they are at the right height compared with being too low. A point to consider when designing hive stands.
- In home apiaries it is best to site the stocks out of sight of neighbours if this can be done.

- Bees in the stocks will at some time swarm despite the best efforts of the beekeeper to prevent this happening. Shrubs and trees around the stocks are useful for the swarms to hang on.
- A certain amount of shade from nearby trees is useful particularly at mid-day during the summer. Stocks should not be sited under trees where rain drops can fall from them onto the hive in winter; it disturbs the colony.
- Provision should be made for storing spare equipment near to the apiary, preferably a discrete shed for the multitude of bits and pieces.

1.8.2 The provision of an apiary water supply.

1.8.2.1 Reasons for providing a supply. Bees will require water if there is no nectar flow in progress; they are forced into a situation where they have to use their own stores. This is particularly so in the spring when the average colony requires about 150g water/day for diluting stores to 50:50 ratio and in dry hot weather for cooling, this can increase to 1kg/day. It is essential in an urban apiary that bees are not annoying the neighbours by taking water from their swimming pools, ornamental ponds, drains, etc. At out apiaries it is always good beekeeping practice to ensure that a supply of water is available reasonably close to hand; generally this is not a problem in UK and it is not necessary to provide a discrete supply but if drought conditions prevail for any length of time (eg. in 1989 and 1995) problems could arise.

1.8.2.2 Siting of the supply: is important if the bees are to use it regularly. The main criteria are as follows:

a) It should be close to the hives in the apiary.
b) It should be in a sheltered spot out of the prevailing winds.
c) It should receive maximum sun and be directly illuminated by the sun in the early part of the year when the declination is zero or southerly. Warm water is collected more quickly than cold.

1.8.2.3 Design of the supply. The methods are legion but all should meet two important criteria namely;

a) There must be no possibility of the bees drowning and,
b) It must never be allowed to dry up or the bees will seek a more reliable source.

The requirement for the supply never drying up implies the provision of an automatic system or self discipline on the part of the beekeeper to regularly top it up. Any automatic system is easily engineered with the use of a ball valve either on a gravity feed system or mains fed.

In order to prevent the bees drowning they should only be allowed to take water indirectly, for example from wet sacking, moss, pebbles or stone chippings, etc.

1.8.2.4 Training bees to the water supply. Any training should start at the beginning of the year in early spring. Adding a small amount of syrup to sweeten the source or putting syrup adjacent to it is a simple way of starting off the process. Once the bees have found another source it is very difficult (impossible ?) to wean them off it in favour of your own supply.

1.8.3 Other points.

There is a risk to life, albeit fairly remote, wherever bees are kept and if this is remembered when planning an apiary, the chances of success are well assured. Having said all this, we believe that suburban gardens are becoming so small and houses so close together that they are unsuitable sites for keeping bees and certainly not the place for beginners.

Like all other pursuits we follow today, insurance for injury to third parties is essential. Beekeeping is no exception and cover is provided in the capitation fee to the BBKA, part of an Association subscription.

1.9 Good apiary hygiene.

This must be the easiest part of the syllabus and has been a popular examination question. Good apiary hygiene is summed up in the following, often referred to as the 10 commandments of good beekeeping:

1. Always keep the apiary clean and tidy.
2. Never throw propolis or brace comb on the ground; be sure always to place it in a suitable container and remove it from the apiary.
3. Never buy old combs.
4. Never buy colonies of bees unless it is known that they come from disease free apiaries; never accept stray swarms from unknown origins.
5. Always disinfect second hand hives and other equipment before use.
6. Never feed honey or allow bees to gain access to it; refined sugar is the only acceptable feed for honeybees.
7. If a colony dies out during the winter (or at any other time) and the trouble is not due to starvation, close the hive, pending the examination of a sample comb and bees, to prevent the remaining stores being robbed out.
8. Never exchange brood or super frames/combs between one colony and another unless it is known that all colonies are free from disease. Where possible, supers should be marked and always used on the same colonies.
9. Take care to prevent robbing at all times by observing item 2 and not spilling syrup or having leaky feeders.
10. Arrange all hives in such a way that drifting is reduced to a minimum.

The code is essentially for minimising disease and its spread in an apiary and appears in a modified form in ADAS Leaflet P306 - 'Foul brood of bees: recognition and control'.

There is only one other item that we would incorporate in the list and that is the requirement of renewing comb in the brood chamber once every three years on a rotational basis. It is another way of getting rid of disease pathogens. Having said that it is common practice in the USA to keep brood comb for year after year without detriment.

1.10 The variable temperament of bees in relation to management and public relations.

1.10.1 How the variable temperament of bees arises.

In order to address this part of the syllabus it is necessary to have a clear understanding of why the temperament of our honeybees are variable and how this arose. There is a very wide range of temperaments from the very docile to the very aggressive or put another way from those that exhibit little defensive instinct to those with a very strong defensive instinct whether the colony is disturbed or remains undisturbed.

By various scientific techniques, including palaeontology, it is generally agreed that the origin of the honeybee was in that part of Africa that is now known as Kenya somewhere between 20 and 30 million years ago. This was before India split off from Africa and before the Red Sea and Rift Valley were formed. The land mass now called India carried with it some of the earlier bee like insects which developed into the Eastern species of bees, ie, Dorsata, Cerana and Florea.

Reference now to the diagram of the 'Migration of the Honeybee' in appendix 11 shows the origin in Kenya and the main migration routes marked with double line arrows northwards, southwards and westwards. Major races developed notably A.M.Capensis in the Cape of Good Hope area, Adansonii in the equatorial strip, Fasciata (the Egyptian bee) in the north east and Intermissa (the Tellian or Arab bee) in the north west.

The Tellian bee is considered to be a major race from which many other strains have developed. In its native part of northwest Africa it developed in a very hostile environment and presumably adapted to these conditions by having to defend its colonies against determined predators (eg hornets, etc.) It migrated northwards before the last melting of the icecap c. 10,000 years ago and established the well known races in NW Europe such as Iberian bee, the French Black bee and the English bee. It migrated as far north as Finland in latitude 60°N.

Similarly, the other major race (Fasciata) migrated northwards also providing the Italian bees (Ligustica), Greek, Caucasian Carniolan, etc. After the ice cap melting the UK was cut off from the continent and the Mediterranean was formed isolating Europe from Africa. At that time we had a discrete race of bee in the UK now known as the. English Black bee or the English Brown bee. It was decimated by disease in the early 1900s (nb. Isle of Wight Disease or Acarine) and the Government of the day offered subsidies to beekeepers to import bees from the Continent. The result was that most of the races in Europe were imported and over the last 50 to 80 years these races have interbred and we now have a hotchpotch of mongrels with a very mixed pool of genes.

All the bees with their origins or stem emanating from the Tellian bee have to a greater or lesser degree the defensive instinct while other bees from Italy, Greece, etc. have a very weak defensive trait. Breeding can only be true with pure strains while breeding with mongrels is known to be an erratic and unpredictable procedure.

Herein then lies the root of our problem in the UK. Using mongrel bees and taking pot luck with the matings will result in a wide range of temperaments in the offspring. The only beekeeper who claims experience with the old English bee, and has committed his findings to paper, is Bro.Adam. He considered the bee had some very desirable features but also some very bad ones, notably bad temper. BIBBA claim that there are pockets of the old English bee with a good temper and campaign for its breeding and use in the UK.

Before leaving this introduction to understanding the temperament of our bees it must be pointed out that other characteristics will also be present and variable with mongrels such as high tendency to swarm, heavy propolis gathers, early starters/late finishers, longevity, economy on stores for overwintering, resistance to different diseases, etc. We know from experience that it possible to eliminate bad temper fairly quickly by culling those queens producing bad tempered bees. However, it is nigh impossible to control more than two variables without recourse to specialised isolation and mating techniques. Our own breeding programme concentrates on good temper and minimum swarming tendency which can be achieved by any beekeeper if they put their mind to it. Unfortunately, it is a very small minority who control the temperament of the bees they keep and we put this down to two traits that have developed over the last 50 years as follows:

a) Newcomers have been encouraged to wear very adequate protective clothing which has become available making them 'safe' from stings under most conditions.
b) Few associations encourage their membership to manipulate their bees without gloves.

1.10.2 The defensive qualities of different strains.

We may well ask how we can measure the defensive qualities of the bees we keep and the bees we wish to get rid of?

Lord Kelvin (1824 to 1907) stated on one occasion 'I often say that when you can measure what you are talking about and express it in numbers you know something about it; but when you cannot measure it in numbers, your knowledge is of a meagre and unsatisfactory kind'.

At first sight this seems to be an impossible task but a little thought and the matter is simple. We are all aware that it is possible to open up some colonies of bees without a veil or other protection and it is unlikely that a sting will be suffered by the operator, assuming that he knows what he is doing and handles his bees well. We are also aware that other colonies are virtually impossible to handle. In between these two extremes is the wide variation of temperament. The best measurement to assess the defensive nature of the bees is, in our opinion, to take note of the followers. If, after manipulating a colony, there are no followers 2 metres from the back or side of the hive then it is a suitable bee for keeping in a suburban garden. At 2 metres one should be able to remove the veil and not get pestered by a guard bee or follower.

If bees follow up to 5 metres then, in our opinion, they are unsuitable for a suburban garden. Such bees will need careful handling during a manipulation and would only be suitable in an isolated out apiary.

If bees follow beyond 5 metres then we would consider requeening them in favour of a more favourable strain.

We consider that the use of gloves should be dispensed with except for dire emergencies. If the bees cannot be handled without gloves, then there is something wrong with either the bees or the beekeeper, both of which can be corrected. We record the number of stings we receive from each colony on the record card and this is also a numerate way of measuring the defensive qualities of the stocks. We don't expect to get stung during an inspection but if we do then there must be a reason for it and we do our best to assess the situation. If we wore gloves as the norm we would be unlikely to assess in this way.

Finally on this point, if the colony is becoming difficult to handle then close it down; contrary to what many experienced beekeepers do it is very good beekeeping practice.

1.10.3 Variable temperament in relation to management.

The more bad tempered the bees the longer it takes to undertake routine inspections for swarm prevention and control. Additionally, the enjoyment of managing a few colonies of bees decreases rapidly with even a modest amount of bad temper.

When the colony gets to a state where it is really difficult to handle, the average beekeeper gives up and regular inspections go by the board. Such a beekeeper then starts extolling the virtues of leave alone beekeeping which is usually nonsense. Swarms start to issue and the result is that the bad temper is further promulgated around the area.

Even the best beekeepers occasionally end up with a rogue colony and if this is in a garden apiary something has to be done at very short notice. All beekeepers must have a 'bolt hole', a site where a bad tempered colony can be moved safely away from children, neighbours and livestock where it can be dealt with at leisure and put to rights. Here it must be appreciated that the bad temper may be due to the genetic make up of the queen's offspring or due to the pheromones produced by the queen. If the cause is genetic then it will take a minimum of six weeks after requeening for the temperament to improve; three weeks for the house bee and then another three weeks foraging before it naturally dies. This is a long time during a relatively short season. If, on the other hand, the cause is due to pheromones (our guess at the cause and not proven) the change will be effected in 24 to 48 hours. To the best of our knowledge there has been no scientific work done on this aspect of pheromones and temper. However, by experience we know it to be true and it can be readily demonstrated by reversing the queens. We have experimented with nuclei by swapping queens.

If colonies are left to produce their own queens and mate in the local neighbourhood it is surprising how quickly they deteriorate and up surges the bad temper. In 1986 we moved to Devon and brought 6 well behaved colonies with us for the garden apiary. Other more pressing demands on our time precluded the continuation of our selective queen rearing programmes. In three years had we six very 'grotty' stocks which had to be moved to an out apiary which we had found and established by that time. It is essential for the management of good temper that queens are reared each year and the best selected for use in honey gathering colonies.

The only way that we know, using mongrels, is to rear from the best tempered stock in May and overwinter the queens in nucs for introduction the following spring. By the time spring has arrived the queens will have been assessed for first temper and then nervousness. If they are satisfactory they can be used. The old queens, no matter how bad they are, can be used to keep the nucs going until queen rearing time again. Failing this, it is necessary to buy in queens of known temperament.

We believe that only about 5% of beekeepers do any selective queen rearing with the result that bad temper is a perennial problem.

1.10.4 Public relations and the temperament of bees.

Public relations and the temperament of bees is usually confined to bees and neighbours in the suburban situation. The bees kept adjacent to neighbours must be beyond reproach as far as temper is concerned and they must not be of a swarming tendency. No matter how nice ones neighbours, our bees must not cause nuisance by stinging, swarming or soiling the washing; all are unacceptable.

In all the years we have kept bees in our garden, only once has a neighbour been stung. She was about 6 feet from one of our hives weeding her garden the other side of an open mesh fence. She said it didn't matter but we told her it did matter to us and the offending stock was requeened although it was not in our opinion a bad stock.

It is important to manipulate your bees in a garden without gloves if you are overlooked by neighbours, it tells them that the bees are unlikely to be a menace to them. It is even better if the bees can be kept out of sight from ones neighbours but always ensure that you approach the hives without veil and similarly when leaving the bees.

It is good practice never to open up or manipulate a colony in a garden apiary when the next door neighbours are using their garden.

Good public relations and bees is just plain common sense but do ensure that insurance is kept valid for third party liability. Litigation seems to be the order of the day and attitudes can change dramatically if a serious incident occurs.

1.11 The actions which can be taken to avoid bad-tempered bees causing a nuisance to members of the public.

1.11.1 Actions to be taken.

The actions are common sense as follows:

    1. Select the apiary carefully in accordance with section 1.7.
    2. Site the colonies in the apiary carefully in accordance with section 1.8 ensuring that flight paths do not interfere with any member of the public.
    3. Ensure that colonies of good tempered bees are maintained as detailed in section 1.10.
    4. Move any offending bad tempered bees immediately or, if necessary, kill the stock off.
    5. Requeen if the situation is not immediately serious.

1.11.2 Requeening bad tempered colonies.

Always the problem is to find the queen and it will be a queen that is unmarked and the colony owned by an indifferent beekeeper. They always squeak when in trouble and the situation is desperate. Remove the colony if at all possible is the best advice.

It is always best to have a look at the colony quietly to see if it is really bad tempered. We have had many calls only to find that we could handle the colony without gloves and most of the trouble is the way the beekeeper manipulates the bees. Bad smoker technique, clumsy handling, etc.

By moving the colony. Early morning move the colony away from its normal position (about 8 feet) and put an empty brood box with about six combs in it to catch the foraging bees on return. Remember about 33% of the colony are foragers and sufficient comb should be provided.

At mid-day when all the foragers have gone find the queen and introduce the new one. Next morning swap the boxes over returning the hive to its original stand and the foragers in the place where the hive was temporarily placed. Remove the empty box of frames the evening of the second day. Four days later release the queen if the release is to be supervised or remove the cage if released by the bees.

By using chloroform. This is only for the really bad boys! The colony that sends the bees downwards into your 'wellies' and finds every crack in your armour. Kit up well and carefully because the returning foragers are the problem but these can be avoided by shifting the stock as above.

The method is due to the late Harrison-Ashforth, CBL for Cornwall. It works well and we have used it on quite a few occasions on other peoples bees. About 1 fluid ounce of chloroform is required, two pieces of corrugated cardboard about 3 inches square and a piece of foam to seal the entrance. The method is as follows:

- The entrance block should be in the colony. Drive the bees back from the entrance with smoke.
- Pour one teaspoonful of chloroform onto one of the pieces of cardboard push into the entrance and seal with foam or a rag.
- Do exactly the same with the second piece of cardboard putting it under the crown board; the feed hole should be covered to keep the fumes inside.
- Wait for 2 to 3 minutes.
- You then have about 10 minutes maximum to work and find the queen.
- Remove her and run another one in directly from a cage lying on the top bars.
- As soon as the new queen has walked in close up and open the entrance. The job is complete.

The chloroform affects the central nervous system of the bees and disorientates them. We assume the mechanism is that in a disorientated state they cannot recognise their own queen and immediately accept the new one. The method has, so far, never failed and Harrison - Ashforth also reported similar results with no failures.

1.12 The year's work in the apiary and how this is dependent upon the annual colony cycle and the timing of local bee forage.

The beekeeping year is generally acknowledged as starting after the main crop is removed the previous year. The year's work in the apiary is examined below on a month by month basis starting in August on the assumption that the main flow occurs in July and all the supers have been removed by the beginning of August. Included in the account below are bits of information outside the BBKA syllabus but which all good beekeepers should know.

1.12.1 The year's work in the apiary.

August: This is the month that work commences to prepare the colonies for winter. For a colony to overwinter successfully the following criteria must be met:

a) The colony must be disease free (clustering is the ideal condition for the spread of all diseases) and strong in winter bees.

b) A young fertile queen is required to head the colony.

c) 35lb of honey or the equivalent in sugar syrup is required.

d) A sound and weatherproof hive.

e) Protection from the ingress of mice.

f) Some protection from the prevailing winds.

- After supers have been removed, examine the colony and determine the quantity of stores in the brood chamber. This should be estimated frame by frame both by eye and by feeling the weight; an assistant to write down the figures is useful. Take a sample of bees at this inspection to examine for adult bee diseases. If reduced entrance blocks were not inserted when supers were removed, do this at this inspection; robbing is a serious problem at this time of the year when the flow stops fairly abruptly.
- Await the results of disease diagnosis; these results are crucial before starting to prepare the colonies for winter, ie. uniting, re-queening and feeding. Only disease free colonies should be united, never those that are being treated for disease; there is the possibility that the treatment may be unsuccessful.
- Treat for Acarine before feeding starts (feeders get in the way and the operation is easier without them).
- Feed all colonies for winter, treating those colonies for Nosema as required with Fumidil 'B' in the feed. If after inspection a colony has 15lb of stores, it will need a further 20lb of additional stores to see it through the winter; this is equivalent to feeding the colony with 16lb of sugar (nb. ripe honey contains c. 80% sugar). It has been recommended by some sources to feed Fumidil 'B' to all colonies as a prophylactic. Many bacteria can develop resistant strains when continually subjected to antibiotic treatment. There is some doubt about this mechanism working in the case of Nosema mainly because the pathogen is a protozoa and not a bacterium. Until proof is forthcoming, it would be prudent to err on the side of safety and treat only those colonies with the disease.
- If the colonies are kept in a Varroa infested area they should be treated with Bayvarol or Apistan. If these strips are used they must remain in the colonies for a minimum period of six weeks. Therefore, it is important that they are inserted in the colonies by mid August for removal at the end of September.
- Any necessary re-queening required should be completed before the end of August. The authors consider it best to avoid re-queening at this time if it is possible. If something goes wrong and a colony has to put itself to rights by raising emergency queen cells, there is a dearth of drones at this time of the year for ensuring a successful mating.

September/October: Stocks that have been to the heather will be returning during early September and these will require checking for stores and feeding if required. It is seldom that colonies come back without their brood chambers adequately filled and feeding is a rarity. The final preparations for winter are to be completed and these are done just before the autumn evenings start to develop a chill and a drop in temperature is evident.

- Mouse guards should be fitted early rather than late; mice are also making their winter preparations and seeking a dry warm place to hibernate.
- Ventilation requires attention, c. 4 gallons of water will be produced metabolising 35lb of stores. Lift the crown board by inserting matchsticks at each corner and close the centre feed hole (the roof ventilators now become inoperative). Any air flow through the hive will be in through the entrance and out under the crown board and down the sides of the hive under the roof, the smallest opening at either the top or the bottom will control the rate of flow in conjunction with the internal temperature.

- If the green woodpecker is troublesome in the apiary area then protection should be added to the stocks. Polythene can be taped or tied onto the hive sides to deny a foot (or toe) hold to the bird, in which case care should be taken not to interfere with the ventilation. Chicken wire attached to the hive and kept a few inches off it to deny the bird's beak access to the woodwork is also a suitable method of protection.
- The final preparation for winter is the roping down of the stocks if this is considered necessary. If the roofs of single walled hives have been constructed to the correct dimensions it is nigh impossible for them to be blown off. The shallow roofs of the WBC hive needs roping down for winter. The habit of placing house bricks on top of roofs is quite futile.

November/December/January: Providing all the preceding preparations have been completed satisfactorily, there is nothing the beekeeper can do to assist his bees to get through the winter to the next spring. Apiaries should be inspected regularly (say once a fortnight) or after a particularly bad spell of weather to ensure all is well. The hives should not be touched, even taking the roof off will raise the temperature of the cluster unnecessarily. If something is amiss then, of course, it must be put to rights; most mishaps seem to be associated with vandalism unfortunately. Heavy snow falls can cover the hive entrances; any snow should be very quietly cleared away without alarming the colony in order to maintain the ventilation at the bottom. The practice of feeding candy on Christmas Day still seems to persist quite widely around the country. It is a nonsense and an unnecessary disturbance to the colony if it has been prepared properly for winter.

February/March: The work to be done will depend very much on the weather and whether the colonies are flying. In the south of England the first warm day after the 3rd week in February is the author's guide.

- The first task is to change all the floorboards in the apiary and collect all the scrapings as one large apiary sample and send it away to Luddington for the Varroosis search programme if living in an area where Varroa has not yet been found. For those who already have Varroa then an inspection of the debris is always informative on the level of mite drop out that has occurred during the winter months.
- Mouse guards should be removed and reduced entrance blocks put in.
- The last job is to quickly check for sealed stores, remove the matchsticks, lower the crown board and at the same time uncover the feedhole to provide some top ventilation. This all takes a couple of minutes per hive or less with two people; the bees are hardly disturbed.
- When the first task is undertaken on a colony, the hive record for the season should be started and the first entry made. The authors keep two records, one on a hive card kept in the hive roof and the other as a computer printout on a clip board which is up-dated in manuscript in the apiary and then later on the computer. The latest version from the computerised records are taken on the clip board on the next apiary visit.
- In some areas of UK where there is an inadequate supply of early pollen, stocks which are to be used on the rape are fed pollen patties to stimulate brood rearing rather earlier than would have occurred naturally; the patties are put on about the beginning of the month.
- As the weather becomes warmer so the colony will start to fly and forage, with a result, stores are used up at a much greater rate. Water has to be collected to dilute the stored honey (only a 50% sugar solution can be metabolised) and this is a good time to start training the bees to a water supply close at hand.
- It is important to record on the hive record card from February to the end of April the colony 'build up'. The number of frames of bees and the number of frames of brood (eggs, larvae and sealed brood) should be recorded. There should be a steady increase in both.

March: If queens have been overwintered in nuclei this is the time for introduction on a warm sunny day and the bees are flying well. At each inspection when the colony is opened the following points should be recorded:

Are there sufficient stores to last to the next inspection if there is no income available?
Is the queen present and is she laying normally?
Is there any sign of disease?
Is there sufficient comb space for the queen to lay and for the bees (remember many foragers may be out when the colony is inspected)?
Has the colony built up since the last inspection and/or are there preparations for swarming?

- This is the first time that the colony is inspected and while removing and caging the old queen, the colony should be assessed and a sample of bees taken for testing for the adult bee diseases. Queens from the over-wintered nucs are then caged after marking and clipping if this is your style of beekeeping; in the author's opinion both are virtually essential. If colour coding is used, a quick method of remembering the colours is as follows:

COLOUR	LAST DIGIT OF YEAR	READ DOWN
W hite	1 or 6	W hich
Y ellow	2 or 7	Y ear
R ed	3 or 8	R eared in
G reen	4 or 9	G reat
B lue	5 or 0	B ritain

- the old queens are introduced, in Butler cages, into the nucs to keep them going until queen rearing starts again later in the year. The newly marked and clipped queens are introduced into the colonies also in Butler cages. The whole operation can be completed very quickly and the failure rate at this time of the year is very low. The advantages of this system are:

While the new queens are in nucs from May to March the characteristics of the queen's protugu can be assessed; only those that are suitable are used.
Finding queens in March with small colonies is made much easier.
The nuclei are virtually self-supporting and already made up at queen rearing time (something less to do at a busy time).
Spare queens are available at any time of the year if something does go amiss.

- All the queen cages should be removed during the following two days and a quick check made to see that all is well and the queens are laying in both the nucs and the colonies. Any colonies which are short of stores should be fed.

April: The spring flow will start during the month.

- This is the time that regular colony inspections for swarm control should commence.
- Old comb for replacement is placed at the outer edges of the brood box ready for replacing during the 2nd or 3rd week in the month.
- If any brood chambers are to be changed for repair, maintenance and disinfection, the colony can be quickly changed to a clean box at this time of the year before supers are required. Supers are added as required above the queen excluders which go on with the first super.

- Supers are added when all except the two outside frames are covered with bees (rule of thumb for both brood box and supers). Colonies should be building up very quickly and it is better to over super rather than under super early in the season.
- Colonies should be selected for fruit pollination and for going to the rape which will be coming into bloom during April.
- Any colony which is not building up or seriously lagging behind other colonies should be singled out for a special investigation to try and determine the reason. If it can be shown that it is disease free then a re-queening job is more than likely necessary. The record card should provide the evidence.

May: Usually a very busy beekeeping month with stocks being brought back from the rape and from pollination contracts.

- Regular inspections are continued for swarm control and supers added as required. We must repeat, at every inspection of the colony the following should be checked:

  Are there sufficient stores to last to the next inspection if there is no income available?
  Is the queen present and is she laying normally?
  Is there any sign of disease?
  Is there sufficient comb space for the queen to lay and for the bees (remember many foragers will be out when the colony is inspected)?
  Has the colony built up since the last inspection and/or are there preparations for swarming?

- Towards the middle of the month queen rearing should start and arrangements made for making up any nucs that may be required.
- Removal and extraction of the spring crop may also be done during the month and will be necessary if the crop is rape to prevent granulation in the comb. On this point it is necessary to know your area well; although the stocks in the apiary may not have been moved to the rape, it is extremely attractive to bees and they will fly a long way to work it particularly if other sources of nectar are a bit sparse.
- Depending on the weather and colony size the reduced entrance blocks may be removed.

June: The objective is to provide the maximum foraging force and colony size by the end of this month in order to take full advantage of the main flow.

- The colony should still be expanding and further supers may be necessary. This month is notorious in UK for a dearth of nectar and known as the June gap; occasionally it does not happen (eg. in 1989 when nectar continued to flow from March through to end of July).
- If a spring crop has been extracted, colonies may be so short of liquid stores as to require feeding. This requires extreme care to ensure that sugar syrup is not stored in the supers.

July: The main flow usually starts (UK south coast) during the first week of this month and this is what the beekeeper has been preparing for since last August. The colony should be at its peak population just as the flow starts. It is all over by the last week of the month.

- Swarm control inspections are required but it is unlikely more supers will be required for bees (hopefully for honey if the supers are being filled and capped). With 3 or 4 supers on the colonies it is a hard work lifting them off for swarm control and life is much easier with two people at the job.

- When the flow is complete and the crop ripe then it should be removed and extracted straight away.
- Reduced entrance blocks should be put in to discourage robbing.
- The wet supers should be returned to the hives for drying up after extraction unless it is preferred to store them wet. In a home apiary near neighbours it cannot be over emphasised that wet supers should only be returned to the stocks after dark. Many beekeepers do not understand the reason for this and why literally hundreds of foragers will go milling round the apiary for up to c. 100 metres causing great annoyance to any neighbours in a matter of a few minutes (nb. the round dance and the aroma of honey on the outside of the supers direct from the extracting room). There is a very great possibility that robbing can be started under these conditions.
- After removing the main crop, any stocks which are scheduled for the heather must be prepared and transported (generally by the end of the month on the south coast). The essentials for the heather stock are:

  1. A current year queen (re-queening may be required) to try and keep the brood production going.
  2. There should be a very full brood chamber with brood on all frames.
  3. The colony should have plenty of stores to see it through until the heather starts to yield.
  4. There are mixed opinions on whether the stocks should be manipulated and managed while on the moor (eg. removing brood frames when they are empty to induce greater storage in the supers).
  5. Drawn comb is generally necessary (usually very cold at 1000ft. altitude) in the supers.

1.12.2 The annual colony cycle in relation to the year's work.

Before considering the year's work in relation to the annual cycle it will first be instructive to examine why the curve has the one characteristic peak which occurs just before the main flow.

The original bees came from a tropical environment where there are two distinct seasons or monsoons creating two distinct flowering periods each year. Tropical bees have adapted to this environment where there are two main flows per year. The colonies are very prolific in order to build up to strength to utilise them to the full. If a curve was prepared for this type of bee it would have two distinct peaks where the population is a maximum just before each flow.

As the bee migrated further north to the sub tropics (Mediterranean area) the monsoons disappear and the environment is characterised by a continual flowering period throughout the year. The bees which inhabit this part of the world have a steady brood pattern throughout the year whereby the queen does not stop laying as she does in temperate zones. The yellow Italian queens have this trait and this is one of the reasons many experienced beekeepers in the UK dislike them. It is inbuilt in their genes that there is no such thing as winter and the queens continue laying very late in the year thus requiring more stores and artificial feeding.

Coming further north still to the temperate climate of UK the flowers have evolved generally to bloom in the spring and in the summer to provide the fruit and crops in the autumn. The winter conditions are too harsh for flowers to bloom and nectar to yield. The honeybee of NW Europe, *Apis mellifera mellifera*, has evolved to exist under these conditions.

Consideration of the graph in appendix 7 will indicate that the colony population is at its lowest in February and starts to increase steadily up to the end of June. The colony builds up on the spring flow to its peak generally using most of its income. The main flow starts and a large income, well in excess of requirements, is collected in a short time at the expense of large numbers of foragers which die in the fields. The flow stops abruptly and the colony prepares for winter with reduced laying of the queen until she stops completely for the winter period.

Modern methods of agriculture and intensive farming tend to upset the idealised curve as presented. Notably very heavy flows from crops such as oil seed rape, borage and lavender may be quoted.

1.12.3. The beekeepers part in the annual cycle.

During the annual cycle the beekeeper has additional work to do over and above the work outlined above. The following points we consider to be very important.

- Every two weeks the grass should be cut in the apiary and out apiaries and the grass 'strimmed' around each hive. If the hives are raised above ground level it makes it easier to cut the grass and easier to manipulate the colonies. We have usually found that in a well kept apiary, with the grass regularly tended and the hedges and fences maintained in good order, the bees and colonies are also in good shape.
- Every two years each brood chamber requires to be overhauled by scraping, blow lamp scorching, cleaning and greasing runners and finally creosoting. The same goes for all supers except that it unnecessary to scorch them as they are only used for part of the year. Any damaged woodwork requires repair to ensure that the equipment is bee proof. A phased programme is required to undertake this work on a regular basis. Roofs require to be included in the programme.
- Floorboards and entrance blocks require the same treatment every spring after they are removed from the stocks and replaced with clean ones. Also included in the annual routine are the queen excluders in August before storing for winter. The blow lamp will melt wax and propolis and disinfect all in one go.
- When supers have been recovered from the hives after extraction of the crop and drying by the bees, all the boxes and frames should be scraped clean before storing with PDB and newspaper.
- In the months of May and June there is much grass cut all over the country often by the sides of roads. It dries quickly in good weather and turns into hay. Collect a sack (hessian) full in a matter of a few minutes and the smoker fuel problem is solved for another year.

1.13 The drifting of honeybees, the dangers caused and techniques used to minimise the problem.

1.13.1 The definition of drifting and general considerations.

It is generally accepted that drifting occurs when a bee leaves one hive and **mistakenly** joins another hive either as a result of confusion or as a result of the bee being blown off course by the wind.

When drifting occurs and the wrong worker bee attempts to enter the wrong hive, it is usually challenged by the guards. The drifting bee's behaviour is different to those of other worker bees entering the hive; it can readily be observed that it 'bribes' the guards by offering some nectar (they are usually returning with a full load) while it is being examined by them. No fighting occurs.

On the other hand, drones drift much more freely than worker bees and appear to be readily accepted into any hive generally without being challenged.

Drifting occurs most in young bees during the first 4 days of their adult life and N.E. Gary claims that this happens with about 20% of these young bees. This happens during 'play flights' when the young bees start to take orientation flights (also simultaneously cleansing flights). It is an unusual behaviour pattern because many young bees do this in quite large numbers and can be seen hovering in front of the entrance for a few minutes which ends quite abruptly and the activity at the entrance returns to normal. Subsequent play flights are extended in range away from the hive and this is when the drifting is more likely to occur.

Drifting only occurs in man made apiaries. It does not occur in feral colonies because they are so widely separated under normal circumstances.

1.13.2 Apiary configurations and associated disadvantages.

When hives (usually of the same colour and design) within an apiary are sited in the same direction in long rows severe drifting may be expected; and the closer they are together the more severe the problem. If there is no effects by a prevailing wind then it has been observed that the centre colonies of the row are weakened at the expense of the end colonies of the row. If there is a prevailing wind effect then the colonies to leeward will be strengthened.

If the apiary has more than one row of hives also facing in the same direction, then the front row will be strengthened at the expense of the rows behind (the bees drift forwards).

In the situations outlined above it has been noted, in America, that the difference in yield amounts to about 20lb per season in the hives that have been fortified with drifting bees.

The disadvantages of selecting a poor layout are as follows:

> a) In large apiaries in rows it would be necessary to balance the colonies to maintain them at roughly equal strengths. When some colonies become very strong while nearby colonies are weak, then this is a recipe for robbing to start when a flow comes to an abrupt end.
> b) If there is disease in a colony the bees drifting from this colony can carry the disease pathogens to the other colony. All the bee diseases can be transmitted to hives in the same apiary by this mechanism.

1.13.3 Methods of minimising drifting within the apiary.

The most important feature of any apiary layout to prevent drifting is to adopt an irregular pattern of hive layout with the hives facing in different directions and adopting curved lines, arcs, circles, etc. Perhaps the best regular pattern to adopt is having the hives in blocks of four each facing in different directions at right angles to each other (eg. N, S, E & W). These blocks of four can be repeated about 5 metres spacing between the blocks. We use this in one of our apiaries and find virtually no drifting occurs with worker bees.

Our home apiary of six colonies is by necessity in a long row (there is no other way) with 9 ft between each hive. Drifting is quite prevalent but it something that we have to accept. Matilda Herz showed by experiment that it was possible to train bees to recognise marks at their hive entrances. They are able to recognise the difference between solid and open patterns but unable to distinguish between solid shapes or between open shapes. We tried this in our own apiary by making the shapes in white formica about 6 in x 6 in and attaching them, alternately solid and open, onto the alighting boards of each hive in the row. We could not confirm the results claimed by Matilda Herz and drifting still occurred.

Other methods of providing aids to navigation within the apiary are:

a) Hive entrances of different colours. This is very popular in Germany and elsewhere on the Continent.
b) Providing a discrete marker at or adjacent to each hive entrance, eg. a stone, a bush etc.

1.13.4 Other points of interest.

• Queenless colonies are an attraction especially at queen rearing time. Although this is technically not a drifting problem, virgin queens from swarms will drift in if in the near vicinity. We had our queen rearing programme ruined one year by a stray swarm alighting on a tree in our home apiary and virgins from the swarm entered our cell builder and destroyed all our cells!
• Our experience has been that no matter what apiary layout we have adopted, drones hop in and out of any hives, willy-nilly, the whole season.

1.14 The principles involved in feeding bees, including types of feeder, amounts of food, types of food and timing of feeding.

1.14.1 The principles of feeding a colony of bees.

The reasons for feeding a colony sugar are shown below:

a) To provide adequate stores for winter (rapid feeding).
b) To provide emergency stores in the season between colony inspections (rapid feeding).
c) As a means of administering drugs (generally rapid feeding).
d) To stimulate the queen to lay (usually slow feeding).
e) To prevent starvation when the colony is about to succumb (rapid).
f) To enhance wax production and the drawing of foundation and comb (slow or rapid depending on circumstances, eg. a swarm on foundation is fed rapidly).
g) When a colony has an inadequate foraging force, eg. an artificial swarm which is short of stores (rapid feeding) or after spray poisoning losses.

The precautions to take when feeding honeybee colonies:

a) There should be no spilling or dripping of syrup anywhere in the apiary.
b) Precautions should be taken to prevent robbing (reduced entrances and bee tight hives).
c) Feed should only be administered in the evening just before dark.
d) No sugar syrup should find its way into the supers and be mixed eventually with honey for extraction and sale.
e) Only pure white refined granulated sugar should be used.

Preparing syrup for feeding: Generally there are two types of mix, a thick syrup for autumn feeding which will be stored more or less immediately and thin syrup for spring or stimulative feeding which is to be consumed without storing. Most of the literature quotes the following:

Thick – 2lb. sugar to 1pint of water gives 61.5% sugar concentration
Thin – 1lb. sugar to 2pint of water gives 28.0% sugar concentration
Medium – 1kg. sugar to 1 litre of water gives 50.0% sugar concentration

Since the bee requires a concentration of 50% for it to digest and metabolise the sugar then it is clear which is the best one to use if they are to use it straight away. If sugar syrup is to be mixed with cold water, it will be found difficult to obtain a complete mix with 2lb to 1pint The authors use a mix with cold water of 7lb to 5pint in an old washing machine (top loader with central agitator). The concentration works out to be 52.8%, less than 61.5% and hence giving the bees a bit more work to do ripening it to 80% for storing and sealing. As we feed for winter immediately after extracting in August, this causes the bees no distress as they have plenty of time to get their larder in the order they require it before the cold nights set in.

1.14.2 The most common types of feeders in use.

The requirements of a good feeder are to allow the bees to take the syrup at the rate required by the beekeeper for the management of the colony, while at the same time preventing the bees from drowning in the syrup. Finally, when the feeding is finished, access should be provided for the bees into the feeder so that the bees can clean and dry it up (a job they can do very efficiently given the chance). There is quite an array of feeders available, not all of them meeting the criteria above and many of them being manufactured in materials that can corrode or are difficult to clean. A further disadvantage of some types is that they are capable of being propolised by the bees so that without maintenance they become unusable. The various types commonly available are listed below:

Contact feeders: these come in a variety of shapes and sizes but are all similar in design having a container with a close fitting lid. The lid has a series of small holes or a small piece of gauze through which the bees take the syrup when it is turned upside down over the feed hole or directly onto the frames in the colony. The number of holes regulate the speed that the bees can take the contents. It has the advantage of being cheap and can be readily made at short notice from a bewildering assortment of household containers. The disadvantages are as follows:

a) The bees quickly propolise the small feed holes as soon as it is empty.
b) As the contents are coming to an end, a change in temperature can force the last

remaining contents out causing a minor flood of syrup in the hive (usually cleaned up quickly by the bees).

c) They are a bit messy to fill and invert without spilling syrup unless one is very careful.

d) An eke is required in order to house the feeder under the roof.

Round top feeders: are very widely used in UK and are intended to be placed over a feed hole in the crown board. The capacity varies from c.1 pint to 2 or 3 pints depending on the diameter. The height is usually about 3 inches. The entry is via a tube in the centre and down the outside of the tube to the syrup. The whole of the centre feeding area is enclosed by a removable cover for cleaning. Older versions were made of metal but now most are manufactured in plastic which is better from a corrosion point of view. This type of feeder is easily filled in situ without the bees escaping in the process. Again an eke is necessary.

Miller feeders: were designed by Dr.C.C.Miller in USA and consist of a tray, about 3in (76mm) deep, with dimensions in the horizontal plane exactly matching the external sizes of the brood chamber or supers of the hive it is intended to fit. The entry for the bees is via a slot in the centre extending from one side to the other; again it is provided with a cover to prevent the bees from escaping. The capacity is from 1 to 2 gallons. It allows many bees to feed simultaneously thereby allowing very rapid consumption of the syrup (a strong colony can finish the contents in 24 hrs.). Construction is generally in wood with all joints glued to prevent leakage. For bottom bee space hives, a bee space is required on the under side of the feeder.

Ashforth feeders: are virtually identical with the Miller feeder except that the feeding slot is placed at one side allowing the hive to be tilted slightly thereby permitting all the syrup to flow towards the feed slot which is impossible with the Miller type and therefore an improvement. The advantage of allowing all the syrup to be consumed before the tray is opened to the bees for cleaning is that there are no pools of syrup for the bees to drown in.

Bro. Adam feeders: are similar to the Miller and Ashforth except that they have a central entry similar to the Round top type feeders. They are becoming more popular in UK due to some equipment suppliers now manufacturing them. The feeders on the stocks at Buckfast Abbey double up as a crown board (therefore every stock has its own feeder).

All the feeders quoted above are designed for top feeding. Other feeders are available for internal feeding and bottom feeding (which is seldom practised in UK). The internal feeder is in the form of a brood frame with wooden sides and an opening at the top to allow access to the bees. The frame feeder is used for feeding nuclei; the capacity is inadequate for a colony and few would wish to open the colony in order to feed it. A disadvantage of this type of feeder is the bees propolising the float arrangement (to prevent the bees drowning) in the frame feeder at the bottom when the contents have been consumed.

1.14.3 The amounts of food to be fed.

Emergency feeding. It is necessary to know the amount of food that a colony requires during the season so that, after an inspection, the beekeeper can determine whether it shall require feeding or whether it has sufficient stores to the next inspection. The worst case must always be considered and that is when the colony sends out its foragers and they are unrewarded in their search for food.

A flying bee uses 10mg honey per hour while foraging for an average time of 5 hours per day. If the colony has 13,000 foragers ($\frac{1}{3}$ of the total population) and the next inspection is 7 days away, then the colony should have 10lb of liquid stores.

ie. $10lb = (13000 \times 10 \times 10^{-3} \times 5 \times 7) \div 454$

Therefore, if the colony has less than 10lb of stores it may require emergency feeding if there is no income and the weather is inclement. The amount required is likely to be small, ie. a few pounds.

The same considerations are applicable to nuclei and many a nuc has died out due to starvation because of ignorance of the beekeeper not understanding the little colony's food requirements.

Winter feeding. We are alarmed and distressed by the large number of beekeepers who either don't know how much food a colony requires for winter or, if they do know, have no idea how to calculate how much it should be fed. Most losses each year in the UK are due to starvation and amount to thousands of colonies according to a MAFF survey some years ago. We doubt if the situation has changed. If the RSPCA knew more about bees they would be taking some action against the offending beekeepers.

The calculation is a simple bit of arithmetic and the starting point is a colony inspection in August. Each frame in the brood chamber is inspected and the amount of liquid stores estimated on the basis that a BS frame when full and sealed with honey weighs 5lb. A Commercial frame holds 7lb.

A strong colony requires c. 35lb to see it through to the spring without feeding early in the new year when stores are used up very quickly. It is often said that a beekeeper who has to feed his colonies in the spring should not be keeping bees! To illustrate the simplicity of the calculation, assume the colony has 25lb of stores after the inspection. The colony requires 35 – 25 = 10lb of additional stores or the honey equivalent thereof. How much sugar must be fed in syrup form to provide the equivalent of 10lb of honey? 1lb of honey contains c. 0.8lb of sugar, therefore, 8lb of sugar should be fed in syrup form. If the colony required 15lb of additional stores then the amount of sugar = 15 × 0.8 = 12lb sugar. It is as simple as that and yet very few beekeepers take the trouble to do the job properly and many colonies starve to death.

1.14.4 The types of feed that are fed to bees.

The types of feed that are fed to colonies of honeybees:

1. The standard feed is white refined household quality sugar either from cane or beet sources (ie. refined sucrose). No brown or unrefined sugar is permissible.
2. It was recommended at one time to feed candy or fondant. It is now used only for special applications (eg. micro mating nucs or the like). If cream of tartar or vinegar is contained in the recipe, both are toxic to bees cf. refined sucrose. It is best not to feed either candy or fondant if it can be avoided.
3. Dry sugar (again refined sucrose) is used by some beekeepers in a tray type crown board usually in the early part of the year supposedly as an insurance policy. It is not recommended because unless water is provided it is extremely difficult for the bees to produce enough saliva to dissolve the crystals.
4. Honey. This should only be fed when it comes from the beekeeper's own apiary and

is known to be disease free. Many imported honeys carry AFB spores and are highly dangerous and must under no circumstances be used.

5. Pollen patties are often fed in the early part of the year to provide additional protein where pollen may be in short supply or where colonies are being induced to start brood rearing early. There are two types namely, pollen substitutes (fat free soya flour) and pollen supplements (using trapped pollen; again the source should be from the beekeepers apiaries from disease free colonies).

6. A comb of sealed honey can often be usefully taken from a disease free colony and used in another requiring urgent liquid stores.

1.14.5 The timing of feeding a colony of honeybees.

All feeding of colonies of honeybees should be undertaken only in the evening when it is just getting dark. The reason for this is not explained at all well in most books on bee husbandry. This is curious because it is so important particularly when bees are being kept in gardens at close quarters with neighbours.

The reason is that as soon as food is given to a colony during daylight hours, the scout bees will be alerted and will start roaming the immediate neighbourhood for the source. It seems to be a shortcoming of the communication system of the bees. Presumably a round dance occurs and out go the foragers to seek the source and mayhem starts in the apiary with the attendant possibility of robbing being started also. It seems that the colony has no sure means of indicating to the other foragers in the colony that the source is just above them over the brood chamber in a feeder.

Bees are not equipped for night flying and will not fly in the dark. Hence, all feeding should be done at night. The same goes for putting wet supers back on a colony for drying up after extraction.

1.14.6 Other points of interest.

- Each hive should have its own feeder. When feeding starts, particularly in the autumn, all stocks should be fed at the same time.
- There are advantages in combining the feeder as the permanent crown board; it is always available for use and if it stay on one stock it cannot pass on disease by using it on another colony.
- Open tray feeders with straw or polystyrene chips floating in the syrup are messy and not particularly efficient, the bees often seem to find the 'deep end' and drown in the syrup. Not recommended.
- It is good practice to check the feeders each year for leaks with water before being brought into use.
- Communal feeding has been advocated by some authors by providing a common feeder in the apiary for all colonies to fly to and help themselves. We do not recommend it as the disadvantages far out weigh the advantages. No control can be exercised over what each stock needs and takes. Disease can be spread by this means and you are likely to be feeding someone else's bees!

1.15 The value of honey and pollen to the colony.

1.15.1 General.

- Nutrition in the animal kingdom is a chemical process changing carbohydrates, fats, proteins, etc. into bodily materials (muscles, tissues, etc.) and also into energy, both mechanical and heat.
- Honey / nectar (carbohydrates) is broken down into simple sugars and then converted into fat and glycogen during the nutritional process.
- Pollen (protein) is split into basic building blocks called amino acids and fats which are either absorbed or broken down to glycerol or fatty acids.
- Honey is the energy source and pollen is for growth, repair and development.
- Little is known about the digestion of fats and vitamin requirements of the honeybee.
- Most of the research work on nutrition in connection with honeybees was undertaken a long time ago and very little work on the subject has been undertaken during the last 20 to 30 years.

1.15.2 The value of honey to the colony.

- The major carbohydrates in nectar or honey are sucrose, glucose and fructose. In addition honey contains many other sugars (trisaccharides and higher orders) but only 5 are understood to be sweet and nutritious to the bee (Von Frisch, 1934).
- All the higher order sugars represent a very small percentage of the total sugars and from a value to the bee aspect, they may be ignored.
- Energy required during flight is derived exclusively from the breakdown of carbohydrates. The blood sugar content is very important and the following values should be noted:

Hive bee has	blood sugar level	c. 2%
Flying worker bee has	blood sugar level	c. 3%
Unable to fly if	blood sugar level	<1%
Motionless if	blood sugar level	<0.5%

- Flying bees require c. 10mg per hour and drones c. 30mg per hour.
- Ambient temperature is very important, Olaerts in 1956 found with caged bees :

  at c. 52°F (11°C) a bee requires c. 10mg sugar per hour
  at c. 98°F (37°C) a bee requires c. 0.7mg ditto
  at c. 118°F (48°C) a bee requires c. 1.4mg ditto

- Hypopharyngeal gland development is not initiated on nectar / honey only, pollen is a necessary part of the diet.
- Beeswax is produced by the metabolism of sugars by the fat bodies and wax glands.
- The chitin of the exoskeleton is a nitrogenous polysaccharide made up of glucose molecules in combination.
- The amount of honey required to rear one worker bee has been estimated to be c. 100mg in the range 50 to 150mg

1.15.3 The value of pollen to the colony.

Pollen is the male germ cell of flowering plants (angiosperms); it has two major uses:
    a) It is the principal source of protein, fat, vitamins and minerals in the honeybee diet,
    b) It can provide a surplus product from the apiary.
In this section of the syllabus we are only concerned with (a) above.

Pollen demand in the colony is related to the amount of unsealed brood. Bees cannot rear brood without pollen because the nurse bees would not be able to produce brood food from the hypopharyngeal glands. A strong colony will collect c. 50 – 100lb during a season.

It requires 70 – 150mg of pollen to rear one adult bee.
About 200,000 bees are reared during a season thus accounting for more than 50% of the income.
The balance is used by the adult bees preparing for winter (increasing their fat bodies) and/or stored in the comb for use early the following year before new supplies become available.

Note the weight of a worker bee = c.90mg and that 1lb of bees contains c. 5000 bees.

Pollen is rich in protein and is essential for body building material for growth/development and for the repair of worn out tissue. It also has the very important function of stimulating the development of the hypopharyngeal glands and the fat bodies of the winter bee. The protein content varies between different pollen types and also from flower to flower in the same foraging area. A protein content of c. 35% is typical of a high protein pollen eg. beans. Bees can discriminate between pollens by colour and odour; they cannot distinguish between the quality (protein content) of various pollens. Pollen is sometimes known as 'bee bread'.

Pollen contains:
- proteins   7 – 35%
- lipids (fats/oils)   1 – 14%
- amino acids   ?
- carbohydrates   ?
- minerals   1 – 5%
- vitamins   ?
- enzymes   ?
- water   7 – 15%
- sugars   25 – 48%

There are wide variations in the content of different pollens and the bee more than likely receives a balance diet due the variety of pollens collected and used. (? = no information found).

The use of pollen for brood rearing and development of the adult bee:

1. Worker larvae are fed brood food only from 0 to 3 d. and then on 4th and 5th day with pollen, honey and brood food.
2. Queens both adult and larvae are fed exclusively on royal jelly.
3. After emergence of the worker bee, pollen is essential for it to reach maturity in a healthy state. It depends on pollen for its orderly development of its glandular system while it is a house bee.
4. The pollen required to rear one bee = c. 120mg. If 200,000 bees are produced in the course of one year, then c. 50lb of pollen is required to be collected.
5. Pollen is also required for the glandular development of the newly emerged bee. First the hypopharyngeal glands and finally the sting glands just before it takes up guard duties prior to foraging.
6. The conversion of pollen into protein has been calculated to have an efficiency of about 40%, ie. 10mg of pollen will produce about 4mg of protein.
7. A strong colony at the peak of its brood rearing requires about $\frac{1}{2}$lb pollen per day.

In areas where natural pollen is in short supply, particularly in the spring, pollen patties can be fed to colonies to stimulate spring build up. Pollen shortage often occurs where colonies are foraging on honeydew in pine woods.

1.15.4 Other points in connection with honey and pollen.

There are other important items in connection with nutrition which should be noted. These are:

Lipids – little is known in relation to the honeybee.

Vitamins – pollen is known to have a high vitamin content but again the effects of the various vitamins is largely unknown and little work has been undertaken. Vitamins are essential for the growth and development of living organisms.

Minerals – much the same situation exists with minerals as with vitamins but to a worse degree. The study of minerals in the nutrition of the honeybee and insects in general is probably the most neglected area.

Water – is essential for life in the animal and plant world.

1.16 The principles of supering honeybee colonies and the relationship between supering and swarm prevention.

1.16.1 The principles of supering.

1.16.1.1 Definitions:

Super. A box containing frames/combs placed above the brood chamber for the eventual storage of honey. The word 'super' is derived from the Latin word super meaning above (eg. super-script as opposed to sub-script). Supers are generally shallower than brood chambers because of the weight when full of honey; other than this, there is no technical reason why they shouldn't be any depth providing the frames can be accommodated in the extractor.

Supering: is the process of adding supers to a colony above the brood chamber either with or without a queen excluder under the super(s).

Top supering: is the term given to adding further supers to a colony but always adding them on top of any existing supers.

Bottom supering: no prizes for guessing that the supers are added at the bottom of the pile and always next to the brood chamber.

1.16.1.2 Principles involved.

Reference to the annual colony population cycle graph (appendix 7) shows the very rapid increase in adult bee population from the beginning of March. It is not long, providing the weather is fine, that the brood chamber starts to fill up with both brood and bees and if nothing is done there will be insufficient room for the emerging brood. Additional space is therefore provided by adding supers, usually one at a time, as required by the colony build up.

On this basis, supers are for bees and, indeed, this can be very true if the colony is using most of or all its income. In such a situation nothing will be stored in the supers and it will be used solely as a parking place for bees in the colony. If this additional space is not provided, overcrowding will occur and this congestion in the hive leads to a breakdown in the food sharing pattern and subsequent distribution of queen substance with a result that the liability to swarm is greatly enhanced.

When the honeybee undertakes the manipulation and ripening of nectar to honey, large areas of comb are required for the nectar / honey to be 'hung up' to dry in order to evaporate the water. The change in volume of nectar (30% sugar concentration by weight) to honey (80% sugar by weight) is approximately 100:30 thus requiring c. 3.3 times the space for nectar compared with the space required by the finished product.

The calculation looks like this:

    1 litre honey weighs c. 1400g   (80% sugar 20% water by weight)
    1 litre of water weighs 1000g

        1400g honey = 1120g sugar + 280g water
and   1000ml honey = 720ml sugar + 280ml water
∴   1g sugar has a volume of 720 ÷ 1120 = 0.64ml

CONCENTRATION	SUGAR	WATER	TOTAL
Nectar 30%	30g	70g	100g
	19.2ml	70ml	89.2ml
Honey 80%	30g	7.5g	37.5g
	19.2ml	7.5ml	26.7ml

It will be seen that 89.2ml of nectar (30%) when processed to honey only requires a volume of 26.7ml; this is a change of 89.2 ÷ 26.7 = 3.3.

There are only two principles involved as detailed above and summarised below:

    1. Primarily to provide space for bees, and
    2. To provide comb area for ripening nectar.

If adequate space is provided for evaporation then it will be clear that there will be adequate space for honey storage.

1.16.1.3 Other points related to supering:

    a) By experience it has been found that a good working guide for supering is to add a super when the bees are covering all but the two outside frames of the top box or initially the brood chamber.
    b) It is better to super early in the spring and be somewhat tardy about adding supers in July when the main flow is on unless this is absolutely necessary.
    c) In general, top supering is the most widely used method of adding supers. Bottom supering is advantageous if the frames in the super contain only foundation; ie. placing

them above the brood chamber, the warmest place in the hive for the wax makers to work.

d) There are quite a few beekeepers that super without the use of a queen excluder; however, the majority use an excluder. Again there are beekeepers who advocate not using an excluder in the spring when the first super goes on to encourage the bees into it more quickly. It is true the bees always seem to be somewhat tardy about occupying the first super but this may be due to observing the rule of being just a little ahead of the bees requirements (super when the two outside frames are uncovered).

e) See section 1.5 on spacing of frames. Narrow spacing is essential when starting with foundation which can be widened out to 2in (51mm) when drawn and being filled with honey. The maximum of 2in (51mm) is the maximum that a colony will build for the storage of honey in the wild state and cut comb containers have been designed on this thickness.

f) If the super contains frames with foundation only, one or two frames of drawn comb in the middle will encourage the bees into the super more quickly.

g) Wet stored supers are more attractive to the bees in the spring cf. dry supers.

h) The first super above the queen excluder is likely to have some pollen filled cells in it. Pollen will always be stored above the brood where it is to be used. Ensure that supers for cut comb or any kind of comb honey are above the first super. Pollen in comb honey is unacceptable for sale; it has a bitter taste.

1.16.2 The importance of supering as a factor in swarm prevention.

The most important factor which causes a colony of bees to swarm is the lack of an adequate threshold level of queen substance throughout the colony which was discovered and proved by a series of experiments by Dr.C.Butler at Rothamsted in the 1950s.

However, it is known by observation, but not proved, that other factors appear to have an influence on swarming. These other factors include:

Season	Weather
Shade	Ventilation
State of flow	District
Strain of bee	Comb space (queen)
Manipulations	Comb space (honey)

Considering the two principles of supering, it will be clear that by providing additional empty comb and thereby additional space, not only are the last two conditions relieved but ventilation is also improved. The additional comb space in the supers provides the needed storage space for nectar and honey leaving the comb in the brood chamber for the queen to lay in. The overriding factor is the prevention of congestion within the hive and the efficient distribution of queen substance. There has been virtually no work done on the absolute threshold level of queen substance required by worker bees and in the absence of this knowledge young queens producing the maximum amount is the best course of action. The strain of bee is an important factors and some strains do swarm very much more than others. We do not believe that manipulating a colony will induce it to swarm. On the contrary, the leave alone beekeeper who never looks inside his colonies is unaware of any swarming! Season, shade, weather, ventilation and state of the flow are all claimed to have some effect on swarming; however, we have never established any direct link over many years of beekeeping. The final one is district and the only reference to this that we are aware of is in MAFF Bulletin 206 'Swarming of bees' which is regrettably out of print. Records were kept of swarming in Wiltshire and Essex many years ago and while Wiltshire experienced heavy swarming, Essex was comparatively light.

1.17 The prevention, detection and control of swarming.

1.17.1 The definitions and what is involved:

- **Swarm prevention:** is the action(s) taken by the beekeeper to prevent the colony reaching the state whereby it starts to build queen cells.
- **Swarm control:** is the action(s) taken by the beekeeper to thwart the colony in its endeavours to swarm once the preparations for swarming have been started thereby preventing the loss of bees.
- **Detection of swarming preparations:** this is necessary before any swarm control measures are put into practice. The ability to detect the preparations is prerequisite to any control actions.
- **Frequency of inspections:** for swarm detection is dependent on whether the queen is clipped or unclipped (see appendix 4).

Each will be examined separately. However, a further basic distinction must be made and that is between the stocks in the home (or fixed) apiary and those stocks which have been moved for pollination or to exploit a source of nectar (eg. rape in the spring). The control method is likely to vary depending on whether the stock is close to hand where additional spare equipment is readily available or on a remote site where spare equipment is not readily available. On this basis two methods of control will be discussed.

It is necessary to control swarming for a number of reasons which are frequently overlooked by many beekeepers, these are:

- A colony that swarms is unlikely to produce a surplus cf. the colony that does not lose its bees; this is to the detriment of the beekeeper but of little consequence to anyone else.
- Most of the general public are petrified of bees and if not petrified then they have an innate 'api-phobia'. In an urban environment it is essential that no swarm settles on a neighbouring property (this cannot be guaranteed).
- When a colony swarms, there are many thousands of bees flying around which most people find very frightening and can be classed as a nuisance in an urban or suburban environment.

1.17.2 Swarm prevention. It is imperative that the role of queen substance in relation to swarming is thoroughly understood before proceeding further. In section 1.16 the importance of supering as a factor in the prevention of swarming was examined. It is important to understand the role of queen substance and the inter-relationship between food sharing and congestion in the colony as the trigger in the process of swarming. The prerequisite in swarm prevention is that the colony must be headed by a young queen in order that each bee in the colony is assured of its minimum threshold quota of queen substance (see appendix 5). When an adequate supply is available at its source (ie. the queen), the next most important factor in swarm prevention is to ensure that the supply can be distributed around the colony; this can only happen if there is plenty of comb for the bees and hence no congestion. Add good hive ventilation and the beekeeper can do little else in the way of prevention. Nevertheless, having done all this a colony may proceed to build queen cells and it is incumbent on the beekeeper to control the issue of a swarm.

In connection with congestion Lenski and Slabazki investigated population density (PD) within the hive and showed that there was a direct relationship between PD and the number of queen cups which are built. Their findings are summarised below:

PD = 0.64 bees/ml
: The queen can move freely over all the frames depositing footprint odour.

PD = 1.4 bees/ml
: Colony becoming overcrowded and bees begin to congregate at the bottoms of the combs and the queen does not visit this area. The result is that the colony builds queen cups at the bottom of the combs. Our own observations indicate that this happens at all the edges of the combs.

PD = 2 bees/ml
: Queen cup threshold.

PD = 3 bees/ml
: 4 queen cups were built at the bottom of the comb.

PD = 5.5 bees/ml
: 8 queen cups built.

PD = 9 bees/ml
: 16 queen cups built.

PD > 2.3 bees/ml
: The number of queen cups built is directly proportional to the population density.

The above work by Lenski correlates with the work done by Butler, whereby the number of queen cells built was directly related to the time the queen was absent from the colony.

1.17.3 Detection of swarming preparations. It is very important for every beekeeper to be able to recognise the preparations for swarming while undertaking a routine inspection. At the beginning of the season the colony will have no drones and no queen cups (easily recognised; being almost identical in shape and size to acorn cups). As the colony builds up drones will appear and queen cups (known in some parts of the country as play cells; reason unknown) will be built around the outer limits of the brood nest. It is important to examine them closely. If eggs are found in them it does not follow they will be turned into queen cells; in many cases the eggs are eaten by the bees. However, if the cup contains royal jelly, a larva will also be present which is sometimes difficult to see floating in the pool of liquid as the egg may have only recently hatched. This is the sign that preparations for swarming have commenced and swarm control proceedings must be initiated. The simple rules are:

1. Dry queen cups (nothing in them or egg only); the situation can be left to the next inspection.
2. Charged queen cups (containing royal jelly); initiate swarm control procedures.

If all the queen cups have a dull matt finish on the inside, preparations for swarming have definitely not started; the cells will be polished before the queen will lay in them.

When swarming is imminent there will be a marked reduction in the laying of the queen and fewer eggs are likely to be seen.

1.17.4 The frequency of inspections (Reference should be made to appendix 4 – Colony Inspections – timing).

In order to determine the timing of inspections for swarm preparation it is necessary to understand the mechanism involved and the process of events inside the colony. Subject to the weather being favourable, a swarm will issue with the old queen just after the first queen cell is sealed. If the weather is inclement, then the swarm will not emerge until the weather has improved. The swarm can contain the old queen plus virgin(s) if the time is 8 days after the first queen cell was sealed or rarely virgins only (the old queen having been killed by the virgin(s)) if the time is 8 days or more. Inspection 1 reveals no preparations for swarming and the diagram assumes that immediately the inspection is complete, the colony decides to start preparations to swarm. The process of events is shown for both an unclipped queen (swarm out and lost at sealing of the first queen cell) and a clipped queen (swarm out and back without the queen at the same time). The colony that had a clipped queen will swarm with the first virgin(s) to emerge at day 16. This all assumes that the beekeeper takes no action after the inspection postulated at day 1.

Inspection 2 reveals unsealed queen cells and the old queen still present at the end of day 6. All the queen cells are now destroyed. It is possible for the colony to build queen cells over 3 day old larvae (the oldest larvae that can become a queen) immediately after the inspection is complete when the old queen is still present. If this happens the diagram shows the process of events if no action is taken by the beekeeper. With an unclipped queen a swarm issues 2 days later and with a clipped queen it issues and is lost in 10 days time.

From the diagram it will be clear that with an unclipped queen inspections must be on a regular 7 day basis (INU – Inspection normal unclipped) and for a clipped queen every 9 days on a regular basis (INC2). However, with a clipped queen inspections may be on a 14 day basis (INC1) until such time as swarming preparations are found.

1.17.5 Swarm control. Over the years there have been three theories of swarming, namely:

   – Brood food (postulated by Gerstung in 1890).
   – Congestion (postulated by Demuth in 1921).
   – Queen substance (postulated and **proved** by Butler in 1953).

Only the latter satisfactorily explains why a colony swarms and is now accepted as the only correct theory of swarming. Congestion prevents queen substance from being distributed around the colony and is therefore, in itself, not a theory. The brood food theory was accepted for a long time but is now regarded as being incorrect; it is based on the surmise that as the colony builds up, an excess of brood food is produced and this is used in queen cells that are built to absorb this surplus.

Most swarm control methods involve finding the queen and some require finding and destroying queen cells which in turn requires shaking bees off frames. Allied with these operations of controlling, regular inspections are required to know when to undertake them. Such inspections and control can only be undertaken with good tempered bees and ensuring the 'right strain' is **a necessary part** of swarm control. When the colony becomes bad tempered, regular inspections get abandoned, the colony swarms and the bad temper is promulgated further around the district. This indeed must be classed as anti-social behaviour on the part of the beekeeper. The authors believe that a major contributory cause of such situations arising is the present day obsession to wear gloves to manipulate the colony. If the norm were no gloves (kept in reserve for the real emergency) then colonies would be requeened before situations got out of hand. If colonies cannot be handled without gloves, then the handling technique or the strain of bee is at fault and should be corrected without delay. Anyone keeping bees in an urban garden should consider this point long and hard.

Two methods of swarm control are described in section 1.20 as required by the syllabus.

1.18 Methods of taking and hiving swarms of honeybees.

1.18.1 General considerations about swarms. Before considering how to take and hive a swarm, a few points of interest are listed below which will assist in understanding the task to be undertaken:

- There are two types of swarm, a prime swarm and a cast. They differ in size, the prime swarm containing about 50% of the original colony and the casts being very much smaller (as little as a cupful of bees in some cases).
- Swarms settle initially within a few metres of the original colony. The prime swarm is generally predictable in its behaviour, remaining where it first settled until it has decided on a new nesting place before moving (a matter of a few hours or rarely a over a week). In very rare cases they never make up their 'mind' and try to establish comb and a nest outside where they have settled; they invariably perish with the onset of cold and bad weather. Conversely, a cast is very fickle and will take off quickly (can be within the hour) and resettle somewhere else close at hand or at a distance. A cast usually has a virgin(s) queen which provides less queen substance than a fertile queen and therefore the colony cohesion is poor with casts; hence their fickle behaviour.
- The settling place can be almost anywhere; on a post, on a wall, in a tree or bush, on a fence, under eaves, high or low, etc. Because of this diversity, only broad guidelines can be enunciated for taking them and the beekeeper will have to use his own ingenuity depending on the situation.
- Swarms when they first emerge are generally very docile (even bees of doubtful temper) because they have gorged themselves full of honey before departure for immediate future comb building operations. The longer the swarm hangs up after its emergence, the more its behaviour will return to the normal temperament of the bees and this can be anything from good to aggressive. For this reason swarms from unknown sources should be approached with caution and every effort made to determine their history (eg. how long has the swarm been there?).
- After the swarm has settled it forms a cluster with an outside shell of bees about 3in (76mm) thick with a hollow centre. The outer shell has a small entry exit hole about 1in (25mm) diameter. Close examination of the outer surface will reveal, after about an hour, dancing bees. There may be dances indicating different locations while the swarm is 'arguing' until concensus is reached on which site to choose as a final resting place.
- Swarms can vary very considerably in size and therefore weight which can range from a few ounces for a cast to 8 or 10lb for a prime swarm. The skep or box to transport the swarm must be capable of carrying the load.
- Swarms can carry disease and swarms from an unknown origin should be hived in an isolation apiary in the first instance until their state of health has been determined.

1.18.2 Taking a swarm. There are different methods depending on the situation of the swarm; these can be classified into the following broad categories:

1. Shaking the swarm into a skep.
2. Smoking the swarm up into a skep.
3. Enticing the swarm into a nuc with a chemical swarm lure.
4. Using a frame of brood to attract the swarm onto it.
5. Brushing the whole swarm down into a more convenient place so that it can walk into a skep.

The prerequisite of taking any swarm is to get the queen into the skep. Once this is done all the rest of the bees will join her.

The essential equipment required for taking swarms is as follows:

a) A good sized skep, mouth to be 14in (356mm) diameter or larger. Some swarms are often quite wide and anything smaller makes the operation that much more difficult.
b) A second small skep, about 9in (229mm) diameter. This is useful for collecting any stragglers if the first shake is not as clean as it might be.
c) A piece of cloth or net curtain to close the mouth of the large skep by gathering it up and tying over the top of the skep.
d) Secateurs, string and small block of wood to put under the skep (there never seems to be a suitable stone in sight at the right time).
e) Butler cage for caging the queen if she is found.

All the above can be kept in the skeps and ready for immediate use (maybe in the back of the car!). Additional items are:

Smoker, fuel, matches, hive tool and veil.
Steps and/or ladder.

Many beekeepers take swarms not because they want them but to provide a service to the community. Prompt efficient action to a call is not only appreciated by the person concerned but it is good public relations and enhances the general image of beekeepers.

Shaking directly into a skep. Clear away, with the secateurs, any small foliage to allow the skep to be brought up and under the swarm as close to it as possible. One sharp jerk of the main branch that the swarm is clustering on should get 99% in the skep in one go. The preparation before shaking pays dividends. Slowly turn the skep over and place it in the middle of the sheet on the ground below where the swarm was clustering propped up on one side with a small block of wood or stone to allow the bees to get in and out. In about 20 minutes all the bees will be in the skep and foraging is likely to be starting. Leave until the evening when all the bees have returned, remove the block, gather up the sheet round the skep, tie off and carry away for hiving.

If the queen has been missed in the shaking process the swarm will start coming out of the skep and resettling with the queen, more than likely in the same spot. The small skep is useful now for a second shake if this happens. Throw/shake these bees into the large skep when it is turned over, momentarily, the right way up. It is always best to wait about 20 minutes to see that all is well before departing until the evening. Collecting swarms is much easier with two beekeepers especially if steps or a ladder is involved.

Smoking upwards. Quite often the situation arises where the bees cannot be shaken off (eg. on a wall or a rugged post) and they can then be smoked up into a box or skep. Bees will always walk upwards into a darkened space. When a swarm is on a wall or flat surface this is the only time a cardboard box is better than a skep (a long flat side can be laid against the wall above the swarm). Remember to push some slivers of wood through the box to support the swarm when it is inside. The box is brought in contact with the swarm and it is gently smoked to get them marching in. Once in they are put on the sheet on the ground as above and left to fly until the evening. Smoking a swarm upwards is a much slower operation than shaking and if the box/skep can be temporarily be fixed in position it will be a lot easier than holding it for half an hour.

Using a frame of brood. This always works in a difficult situation providing the frame can be brought in contact with the swarm. The bees soon cover it and can be shaken into a nuc box and then the frame can go back to the swarm for more bees. If the queen is seen, then the Butler cage will come into its own; with the queen inside the cage and in the nuc box or skep the bees will follow with no prompting. The queen can be released later when the swarm is hived.

Chemical swarm lure. The authors have only tried this once on a cast on a rose bush close to the ground. Two frames of drawn comb were placed in a nuc which was placed with its entrance close to the swarm. The entrance inside the nuc was treated with about in (13mm) of swarm lure (French brand; in a tube to be squeezed out for use like toothpaste). The idea was to come back in the evening to collect but in minutes the whole swarm was inside the box. Her ladyship, whose garden we were in, thought it magic – and so did we! The experiment seems to have some merit for future use and adaptation for taking swarms in difficult positions.

1.18.3 Hiving a swarm. An interesting phenomenon about a swarm is its loss of 'memory' of its old nest or hive a short while after it has emerged and settled. The swarm can be taken straight away, hived anywhere in the same apiary and the foragers do not return to the old site. It is analogous to erasing the information on a computer disc. Why such memory erasure should take place during swarming is unknown. Bees have a memory of their original site lasting about 2 to 3 weeks when they are not in the swarming mode. However, having said that, it is well known that if half a cupful of bees are taken from a swarm and dusted with flour and then thrown into the air they can be observed returning to their own hive in the apiary.

There are two basic methods of hiving a swarm:

    Swarm board.
    Shaking into an eke.

The first is fun and amuses both the beekeeper and any spectators. It allows inspection of the swarm and the queen(s) present as they march in. The second method is for the beekeeper who has used the first method so many times that he no longer finds it amusing or if time is at a premium, it is quick and efficient. Swarms are in just the right state for drawing foundation and building comb and such an opportunity should not be missed. If possible, always put a swarm onto foundation except maybe for one drawn comb.

Swarm board: is so called because a board, 2ft square (610mm × 610mm), is placed in front of the hive sloping up from the ground to the hive entrance, covered with the sheet from the skep and the swarm shaken on to it. Bees always walk upwards and in a few minutes there is a steady procession walking up into the hive. If the bees are reluctant to start a few taps on the board with a pencil or hive tool will start the proceedings. It takes about hour. The brood chamber that the swarm will occupy should have one drawn comb if the swarm is of unknown origin; if eggs are in this comb 2 days later it indicates an old queen, if there are no eggs it is likely to be a virgin and it should then be left for about two weeks before inspecting again. A feeder with 1 gallon of syrup should be provided straight away.

Shaking into an eke. A shallow eke is placed on the floorboard with the brood chamber complete with frames of foundation over the eke. The entrance should be closed with an entrance block turned through 90°. The brood box is lifted off and the swarm shaken into the eke and the brood box replaced immediately with a feeder with 1 gallon of syrup over. The swarm will walk up into the frames and 10 minutes later the entrance block can be removed (its only purpose was to stop the bees spilling out of the front entrance). The eke should be removed the next day.

1.18.4 Other points.

1. Take a sample of the swarm to check for adult bee diseases.
2. Treat the swarm for Varroa immediately it is hived. This is the best time for treatment as there is no brood and any Varroa mites will be on the exoskeleton of the adult bees ensuring a maximum mite kill
3. When brood is starting to be produced examine it very carefully for brood diseases.
4. Swarms from unknown origins can be a liability because of disease and bad temper.
5. If any bad temper is present when the colony has settled down, take action to requeen it immediately. Lots of stray swarms are bad tempered bees because their owners could not handle them.
6. Two or three swarms can all be shaken into one hive at the same time if there is a surfeit of swarms one day as often there is. The queens will sort themselves out and there will be no fighting amongst the bees.
7. Casts should be hived with a frame of brood from another colony to prevent them absconding.
8. A novel method of collecting swarms with a modified box and vacuum cleaner appeared in one issue of Beecraft. It relies on an electricity supply being available.
9. Beware collecting swarms on other people's estates and damaging their property; it is better to obtain some kind of indemnity statement, preferably signed before starting work, rather than end up with a bill for damages. It is surprising how attitudes change in the event of an accident.
10. Finally the vexed question of whether a beekeeper should make a charge for collecting a swarm from someone else's property. During 1995 our own branch in Plymouth answered over 70 calls from the police and the City Environmental Department. As the City authorities now make a charge of £25 the next port of call was to our members who traditionally have done it for free. The branch is now suggesting a charge of £10 for the collection of a swarm, £5 for the branch funds and £5 for the beekeeper's expenses. His/her time is given free of charge.

1.19 The use, and types, of queen excluder used in the UK.

The purpose of a queen excluder is to exclude the queen from the supers while allowing worker bees access to them thereby keeping all the brood rearing and associated pollen in the lower area of the hive, ie. the brood chamber. Theoretically only honey would be stored in the supers but in practice it is found that the first super often has quite a few cells with pollen stored in them. There doesn't seem to be any answer to this if the brood nest extends close to the top of the brood frames because the bees will always store pollen directly adjacent to the brood where it is required for use. The queen excluder is attributed to Abbé Collins in the year 1865.

The general principle is a flat sheet with slotted holes just large enough to allow a worker to pass through (it not only prevents the queen passing through but drones as well). Zinc sheet is a popular material; the size of the slots was $^5/_{32}$in (4mm) or 0.156in but most slotted types are now made with slots of 0.162in or 0.163in (4mm) depending on which book is read. The same effect can be obtained with a grill of parallel wires. Note the problem of converting to metric.

1.19.1 Slotted types: Generally made of zinc but galvanised mild steel slotted excluders are now available. They were made in two versions, one with a series of short slots, c. $1^1/_2$in (38mm), and the other with long slots, c. 3in (76mm). The design is for bottom bee space hives to allow the flat sheet to lay directly on top of the frames. The long slot variety was easily damaged and the short slot version is generally preferred. It is possible to frame this type of excluder as a DIY job; they are not available commercially in a frame. They are the cheapest of all excluders to buy. The mild steel short slot version is probably the best of those available.

1.19.2 Wire types: have all to be constructed with strong rigid wires to prevent damage and bending of the wire during use. The construction must be able to withstand damage by burr and brace comb when it is removed from the hive during manipulations. The gaps between the wires must not be greater than 0.165in (4mm). All wire type excluders are framed and should have a bee space on one side only; some are on the market with a bee space on both sides which is wrong and they should be avoided. The framed wire type is known as the Waldron excluder and similar types from Germany are known as the Herzog excluder. Both are more expensive than the slotted types. A further type with wood/wire/wood construction is available in USA at an even greater cost; it is claimed the bees 'like it better'(?) than other types. Better ventilation through the hive is achieved with the wire types compared with the slotted types.

(Note in 1.19.1 and 1.19.2 above the futility of converting Imperial to metric and rounding up to the nearest whole milli-meter).

1.19.3 Other points of interest:

a) If the excluders are electro-plated with zinc (and most are) they should be cleaned with boiling water or the careful use of a small blowlamp. They should not be scraped, the plating will be damaged and rusting will occur.
b) When replacing an excluder ensure that the top bars are clear of brace comb which may distort the excluder or worse still, damage it.
c) It is quite amazing how often the excluder is put on the wrong way round, the bee space should be below on a bottom bee space hive. Which way should it be placed on the frames; parallel to the frames or at right angles to them? In practice this does not matter as there is a bee space on both sides of the excluder when in use.
d) At one branch meeting the Authors saw a Waldron type excluder jammed full of dead worker bees stuck in the slots between the wires. It turned out that the beekeeper had been sold an excluder for Apis cerana which is a smaller bee cf. the Apis mellifera – most unusual!

1.20 One method of swarm control used in small scale beekeeping enterprises.

1.20.1 General. The subject of swarm control is so vast that to confine the discussion to only one method would defeat the object of having a reasonable understanding of the subject for examination purposes. Firstly, it is necessary to clearly understand the difference between prevention and control and secondly to be able to detect the preparations for swarming and to know how often to inspect the colony in order to detect the preparations (see section 1.17).

Many swarm control methods involve the use of double brood boxes (eg. Snelgrove, Demaree, etc.); it is not proposed to discuss these here, but to confine the discussion to one method requiring additional equipment (ie. the 'Artificial Swarm') and the other method requiring only a drawing pin (ie. the 'Destruction of Queen Cells'). If these two methods, suitable for single or double brood box management, are thoroughly understood they can be used for the whole of ones beekeeping career. Note that because these two methods are discussed, it does not mean that they are being recommended; there are plenty of other ways of achieving the same end. The destruction of queen cells method requires a clipped queen. As queens have to be found it is infinitely easier to find them if they are marked and marking is regarded as a high priority for effective swarm control.

The Artificial Swarm. This method, which must be common knowledge to anyone keeping bees, is so well known and documented that only a few comments are necessary. Briefly, when the operation has been completed the queen and one frame of bees plus empty comb to fill a new brood chamber remain on the original site and the colony with all the queen cells and remaining bees is put on a new site. All foraging bees return to the original site and, with the queen, form the artificial swarm. The old colony with only house bees and queen cells rear a new queen without swarming. This is the basis of the method, known also as the Pagden method, other points of interest are as follows:

a) If the colony has supers, then where should these end up; on the artificial swarm with the foragers or on the original stock with the queen cells? Most books show the supers on top of the artificial swarm on the original site. The old stock (now weakened by c.$\frac{1}{3}$ of the total original number of bees) on a new site may need feeding and could be robbed. It seems logical to put the supers on the old stock and feed the artificial swarm which in all probability will have foundation to pull out and also, doing it this way, there will be no possibility of contaminating the supers with sugar syrup.

b) Again many books recommend moving the original stock a second time to draw off any additional foragers 7 days after the manipulation and before a virgin has emerged. Unfortunately the rationale behind such a move is not explained. It does provide additional foragers for the artificial swarm but is not essential to the success of the manipulation.

c) It is unnecessary to destroy all but one queen cell in the original stock as the removal of foragers reduces drastically the strength of the colony and the bees will undertake the destruction themselves.

d) If necessary, the operation can be completed on the same site with the artificial swarm below and the old stock on top above a swarm board or similar. If it is done this way, then any feeding will be confined normally to the top stock.

e) The advantage of this method is that it is virtually 100% successful and can be performed on any stock. Additionally, brood rearing continues with the old queen and the two units can be united at a time suitable to the beekeeper. The disadvantage is that additional equipment is required. As an example, the authors had 8 colonies on the rape in 1988 and all wanted to swarm; to use the artificial swarm method was just not practicable away from our home apiary, and further we did not have enough equipment available at the time. There are horses for courses, and the beekeeper has to make up his own mind how to manage the situation.

The Destruction of Queen Cells. This method thwarts the natural intentions of the bee as opposed to the artificial swarm which complies with their intended actions. Does this have any adverse effect on the colony? There seems to be no straightforward answer to this question because how does one measure the adversity? In the authors experience the colonies appear to work just as well as other colonies but of course there is a break in the brood rearing until the new queen is mated and laying which reduces, to some extent, the honey gathering potential of the colony. Again, reference to the diagram in appendix 4 shows that there are likely to be two conditions at the inspection, ie. swarming preparations are detected and either the queen is present or she has been lost.

1. If the queen is present:

- Find and cage her (use her in a nuc or destroy later).
- While the queen is being found, select a good queen cell preferably an open one (sealed ones are sometimes empty!).
- Mark the frame with the queen cell with a drawing pin (always a good idea to have a spare one inside each hive roof ready for the occasion).
- Now, and only now, destroy all queen cells except the selected one. The selected frame should be brushed free of bees to ensure that only the one selected cell is left, do not shake it. All other frames must be shaken free of bees otherwise a cell may be missed.
- 7 days later destroy all QCs except the chosen one, again by shaking every frame except the chosen one which should be carefully handled and the bees brushed off.
- 21 days later a laying queen should be present (the colony should not be disturbed during this time).
- With a new queen laying, it is a waste of time doing any more inspections for swarm control during the rest of the season.

2. If the queen is not present:

- If there are no eggs present, this is a sure sign she has gone and is the first thing to ascertain.
- Select a good queen cell (preferably an open one) but this time, depending on the inspection timing, they may all be sealed and mark the frame as before.
- Proceed as above at 7 and 21 days.

When swarming preparations are first observed and the queen is present, all frames can be shaken and all QCs destroyed. Sometimes the bees give up the idea of swarming (in the authors experience in about 25% of the colonies). As long as the queen is present this can be done a second time. The 3rd time action must be taken.

Requeening every year or at the most every two years, the authors have found over a long period that each year about 10% of the colonies want to swarm. This happens when we breed with the queen from our best tempered stock that hasn't wanted to swarm the previous year.

1.21 The methods of making nuclei and the uses to which nuclei can be put.

1.21.1 Definition of a nucleus.

Before looking at the methods of making a nucleus (popularly referred to as 'nuc' in the singular and 'nucs' for the plural of nuclei) it would be as well to examine the definition of a nuc to understand what has to be made. The BBKA standard (based on the old BS - see appendix 3) is that it shall be 'a colony occupying not less than three BS (British Standard combs, 14in × 8in (356mm × 216mm), of bees and not greater than five BS combs with the brood (eggs and worker brood) area not less than half the total comb area'. As this is a standard for sale it also covers the amount of food and that all the frames should be well covered with bees, etc., etc. The standard for a colony is six BS frames and greater. There seems to be no formally accepted definition of a nuc in past literature but the BBKA standard above will serve our purpose reasonably well as a target to aim at when making a nuc. The number of bees on a well covered BS frame ranges from 1000 to 2000 bees; say an average of 1500 bees (750 on each side). With 3000 bees it is unlikely that any part of the comb will be seen. It follows that using these figures the number of bees in the minimum sized nuc (3 BS frames) should be about 4500. For the maximum sized nuc (5 BS frames) 7500 bees would be required, c.1.5lb (0.7kg) in weight. Nucs on other sized frames would be proportionally sized but with very large sized frames the minimum could not be reasonably less than 2 frames to allow a brood nest temperature to be maintained between the two combs. Other nucs, such as 'mini nucs' and 'micro nucs' are very specialised for queen mating and are beyond the scope of this book. However, their existence should be noted and that they would not fit the definition postulated above.

1.21.2 The nuc box.

This is in effect a miniature hive but with some specialised requirements. To consider the principles involved, the definition of a nuc as above will be used. The requirements are as follows:

- It shall be capable of holding 5 BS frames plus a dummy board.
- The inside width to accommodate this shall be $5 × 1\frac{1}{2}$in (38mm) = $7\frac{1}{2}$in (191mm) plus $\frac{1}{2}$in (13mm) for the dummy board plus $\frac{1}{4}$in (6mm) clearance making a total of $8\frac{1}{4}$in (210mm). If Hoffman spacing is used, $1\frac{3}{8}$in (35mm) then the clearance will become $\frac{7}{8}$in (22mm). If $1\frac{1}{2}$in (38mm) spacing is used it would be preferable to increase the clearance; it is soon used up when inserting a Butler cage for queen introduction.
- A dummy board is essential in a nuc because it will only contain 3 frames when it is initially made.
- The entrance arrangement is important; it should be capable of providing plenty of ventilation but be capable of being restricted to prevent robbing. In built mouse guards are useful if the nucs are used for over wintering new queens for the spring.
- The crown board requires two large ventilators at the back and front covered with wire mesh (8 per inch approx.). A feed hole is necessary to accommodate the nuc's feeder.
- Every nuc box should have its own feeder permanently placed on the crown board. Our preference is for mini Ashforth feeders holding about 1pint of syrup; they cannot be bought and we have to make our own. If a frame feeder is preferred then the inside dimensions of the box will have to be greater than above; these are not recommended because of opening

up the nuc to feed which is bad practice when the nuc is being used for queen mating.

- The roof has to be dimensioned to accommodate the feeder; if the feeder is made too large the roof becomes disproportionate in size and creates too much windage. The most essential features of the roof are that it should be absolutely bee tight (because of feeding) and the ventilators should have an area equal to that of the crown board ventilators. Provision should be made for keeping the record card in the roof so that it is readily available.
- The depth of the box requires a clearance of 1in (25mm) below the bottom of the frames to accommodate a queen cell protruding from the bottom of a frame. It does not happen very often but it is useful to have.
- The easy mobility of a nuc is essential and each nuc should have its own travelling screen easily and securely fastened when required.
- Provision should be made to raise the nuc off the ground with two parallel bars on the underside dimensioned so that the nuc has a forward slope, about $\frac{1}{2}$in (13mm) to drain of any condensation when overwintering and to have an air flow under the nuc to keep it dry.

It is impossible to purchase a nucleus box to the above specification and it will be a case of making your own as a DIY activity or modifying one made by the bee supply manufacturers. We put up for many years with commercially made equipment which in many cases would not perform efficiently the task it is intended to do. It is a great pity that others new to the craft have to go through the same loop because designs are not improved.

1.21.3 Making the nuc.

The essential components for making a nuc are a queen, bees, food (honey and pollen) and emerging brood. If the nuc is to be used for mating then a QC can be given to the nuc in lieu of a queen. A nuc can be made from:

   a) a single colony,
   b) from two colonies or
   c) several colonies.

There will be a difference depending whether the nuc is to remain in the same apiary or whether it is to be moved more than 3 miles away, the latter being a much easier task.

Method 1. Three frame nuc (to be transported away). From the parent colony find the queen and cage her. Select two frames of emerging and advanced brood with attendant bees and place in the nuc box. Then select a good frame of food containing fresh pollen and liquid stores, again with bees and also put into the nuc box. Find now a really well covered frame of bees and shake the lot into the nuc. The old queen can be released into the nuc or a new laying queen can be introduced in a Butler cage. The dummy board should be inserted and the space filled on its vacant side with a piece of foam for travelling. Fix the travelling screen and move to the new site immediately. On arrival at the new site open the entrance (reduced) and let the bees fly. If the nuc was destined to receive a QC then the nuc would be transported queenless and without the QC which would be put in at the new site. The nuc should be fed straightaway. Bees will be dying every day through natural causes and these will be replaced by the emerging brood. If a new laying queen is introduced it will be 21 days before any of her protégé hatch out and longer if the QC has to hatch and the virgin to mate before laying commences. During this time the little colony is unbalanced and in a delicate state until it becomes established; therefore, it must be treated with great care to prevent it being robbed. Continual feeding may be necessary.

Method 2. Three frame nuc (to remain in the same apiary). Proceed as in method 1 but ensure that the frame of liquid stores is virtually full so that the made up nuc can survive without feeding for about 4/5 days. The additional bees shaken into the nuc will be greater in this method to allow for any flying bees returning back to the parent colony. Before shaking into the nuc, lightly shake the frame in the parent colony to get rid of the older bees and then shake the rest into the nuc. Do this with three frames and then introduce the queen and place in a new position in the apiary, out of the flight path of other hives, with a reduced entrance lightly closed with grass. Check after 4/5 days and then feed as required.

Method 3. If nucs are made up taking frames and bees from different colonies, it is prudent to spray each frame lightly with a very weak water and sugar syrup leaving the frames well apart in the nuc box and exposed to the light. The bees that are shaken in should also be lightly sprayed. Finally, slowly bring the frames together after smoking well; it is unlikely that any fighting will occur following this treatment. Alternatively, all the frames less bees can be taken from one or different colonies and the bees from another colony. If it is possible to avoid mixing bees from different colonies, then this should be done. Needless to say, nucs should only be made from disease free colonies.

1.21.4 An account of the various uses of nuclei.

Nuclei are an essential part of modern apiary management and are probably more useful for teaching purposes than a large full sized colony. Manipulating a large colony can be a daunting experience for the newcomers to beekeeping and their initiation should always be on a nuc. The small colonies should form part of every beekeeping establishment whether it be a commercial honey producing organisation or a small amateur beekeeper with a couple of hives. The number of uses to which nuclei can be put is really quite remarkable, the important ones are listed below:

1. Queen mating (these nucs can be quite small, nb. mini nucs).
2. Establishing and building into a full colony.
3. Increasing stocks and replacing colonies.
4. Swarm control.
5. Keeping spare queens and breeder queens.
6. Assessing the queen's offspring.
7. Drawing worker comb.
8. Observation hives.
9. Requeening large stocks.

Queen mating: probably tops the list of uses and is probably the most complicated. The size can range considerably from the micro nuc with only a few dozen bees to a 5 frame nuc on BS frames. The important feature is that if no brood is present the little colony is prone to abscond. The presence of brood creates conditions which are favourable to the acceptance of a queen cell and there will certainly be no absconding as a mating swarm. Bees will not leave brood which needs tending whether it be young or emerging. Introducing a queen cell to an established nuc always seems to cause confusion with many beekeepers. How long should the nuc be left queenless? There are the following possibilities:

a) Remove the queen and introduce a ripe QC (14 days old or greater) straightaway. There is a fair possibility that the cell may be destroyed; a cell protector (or a bit of sellotape) is a good insurance policy.

b) Leaving the nuc queenless for about 2 hours gives a high acceptance success rate. Some advocate feeding at the time the cell is introduced but the rationale for doing this is obscure.

c) Leave queenless for 7 days and then destroy emergency QCs before introducing the ripe QC. In our experience this is 100% successful.

Making up a nuc specially for mating purposes is the final option. Care must be taken to ensure the brood is only advanced or emerging. If it is left for two days in a queenless condition the ripe QC will be accepted without trouble. Usually 100% successful.

Establishing and building into a full sized colony. This is the ideal way for a beginner to start beekeeping. The ideal time is to take possession of the nuc in March/April and, of course, this will be an overwintered one. It will be capable of being built into a full sized colony and a surplus obtained during the first season. If the nuc is obtained in June with a current year queen, the build up is unlikely to lead to a surplus during the first season.

Increasing stocks and replacing colonies. Even with the best management and bee husbandry, occasionally stocks are lost during the winter for a variety of reasons. Overwintered nucs are ideal for replacing such losses and will provide a crop during the year of replacement. If stocks are to be increased, then new nucs will have to be made up during the season. The normal time for this is May/June when queens can be also reared and the colonies are strong enough to provide the bees for making the nucs.

Swarm control. Removing bees and brood from strong colonies to make nucs is an effective method of swarm prevention by reducing the colony population. If QCs are present in the parent colony, one of these may be usefully used in the nuc when it is made up. The danger of perpetuating a swarming strain must be taken into consideration with this particular use.

Keeping spare queens and breeder queens. All beekeepers should have a spare queen available for emergency purposes. This means maintaining an overwintered nuc or two in case one is required early in the year when it would be impossible for a virgin to mate due to drones not being available. The life of a breeder queen can be extended by keeping her in a nuc and thereby severely limiting the extent of her egg laying. In fact the genetic material (eggs and larvae) for queen rearing can be obtained directly from the breeder queen in the nuc. Breeder queens can be kept for up to 5 years in this way.

Assessing the queen's offspring. Because of the very widespread problem of bad temper, we consider it essential that new queens are assessed in nucs prior to being introduced into colonies. It is easy to deal with bad tempered bees if they are in small numbers. Other characteristics are observed such as laying pattern, nervousness, amount of propolis collected, etc.

Drawing worker comb. Small colonies produce little, if any, drone comb when compared with large colonies. A nuc will always draw worker comb irrespective of whether foundation has been provided. Therefore, old comb with the drone comb cut out can be given to nucs for repair as well as giving them foundation. All our 5 frame nucs are given 1 or 2 frames of foundation to pull out every year.

Observation hives. These contain only two or three frames of bees and are therefore stocked from a nucleus. A greater use could be made of observation hives for learning and teaching than is done at present. The observation hive can be stocked from a nuc and given starters instead of foundation to observe comb building in progress.

Requeening large stocks. If a queen is purchased or obtained from another source and has been out of the hive for some time, it is best that she is introduced initially to a nuc (there is a better chance of acceptance in a small colony). When her laying has normalised in the nuc, then she can be introduced into the large colony. For successful queen introduction, it seems that the old and the new queen must be in the same physiological state. An alternative method is to make a nuc from the colony to be requeened, introduce the queen to the nuc and when laying normally the nuc is united with the parent colony, after first removing the old queen, thus bringing it back to its full strength. We recommend, as an insurance policy particularly if the queen is yellow and the colony is black, that the queen is recaged for a day when the nuc is returned to the parent colony.

1.21.5 Other points.

- Chalk brood always seems to be a problem with nucs until they become established as well balanced colonies, albeit small ones. The trigger is of course temperature, protein and CO_2 stress. When the nucs are established and good ventilation is provided as per the spec in section 1.19.2, it has been our experience that they seem able to keep it at bay.
- Nucs made up as 3 frames in early June with QCs, build up to 5 frames and generally collect enough stores to feed themselves for winter. They overwinter well with the young queens and provide the replacement queens for the spring.
- Samples for adult bee diseases should be taken from the nucs and treated in a similar manner to full colonies.
- Nucs should never be allowed to raise a queen from their own emergency QCs; scrub queens will result.
- A minimum amount of smoke should be used when inspecting nuclei.

1.22 How swarms and nuclei can be turned into productive colonies.

1.22.1 General. Turning nucs and swarms into productive colonies in UK, means bringing them up to maximum strength by the end of June ready for the main flow. Swarms which usually occur from May onwards will never, during the same season, be large enough to gather a crop comparable with a well established colony; there is insufficient time to produce the bees unless special arrangements are made to add brood from other colonies. Similarly with nucs made up about the same time when queens are being reared, the time is too short. The only nuc which can build up naturally to a full sized colony is one that has been overwintered. The productive colony will have a maximum sized brood nest during the first three weeks in June, which will produce the maximum foraging force at the beginning of July. The number of adult bees in the colony will be about double the amount of brood and the amount of brood will be approximately 20 times the daily egg laying rate of the queen. Putting some numbers to this, we have:

Eggs per day	Total brood	Adult bees
1000	20,000	40,000
1500*	30,000	60,000
2000	40,000	80,000!

With this amount of brood, how many BS frames does this represent? The answer to this, of course, depends on the percentage fill in each frame which will not only contain brood but stores of honey and pollen. Again putting some figures to this on the basis of 5000 cells/BS frame, we have:

Stores	Brood	Brood/frame	20k brood	30k brood
25%	75%	3750	5 frames	8 frames
40%	60%*	3000	7 frames	10 frames
50%	50%	2500	8 frames	12 frames

With a reasonably prolific queen and using a 60%* brood/frame (which from experience seems to be about right), then 10 frames of brood will be required in the productive colony. This could be used as a target to achieve in the build up; it will be a massive colony with 60,000 bees. If the brood chamber is full of brood and a flow starts, then the only place nectar and honey can be stored is in the supers, just where it is required.

Colony size is an interesting concept and writers seem to vie with every other to give a higher number (rather like fishing stories!). Dr. Jeffree, in some of his experiments, measured 510 colonies and the biggest, a really large one in his own words, contained 47,700 bees. So the estimate above is a bit on the large size, but it is interesting to try and quantify it in terms of frames of brood.

Queens do not lay well when there is no income to the colony. Therefore, if there is no flow the colony will require to be fed in order to build it up. A further factor in the equation is whether foundation is to be given or drawn comb; to draw foundation requires a flow or feeding. A flow requires good weather.

We now have all the variables, namely;

    a) the fecundity of the queen,
    b) the weather,
    c) flow or feeding,
    d) foundation or comb.

1.22.2 Management of the nuc to build it to colony size.

There are three basic ways of managing a nucleus to ensure it is at peak strength to effectively produce a surplus on the main flow, namely:

    1. brood spreading,
    2. natural expansion by feeding or on a natural flow,
    3. augmenting from established colonies.

Brood spreading: is an unnatural disturbance of the brood nest done in such a way as to encourage a more rapid expansion than would have occurred otherwise. It is a highly skilled job and is not recommended for the beekeeper new to the craft. In essence, the frames of the brood nest are re-arranged so that one with a small patch of brood is placed between two with large patches of brood; this then encourages the bees to expand the small patch of brood to the same size as those on the adjacent frames. Full descriptions of the manipulation may be found elsewhere. If it is practised, it is most important to never 'brood split', ie. interposing an empty frame between one frame with brood and the rest of the brood nest. Brood spreading is likely to be undertaken in the early part of the year when temperatures can drop quite suddenly. Under these conditions it is not unusual for brood to be lost due to chilling even in a small colony that has not had its brood nest altered; if brood has recently been spread the situation can be worse. In our opinion, the whole operation of interfering with the brood nest should be avoided if possible.

Natural expansion: of the brood nest, and hence the colony, takes place dependent on the income. The 'colony explosion' that takes place, for example, in a nuc put out onto the rape has to be seen to be believed. The management required in this case is to prevent the storage of honey in the brood chamber. The danger is that the brood nest becomes restricted by a large slab of honey at either end at a time when it could easily continue expanding. The management here is the judicious use of the dummy board and supering over a queen excluder while the brood nest is not yet on its full capacity of frames. This forces the colony to store nectar in the super while allowing only enough spare comb in the brood chamber for the queen to lay in. If there is no flow then no super is required and feeding (slow – a few ounces per day) should be resorted to, enough to keep the colony continually building up without storing too much in the brood chamber and blocking the natural expansion. Care should be taken to evaluate when a natural flow of nectar starts to occur in order to put the first super on. It should be noted that in a good spring and a source of nectar such as rape the queen can start to lay at her peak rate per day and the build up becomes very rapid. If feeding is required, it is important that sugar syrup is not processed by the bees and stored in the supers and subsequently extracted.

Augmenting from established colonies: means providing either brood or brood and bees from other colonies, always providing they are disease free. Uniform equipment is essential for this operation. Care must again be exercised in doing this, the salient points are:

• Since the nuc is a very small unit, only emerging brood should be added and this only one frame at a time. The reason is twofold; first, emerging brood is not as critical to temperature variation as younger brood and second, there is only a limited number of bees in the nuc to incubate it. If it is an overwintered nuc, the little colony will be balanced and there will be only enough nurse bees to deal with its own young brood, any addition will put it under stress.
• Adding bees and brood to a nuc is better, so that the balance of bees to brood is maintained. When a frame with bees is removed from the parent colony, it should be lightly shaken to dislodge the older bees leaving only the young ones on the frame with the brood to be added to the nuc or expanding colony. Old bees are not required as they are foragers and will return to their old site if it is in the same apiary thereby defeating the object of the manipulation.
• Will the added bees fight with the bees in the recipient colony? It is our experience that in the early part of the year when such operations are being undertaken bees do not fight if they are exposed to sunlight for about 5 minutes. Therefore, open up a space (enough for two frames say) where the new comb is to go and put the new frame in the middle of the gap and leave for a few minutes and then slowly bring the frames together and then close the colony up. Alternatively, the bees on the three frames concerned can be sprayed with a very weak syrup before closing up.
• When augmenting, feeding should be avoided because of the possibility of robbing. It therefore follows that there should be adequate stores until the next inspection.

It should be noted that flying bees can be added to a weaker colony by exchanging the positions of the weak and strong stocks in the same apiary. This only provides older foraging bees with a limited life and creates an unbalance between old and young bees in both colonies.

1.22.3 Swarms. These are managed in much the same way as the nucs and again the dummy board should be used to prevent storage in the brood chamber. Any swarm from an outside unknown source should be put in an isolation 'bolt hole' away from other bees. It should be immediately sampled for adult bee diseases and treated for Varroosis while no brood is present. Finally, the first brood produced should be very carefully checked for AFB and EFB which are known to be carried in swarms.

1.22.4 The dummy board: is one of the most useful pieces of equipment when building up colonies. It is also not used as much as it should be mainly because its three main uses are generally not appreciated ie. for providing manipulating space in a full brood box, providing a good surface to lever the full complement of frames together at the end of a brood box manipulation and as described above for temporarily limiting the size of the brood chamber. Every brood box should have its own dummy board; once a beekeeper has learnt the value of these inexpensive bits of equipment, he will never revert to being without them.

1.23 The methods used to unite colonies of honeybees, the underlying principles of these methods and any precautions that need to be taken.

1.23.1 General considerations. There are various points concerning bee behaviour and bee-keeping practice which are of interest before considering the possible methods of actually uniting, these are:

a) Both colonies must be disease free; the spread of disease is caused more often by the beekeeper rather than by any other mechanism.

b) In beekeeping literature mention will be made of 'colony odour' and 'hive odour'. Butler (of queen substance fame) postulated that colony odour is genetically produced and each colony has its own characteristics. On the other hand, Bro. Adam is of the opinion that there is no such thing as colony odour but that there is a hive odour which depends entirely on the materials of the hive and the income (nectar and pollen) which in turn depends on the weather. The hive odour is carried by the individual bees. No one has disputed the concept of hive odour but it has not been subjected to any scientific experiments or proof.

c) During times of dearth there are many guard bees at the entrance of a colony, some of these being potential foragers if forage was available.

d) When there is plenty of forage and a flow on, there will be virtually no guards at the entrance. It is likely that all the colonies in the same apiary are working the same crop and the hive odours are likely to be very similar. Under these conditions, drifting bees are accepted in another colony without challenge or fighting.

From the considerations above it is clear that the best time to unite colonies is during a flow. Feeding, particularly with a scented syrup, when there is a dearth is the alternative solution although this is not too easy to feed both colonies separately during the uniting process and feeding both separately beforehand is usually the order of the day.

1.23.2 Methods of uniting. There are a variety of ways of uniting, the more important methods and variations will be described. These are:

1. Newspaper method.
2. Direct uniting.

Newspaper method. This method is probably the most widely used and is generally very reliable and successful in use. The principle involved is very simple; a queenright (QR) colony and a queenless (QL) colony are joined together with a sheet of newspaper between them and the bees chew the paper away and intermingle slowly and hence unite. The paper is deposited outside the hive in the course of the next 24 hours.

- The two colonies to be united have to be brought adjacent to one another (see section 1.28) with their entrances in the same direction.
- The manipulation of uniting colonies should be done in the evening when both colonies have virtually finished flying. The reason is obvious, if the bees are flying then some of the returning foragers will be returning to the entrance of a foreign colony and fighting is likely. Once fighting starts more guards are alerted and then all bees from the other colony trying to enter will be involved. This simple precaution is seldom, if ever, recommended in the literature on practical beekeeping.
- The newspaper requires 3 or 4 pin holes made in it to help start the process of paper destruction. This can be done with the corner of the hive tool blade if care is used. It is useful to cover the paper with the queen excluder to stop it blowing around during the manipulation. Note the requirement to remove the queen excluder the following day after uniting to release any drones above it.
- Prior feeding is required if there is no flow on.
- One colony must be dequeened, the first part of the manipulation. Some books have suggested in the past that the two queens will fight it out and the younger queen will succeed. There is no definite proof that this is so and the possibility exists that the surviving queen may be damaged in the fight. Our advice is do your own selection and be sure of the result.
- Now comes the last, but vexed, question of which goes on top and which goes below? There is the queenright (QR) colony and the queenless (QL) colony and either may be the strong (STR) one or the weak (WK) one. Consultation of 4 books; recommended reading for the BBKA exams gave the following result:

	BK1	BK2	BK3	BK4
QR or QL on top	QR	QL	QR	—
WK or STR on top	WK	—	STR	WK

The curious thing is that although the authors were recommending a particular approach, not one of them explained why their way was presumably the right way and whether either of the two conditions take preference. If anything preference would be given to the strong colony being above the weak colony on the basis that the weaker would have the minimum guards at the entrance to oppose returning foragers. A case could be made for having the QR colony below with a queen excluder over on the basis that the arrangement can be left for 3 weeks to allow all the brood to hatch in the upper box; the top brood box can then be removed. We are of the opinion that it does not matter which way round they go and any combination will be successful if 3 criteria are observed, namely:

- Dequeen one colony.

- Do the manipulation in a flow or with colonies fed for 2 days before the manipulation.
- Do the manipulation just as it is getting dark.

It is not clear where or when the newspaper method originated but it is simple and effective. In some ways it is similar to using a screen between the two colonies for a few days before removing the screen to allow the bees to unite. This method has the disadvantage of requiring a separate entrance for the top colony which is closed when the screen is removed.

Direct uniting. This is usually undertaken with small colonies (eg. 2 nucs to be united) which may, in total when combined, fill a single brood box. The colonies are brought together, one dequeened and again the operation undertaken in the evening as follows:

- Each frame with bees is removed one at a time from the colonies, dusted with flour or sprayed with a weak syrup and placed in the new brood chamber.
- The frames are taken alternately one from one colony and then one from the other and placed in the new brood box also alternately so that there is a complete mixing.
- Care should be taken not to split the brood nests which should combine to make one large one.
- Finally, the bees are heavily smoked and bumped around to create confusion and the colony closed up.

The flour or the syrup gives the bees an immediate job to do and fighting is none existent or else minimised.

The words of Bro. Adam, on the subject of uniting, are of considerable interest; exposure to light has a calming effect on bees and when they have been exposed for some minutes, they will peaceably unite without any other precaution throughout the whole season. We follow his wisdom with small colonies and nuclei but use the newspaper method for larger colonies. A further variation on the direct uniting method is to place the frame with the queen and bees in the new brood box and then shake all the other bees from both colonies in front of the hive, placing the empty frames in the brood box. The shaken bees are sprayed with syrup or dusted with flour and allowed to return to the hive. This method is not one that is recommended these days. The job can be done with less confusion and uproar in the apiary.

1.23.3 Other points relating to uniting.

- Swarms can be thrown together (queens and all) into the same hive within a few days of one another without fighting. When there is a surplus of swarms it is a good way of dealing with them. We have bumped up to 3 swarms all together on the same day and had two brood boxes of foundation drawn out in 2 weeks; when the flow starts such a unit will collect a surplus.
- Some books state that uniting when there are no drones about is a bad time for this operation; the rationale is not understood. Uniting colonies before winter is a classic time for rationalising the apiary.
- It is a well known observation that a strong colony will collect more surplus than two weak ones; it is important to ascertain the reason for weakness. If it is disease or poor queens, then uniting will not alleviate the problem. In general the honey produced by a colony is directly proportional to the size of the colony when the colony size is over about 25k bees. The following figures were derived in New Zealand and demonstrate well the benefits to be obtained by having large colonies.

SIZE OF COLONY(bees)	HONEY PRODUCTON (kg)
10,000	4
20,000	14
30,000	23
40,000	32
50,000	41
60,000	50

Note the difference between 10k and 20k and the linearity above 30k. Therefore, there are advantages to be gained by uniting colonies before the main flow and disadvantages in the autumn by uniting and ending up with a colony too large for the optimum wintering conditions (see appendix 8).

• It has been suggested that a colony of laying workers can be united to a QR colony. Such colonies are virtually impossible to requeen *. We disagree that uniting is a solution because if there are laying workers, the colony will have been QL for 3 weeks or more and all the bees will be old ones. If united satisfactorily they will die off quickly by natural causes and the recipient colony will derive little gain from the addition.

   * Work in France in c.1988 indicated that it is possible to requeen colonies of laying workers by dipping the queen in a solution of royal jelly (70%) and water (30%) and introducing them directly. The success rate claimed is greater than 70%. We believe this to be only of academic interest and has no application from a practical beekeeping aspect.

1.24 Robbing by bees and wasps and its associated dangers, including its prevention and curtailment.

1.24.1 General points in relation to bees robbing bees.

• In nature, a concentration of colonies does not occur and therefore robbing is not a problem. It only occurs where the beekeeper has concentrated his stocks on to a single site to form an apiary. The beekeeper with only one stock will seldom have trouble with robbing.
• Robbers are generally bees from another colony but wasps, hornets and ants can also rob a hive. Ants are not a problem in the UK but overseas in the tropics they are a problem.
• Robbing is for honey only, the other hive products such as pollen and propolis attract no attention as plunder.
• Different strains of bees have different propensities to rob other colonies; the Italian yellow strains being the worst, they are inveterate robbers.
• It is more likely to start after a nectar flow has come to an abrupt halt and in times of dearth.
• It is usually started as a result of bad management practices on the part of the beekeeper.
• Robbing can occur between hives in a single apiary or between hives in two apiaries.
• When robbing occurs in an apiary the only method of communication between the bees is by the round dance which only gives information on distance. Because no directional information is available the bees can only search in the near vicinity which may initiate further robbing if a weak colony is discovered.
• It has been suggested, but not proven, that robbers may release a pheromone to mark the site to be robbed.

1.24.2 Methods to avoid robbing:

- Prevention is always better than cure, and good apiary practice at all times is usually the answer.
- Because bees are only interested in a free supply of honey/nectar or sugar syrup available in quantity then there should be no spillage or trace of syrup outside any colony or within the apiary.
- There should be no way into any colony except via the designed entrance; all equipment should be bee tight.
- Colony entrances should be adjusted to the size (or strength) of the colony and to the time of the year and flow conditions.
- When there is no nectar flow, colonies should not be kept open for too long during manipulations.

1.24.3 Methods of detection of robbing.

There are two types of robbing. The first involves fighting at the entrance of the robbed hive and the second is called silent robbing where no fighting takes place at or within the robbed stock. The behaviour of the foraging bees is quite different in the two cases.

Silent robbing: is characterised by the robbed colony continuing to work normally while at the same time the robbers also enter and leave the robbed colony in a normal manner. The robbed colony can itself be robbing another colony at the same time. The only tell-tale sign is the flight of the bees returning directly to another colony in the same apiary.

Robbing with fighting: has two recognisable characteristics. The first is the fighting outside the robbed hive and the second is the flight of the robber bees approach which is nervous and erratic. The erratic zig-zag flight is curious because it alerts the guards of the robbed colony. Once the robber bee alights and is challenged it becomes submissive and often offers food to the guards.

The characteristic common to both types of robbing is the flight of the laden and unladen bee; rear legs forward in the first instance with a full honey sac and with rear legs trailing astern when unladen in the second instance. The normal rear leg position in flight is reversed, ie. a normal forager should not leave the hive full and return empty.

1.24.4 Methods used to terminate robbing.

There is no effective way to stop robbing the day it starts. Removal of the robbed stock to another apiary is unsatisfactory as it usually gets robbed again at the new site (the colony being possibly marked by pheromone). The robbing stock is likely to find another weak stock and continue robbing. The following actions are all effective to some degree:

- Remove robbers to a remote site isolated from other colonies in the immediate vicinity.
- Reduce all entrances and make the nucs and weaker stocks a narrow tunnel (one bee space wide) about 2in (50mm) long.
- Straw and grass to cover the entrances of both the robbed and robbing hive to confuse both parties has been suggested by some writers.
- Plain glass leant up against the entrance allowing only entrance from the sides.
- Reversal of the robber and robbed colony.

If any signs of robbing do occur, we consider that the first action must be reduced entrances and this is why it is so important to have the hive entrance block always stored in the hive diagonally across the crown board when not in use. Nucs are particularly vulnerable and methods of restricting any nuc entrances immediately must be normal apiary management. Note that many of the equipment suppliers, economising on wood, do not make the trim in the roofs of hives deep enough to take an entrance block – they are very easily rectified by tacking 4 laths to the existing woodwork.

If a robbed colony is moved it is always wise to leave a frame with some stores in it on the site and allow the robbers to clean it out and finish the robbing job to their satisfaction (the one frame can be put in a spare nuc or travelling box).

1.24.5 Robbing by wasps.

Eleven species of wasp are found in Europe and seven of these are found in the UK. The most common are the *Vespa vulgaris* and then the *Vespa germanica* both of about the same size. Hornets, *Vespa crabro*, are also fairly common but in our experience seldom cause problems as robbers of bee hives.

The *Vespa vulgaris* is the main culprit and its robbing can be quite devastating if a colony exists nearby an apiary. This common wasp is physically stronger than the honeybee and in large numbers can easily overpower a quite strong colony. The nests are usually underground in old mouse holes or rabbit holes. As the colony grows so the nest size is increased and this often requires the wasps to enlarge the cavity by moistening the earth and removing it in small pellets to the outside while maintaining a small entrance. Their mandibles are also strong to do this work and to prepare the wood pulp which the nest is built with.

We know of no way of stopping wasps robbing once the process has started except by seeking out the nest and destroying it after dark when all their foragers (and robbers) have returned for the night. The worst year (1995) that we have known for wasps has just passed and we have lost two colonies which were decimated by wasps.

It is not clear whether wasps communicate food sources to their nest mates as do the honeybees. However, the observation of colonies being killed off would indicate that they have some mode of communication considering the numbers involved in their concerted attacks. Examination of the combs of a colony killed by wasps will reveal all the honey stores have been taken together with the brood and only the exoskeletons of some of the worker bees remain, the soft internal viscera have been removed. Wasps are the best insecticide available!

1.25 Spring management of colonies.

It is not at all clear to us what is meant by spring management. A search through the classical bee literature revealed no definition of what may be required. Wedmore's 'A Manual of Beekeeping' came nearest to our own ideas of dealing with the topic.

1.25.1 Definition of spring.

The dictionary definition of spring is as follows:

'The season in which vegetation begins to appear, first season of the year, in the northern hemisphere March - May (Astronomical, from vernal equinox to summer solstice)'

Reference to appendix 2 showing the orbit of the earth around the sun shows an equinox in March (21st) and one in September (23rd) when the day and the night are equal (hence equinox). At these dates the declination of the sun is zero ie. the first point of Aries and Libra respectively. Between these two dates the diagram also shows the summer solstice on about 21st June and the winter solstice on about 22nd December the times of the year when the earth is furthest away from the sun.

So what does spring mean to the beekeeper? We consider that in the south of England it extends from the first inspection usually earlier than the equinox to the end of June just before the main flow is about to start and a little later than the summer solstice. The whole of spring, in our opinion, is concerned with managing the colony in order to maximise the population to take advantage of the main flow which generally starts in early July.

This is where the difficulty of definition starts to come in. The summer solstice is known as mid-summer day implying that summer started earlier and again by definition, summer follows spring. The further north one goes in the UK the flowering vegetation is later by approximately 2 to 3 weeks in Scotland and the north of England. This convinces us even more that the definition should be from first inspection to the main flow starting which is dependent on weather and latitude.

1.25.2 The objectives of spring management.

In arriving at our definition above we have already stated the broad objective and that is **to maximise the colony population by about the end of June**. Many beekeepers do not take cognizance of this objective and seldom give it a thought. It is based, of course, on the assumption that the ultimate objective of managing a colony of honeybees is to maximise the surplus honey yield. In the following parts to this section we will assume that:

• No artificial pollen feeding is necessary, and
• No stimulative feeding of sugar syrup is undertaken.

Both these techniques are a specialised form of management for early crops and in areas where there is a dearth of pollen due to farming practices such as those of the 'barley barons' of the south east.

The major points required to achieve the objective are as follows:

• A good young queen.
• A disease free colony.
• No swarming.

The objectives can never be achieved if the ground work the previous year has not been undertaken in August to October the previous year. It is assumed that the following were carried out:

    a) The colony was adequately fed.
    b) Treatment for Varroa and if necessary for Nosema and Acarine were completed

c) The colony was protected against the ingress of mice.

d) The colony had adequate ventilation in a sound hive during the winter.

1.25.3 Colony management on a month by month basis.

1.25.3.1 February / March.

Is the equipment ready for the season?

a) Smoker overhauled from last season.

b) An adequate supply of smoker fuel should be available right from the start.

c) Hive tool and a bee tight veil.

d) Clean brood boxes and spare frames of foundation.

e) Supers all ready for the season (4 per hive minimum are required).

The first inspection on a warm day in February when the bees are flying and bringing in pollen.

a) Floorboard change – debris search for Varroa. The importance of starting this early is governed by the treatment for Varroa. If the colony has to be treated, then a period of six weeks is required and no supers should be on the colony during treatment. Under normal circumstances supers will be required in the first week of April.

b) Remove the mouse guards and provide a reduced entrance.

c) Remove the crown board and check for sealed stores without removing any frames by smoking the bees down, if necessary. If none can be seen the previous winter preparations were not carried out satisfactorily and the colony must be checked further by removing and examining frames. See appendix 6 'Consumption of stores during winter'

d) Lower crown board if it was raised with match sticks.

e) Start the hive record cards and store on the underside of the roof.

1.25.3.2 March.

During March the first colony inspection should be made. We hear time and time again that opening a colony too early in the year can chill the brood and the queen is likely to be balled. In our experience both are fairy stories. We have never seen chilled brood in a colony all the years we have been keeping bees. Reference to Bailey indicates that brood has to be kept at a low temperature for quite along time to chill it. We have to take brood out of colonies and place it in the refrigerator to chill it for our winter lectures for the BBKA Basic Course which requires candidates to be able to recognise chilled brood (Perhaps this is an unnecessary requirement at this level). As we normally requeen our colonies in March, and we have requeened hundreds over the years, we can report that we have never known balling at that time of the year.

The following points require attention at the first inspection:

1. Are the stores adequate to the next inspection?

2. Take a sample for adult bee diseases. This is important and ignored by over 90% of beekeepers. It is important to know because if the colony fails to build up the reason will be either Nosema or a dud queen. If no disease analysis is undertaken the reason cannot be ascertained.

3. Transfer the colony to a clean brood chamber during the inspection.

4. Check the frames to be changed and work to edge of brood chamber if possible.
5. Check that the queen is laying and note the frames of brood and separately the frames of bees. Ensure that the queen is marked and clipped if necessary.
6. Complete the record card.

Inspections are required every 14 days or every 7 days from now on depending whether clipped or unclipped queens are being used. We strongly recommend clipped queens as it reduces the inspections required until swarming preparations are first noted. We consider March to be the best time of the year to requeen all colonies.

1.25.3.3 April.

Regular colony inspections must now be carried out for the following reasons:

a) To check on stores available to the next inspection.
b) To check the build up of the colony. The number of frames of brood and frames of bees must be recorded; there should be a steady increase through to about the end of May.
c) Search for brood diseases while the colony has a greater amount of brood compared with adult bees. Reference should be made to the annual colony cycle in appendix 7.
d) To detect any signs that the colony may be wanting to swarm and to provide the colony with sufficient additional comb area to prevent swarming. Additionally, to institute swarm control methods as and when required. It is very important to understand the difference between swarm prevention, detection and control.

Three or four brood combs should be changed this month and the first super will be required during the month.

1.25.3.4 May.

This is likely to be the busiest month of the year for most beekeepers.

• Regular colony inspections must proceed as detailed above. Colonies will be reaching their opulent state and swarming is more likely at this time of the year.
• Extraction of autumn sown rape will require to be undertaken in order to prevent granulation in the combs. It is poor management practice to allow granulation in the combs to occur.
• Any queen rearing should be commenced to provide new queens for next season.
• Reduced entrance blocks will require to be removed during the month.
• It is imperative not to allow any swarms to escape. The bees in these swarms are the foraging force required for the main flow and a system of control is required to ensure that they can be utilised to the full.

1.25.3.5 June.

This is the notorious month when there is a gap in the spring flow before the main flow starts in July. Stores can be very low in colonies at this time of the year and feeding may be necessary. This can be occasioned particularly when the rape or any other spring crop is removed in May.

Great care must be taken not to contaminate supers with sugar syrup. In such a situation, all the supers will be full of bees and devoid of stores and the brood chamber should, by now, be full of brood on all frames. There will be little food in the brood chamber. Our method of feeding the colonies in this state during this month is to shake two or three frames in the top super free of bees and fill the comb with syrup pouring it into the cells with a jug and then replacing them in the super. Care is required to ensure that the syrup is consumed and not stored. Some years we have had to do this twice a week for the whole of the month.

Congratulate yourself if you have got all your colonies through to this stage without swarming and all fully supered as the flow starts; your bees will reward you well. The month of July is the time for holidays before another busy summer month starts in August.

1.26 Management of colonies for honey production from oilseed rape.

1.26.1 General.

Oil seed rape (OSR) is sown both in the autumn and in the spring blooming in April and July respectively in the south of England and a little later further north. If reference is made to the annual colony cycle it will be clear that a normal colony will be inadequate in adult bee population to exploit the spring blooming crop to the full unless it is subjected to some special management treatment. The flowering of the crop sown in the spring occurs just at the right time when the colony population is at a maximum. To exploit this crop requires normal spring management dealt with in the previous section, 1.24.

1.26.2 Management objective.

The objective is simple; the colony is to be built up to as large a size as possible by the middle of April in order to maximise the foraging force while the crop is in bloom. This requires large amounts of emerging brood 6 weeks before mid April; that is emerging in large quantities by the end of February/early March. This will allow the emerging bees to spend three weeks as house bees before having their three week foraging period on the rape.

1.26.3 Management to achieve the objective.

The queen must be stimulated to lay as early as possible. There are two ways of achieving this, namely:

    a) By feeding sugar syrup, or
    b) By feeding pollen patties

1.26.3.1 Feeding sugar syrup.

This should start late January and be undertaken in areas where there is no natural shortage of pollen and where the colony has plenty stored from the previous season. The feeding should be slow and a 50:50 mixture used which can be metabolised immediately.

The only suitable feeder will be a contact feeder directly over the frames in the brood chamber and directly over the brood nest. If the weather is cold bees will ignore a feeder where they have to 'come up and over' to the feed'. A couple of pints a week is in our experience an adequate amount and the holes available on the contact feeder should be adjusted accordingly to allow the colony to take this amount in this time scale.

There is advantage in providing some top insulation on top of the crown board and around the contact feeder at this time of the year. Kept warm and with stimulative feeding continued until the third week in March will produce a large colony at the right time.

The colony will require to be inspected to ensure that the there is plenty of comb space available for the queen to lay and frames of food may be judiciously removed and replaced with empty comb.

Some books have advised that brood spreading will help the colony build up quickly. We believe this practice should be avoided. The same result can be achieved by feeding or simulating a very early flow.

1.26.3.2 Feeding pollen patties.

This method is to be used in areas where there is a dearth of pollen such as may be experienced in some parts of the south east. Where autumn pollen supplies are not available, there is likely to be a shortage of spring pollen plants as well.

The additional protein can be provided either as pollen substitute or as pollen supplement in the form of patties. If pollen supplement is used it is essential that it is collected the previous season from disease free colonies and kept in the freezer for use in the spring. Recipes are as follows:

Pollen supplement: 20% pollen, 60% soya flour and 20% brewers' yeast.
Pollen substitute: 75% soya flour and 25% brewers' yeast.

The soya flour MUST be fat free; soya flour with a fat content is damaging to bees. The percentages stated above are by weight and not by volume. The method is to mix the ingredients into a stiff dough using sugar syrup and spreading about 1lb of it on a large piece of polythene. This is then placed on top of the frames and pressed down between the seams and covered with the crown board. Most colonies will take about a week to consume this amount. It is to be noted that the bees prefer pollen supplement to pollen substitute and this is clearly demonstrated by the rate of consumption.

Feeding should be continuous until the colonies start to work the rape.

1.26.4 Other points.

• There are advantages in reaping a crop from the OSR but it does entail additional work preparing the colonies. In many years a lot of beekeepers in the UK would have had very sparse returns without OSR.
• With the early build up and the strong flow from the rape most colonies will turn their attentions to swarming, usually while they are on the rape. Swarm detection inspections are very necessary while the bees are working the crop and the beekeeper must be prepared and have a suitable control method ready to deal with them.
• Noting the swarming probability, it goes without saying that a young queen is essential for

the satisfactory management of colonies on the rape. It is a good time to start queen rearing with such opulent colonies.

- Colonies prepared in the way outlined above may be expected to provide between 50 to 80lb of surplus honey if the stocks are actually adjacent to the crop.
- OSR will support one colony per acre while it is in bloom.
- Do not put colonies onto the rape close to other colonies from other beekeepers. We are aware of more than one case of EFB being contracted in this way. Farmers are not interested in the spread of bee diseases and often welcome any number of beekeepers on to their crop.

1.27 Summer management including the prevention detection and control of swarming.

1.27.1 Definition of summer.

The dictionary definition of summer is as follows:

> The warmest season of the year, in the northern hemisphere from June to August. The astronomical definition is from the summer solstice to the autumnal equinox.

As we used the definition of spring finishing on the last day of June or just after the summer solstice, we believe that the period we should be considering in this part of the syllabus is from early July to the end of September. This is the period when generally the colony size is decreasing from its peak value just before the main flow.

1.27.2 Management during the period under consideration.

Swarms can occur up to the end of September and the latest which one has been recorded in the UK is in October! We consider that after the end of May the probability of a colony swarming starts to decrease rapidly and is low by the beginning of July. On this basis we check our colonies just before going on holiday in July and leave them to their own devices. It is rare, in our experience, to have a swarm as late as this. However, we must add that we always work with young queens in our colonies. The management is detailed in section 1.12 but in summary it is as follows:

July. Continue swarm control inspections and take action accordingly. Many beekeepers tend to add supers unnecessarily during the flow and end up with half filled supers. It is better to over super in the spring and under super during the summer; remember the population is decreasing and swarming is caused through the poor distribution of queen substance throughout the colony. Decreasing population means there is more queen substance per bee and thus reducing the chances of the colony swarming. A nice easy month when the bees are doing all the work!.

August. Extraction of the crop, reducing entrances to prevent robbing, preparing stocks for heather and treating for Varroosis are the prime requirements. These are followed by checking for adult bee diseases and feeding the colony for winter after stores have been assessed. Any uniting can be undertaken to reduce the number of colonies to be over wintered. It is often said that colonies can be requeened for winter at this time of the year. We definitely do not recommend it unless absolutely necessary; spring is the best time for requeening in our experience.

September. Colonies back from the heather to be checked for winter stores and treated for Varroosis. General winter preparation for all other colonies.

1.27.3 Prevention, detection and control of swarming.

Depending on the season and the colony it is possible for a stock to swarm late in the summer although the probability decreases quite rapidly after the peak annual population is reached. Therefore do not be surprised if swarming preparations are detected in August or September and we advise continuing inspections to the end of the season even though we do not practice this ourselves. We usually go on leave during July returning we hope to full supers and a lot of hard work extracting!

In section 1.20 we detailed two methods of swarm control, namely, the artificial swarm and the destruction of queen cells. We believe that candidates should be familiar with at least two other methods of swarm control. In this respect we recommend reading up and trying the Snelgrove system and the Demaree system both of which are well documented elsewhere.

1.28 Moving colonies and the difficulties and dangers involved.

The criteria to be observed when moving colonies of bees from one place to another include optimum distance, vibration, temperature, ventilation and water supply.

1.28.1 The distance: that bees can be moved is well known, ie. 3 feet maximum or 3 miles minimum, if no bees are to be lost from the colony concerned. Note that it is usually the stock that is moved not the colony (BBKA definition) because it has to be moved in some receptacle or another. The reason for the distance restriction is twofold. Honeybees forage generally up to a distance of 2 to 3 miles from their hive and have a 'mental picture' of this area or recognise distinctive landmarks within the area and know how to navigate back using these landmarks. Moving their hive within this known area creates a condition whereby the foragers leave the hive in the new position, re-orientate on leaving the hive but while foraging, recognise well known landmarks and return to the old site.

The navigational ability of the honeybee is extremely precise (a matter of a few inches near their own hive). Moving the hive entrance more than 3 feet will create a condition whereby the foragers will not find their hive and will either drift to a nearby hive or cluster at the original position of the hive entrance. The authors conducted a series of experiments some years ago to test the memories of the bees by moving them to a distant apiary and then returning them to a different site in the original apiary. After two weeks their memories started to fail and all foragers returned to the new hive position in the original apiary. For periods less than 2 weeks, the bees when brought back, continued to return to their original site. Of course during the 2 week period many of the original foragers would have died a natural death and new foragers would have taken their place. The only time that this is not true is when a swarm issues; it can be hived very close to the original site and the foragers do not return to their original hive. It seems that something very curious happens to their memories (?), rather like erasing a computer disc of all its information.

1.28.2 Preparing a stock for moving: starts by removing the crown board and replacing it with a travelling screen, preferably with a space of about 1 in on the underside to allow room for any bees to cluster. When being moved, the entrance should be closed (eg. reduced entrance block foam pushed into the reduced entrance just before moving) and not restricted with a screen as many books recommend. If light is showing at their normal entrance they will attempt to escape at this point and there is the danger of them suffocating in the panic to get out. When being moved, the hive parts have to be secured one with another; this can be done in a variety of ways:

a) Using a hive strap around everything excluding the roof which is always removed for travelling. Two hive straps in opposite directions are safer than one.

b) Screwing plates 4in × 1in (100mm × 25mm) at an angle of 45° across the joins between floor and boxes and the screen being fastened with screws to the to box. Note that the 2 plates on each side should be angled in opposite directions to prevent movement. This method is considered to be superior to all others but it is more time consuming. It should be used for a major move over long distances, say greater than 50 miles.

c) Spring clips to join the boxes together: these use 3 screws, 2 on one box and 1 on the other.

d) Bro. Adam's method of long bolts through the screen, brood chamber and floorboard.

e) Using hive staples; these are a bit outdated these days and a fine way of disturbing a colony when hammering them home. Definitely not recommended.

f) The entrance block needs securing to the floorboard, the safest way is with two 'L' brackets screwed to the front and to the sides of the floorboard.

Other preparations which are necessary before the actual move are as follows:

a) The site and stands at the new location should be ready to receive the stocks immediately on arrival.

b) Prepare emergency equipment for journey, ie. veil, smoker, fuel, water spray for occasional cooling, spare ropes, wide sticky tape for accidental bee leaks, etc.

1.28.3 Moving the stocks: involves observing some simple rules:

a) Place foam in reduced entrance and then remove roof.

b) Place the stocks with the frames in a fore and aft direction so that frames cannot swing if emergency braking or stopping is required en route.

c) Ensure all stocks are roped down securely before starting. Stop after 15 minutes and check all is secure (tension up if required).

d) Corner at slow speed to minimise frames swinging.

e) The stocks should be moved preferably during the hours of darkness arriving at the destination about daybreak. If they are moved during the day over heating must be watched carefully and cooling applied (say every hour) with water spray if necessary.

f) If they are being moved on a trailer ensure that it has a spare wheel.

g) On arrival, set up all stocks in final positions replace all roofs and immediately remove foam at reduced entrances.

h) Next day remove screens and replace crown boards.

1.28.4 Vibration: excites bees and if they are closed up in transport the temperature increase would be dangerous if insufficient ventilation and cooling were not provided. During transportation by vehicle there will be a continuous vibration keeping the colony in a state of agitation and high temperature. It will therefore be clear that vibration in general is closely allied to temperature and ventilation. In order to minimise these adverse effects, stocks should be handled with care during the loading and off loading process.

1.28.5 Temperature and ventilation: go hand in hand and, of course, are allied to vibration. Because of the rise in temperature when a colony is disturbed it is necessary to provide adequate ventilation when moving bees. If very strong colonies are to be moved then it may be advantageous to provide additional space by adding another super as well as providing the ventilation screen. Even with these precautions moving strong stocks during the day in warm weather may be insufficient to prevent dangerous temperature rises, enough to melt wax comb and drown the bees in honey. Spraying the colony with water through the ventilation screen will be required as part of the operation.

1.28.6 Water supply: Water may be required en route as indicated above and it will be obvious that a regular water supply will be required by the colony when it arrives at its new location.

1.28.7 Other points related to moving bees are:

a) Bees should only normally be moved during the flying season, the winter cluster should not be disturbed.
b) Continual movement of bees, for say pollination purposes, puts them under stress and stress is the forerunner to Nosema.
c) It is better to move a stock of bees some days after it has been inspected in order to allow time for the bees to re-propolise all the seals which had been broken. This minimises internal movement of frames etc.
d) Travelling screens should be constructed of a mesh of 7 to 1 in of a wire gauge c. 28 SWG.
e) Colonies being moved to a new site should have a 10 day supply of stores in the brood chamber.

Stories of moving bees are legion, most of them involve the bees escaping and someone being stung. We find no amusement in these stories and believe that if bees are moved properly and the common sense precautions outlined above are taken, then no bees will be lost and no one will be stung. We consider that any bees escaping en route is due to negligence on the part of the beekeeper.

1.29 Different methods of 'clearing' bees from supers.

1.29.1 General points on clearing bees.

• By definition, clearing implies a crop has been collected and the flow is over; robbing can easily be started unless care is taken when removing the crop.
• Bees are generally more irritable after the flow and will be more inclined to defend their stores than before the flow finished.
• Entrances must be reduced at the same time that supers are being cleared.
• If more than one super has been used it is common for burr/brace comb to have been built joining supers together, the brace comb being filled with honey. It is essential to remove this brace comb from the top and bottom bars of the frames 24 hours before clearing, in order

to avoid honey dripping from the supers as they are removed. It is a sticky job to do but well worth having the frames cleaned up and no honey dripping while they are being collected. The brace comb should not be there and emphasises the importance of bee space and the many incorrect frames that are in use. The process known as 'cracking the supers' is not given the attention it needs in modern bee literature. It should be done just before dark. It also prevents the surprise of finding the supers not cleared because of brood in the one next to the brood chamber if the first supers are checked during the cracking process.

• Supers should be removed very early in the morning before the colony has started flying and taken straight to the extracting room for extraction the same day.

1.29.2 Clearer boards. There are basically two types one using Porter Bee Escapes and the other called the Canadian type with long tunnels for the bees to traverse to get from one side of the board to the other.

Porter bee escapes: possibly the most popular device in UK for clearing bees. The following are the salient points about its use:

a) The phosphor bronze springs require very delicate adjustment to a gap of $\frac{1}{8}$in (3mm) and to be free of propolis and wax if they are to work satisfactorily. The vertical alignment should also be checked to ensure that the two springs are central in the case.

b) Two Porter bee escapes per board should be used for rapid clearing and to ensure that if one escape becomes blocked the other one will still be operative.

c) Any clearer board should have an internal bee entrance incorporated in the design with an opening and closing device which can be operated from outside the hive. When wet supers are returned to the hive, the entrance is opened allowing the bees to enter the supers and, conversely, it is closed when they are to be cleared again. It is important that the operating lever allows the roof to be put in place when the supers are off the hive.

d) Approximately 24 to 48 hours are required to clear the supers. The time depends very much on the weather and the flying conditions at the time the board is put on, the better the conditions the shorter the time required to clear.

e) The bee escapes will require cleaning from time to time. Methylated spirit is an ideal solvent for propolis and wax.

Canadian clearer boards: have the advantage of no moving parts to be propolised and go wrong. The salient points of this mode of clearing are as follows:

a) The same time is required (perhaps marginally shorter) to clear; however, if the weather is bad they are not as effective as the Porter bee escape. The bees seem to learn very quickly that they can return to the supers via the same exit route. The supers must be removed at the latest after 48 hours.

b) An entrance capable of being opened and closed from outside the hive is required identical to the board with Porter bee escapes.

c) If by any chance there may be an odd drone in the supers, they can traverse the exit route without blocking it as would happen with a Porter bee escape.

8 way plastic escape: which is pinned to the underside of the board directly below a suitable hole. There are 8 plastic slots for the bees to reach the brood chamber and there are again no moving parts. The principle is the same as the Canadian clearer board. Our findings are that it works no better than the Canadian board.

Scottish clearer board: has 4 holes in each corner leading to a narrowing channel which reduces to a bee space over a distance of about 3in (76mm). We have found that it works no better than the Canadian clearer board despite what the Scots say about it being superior to any other.

1.29.3 Shake and brush method. The method appears to be simple and indeed is, if used at the right time.

    a) A spare empty super is required, to receive the cleared frames, placed on a roof behind the hive (note the roof is not upturned as most books recommend) with a cover cloth over to prevent any flying bees re-entering the cleared frames. The colony is smoked first at the entrance and then at the top to drive the bees downwards in the supers. One frame at a time is shaken free of bees and those remaining on the frame are brushed off with a feather. The frame free of bees is then placed in the empty super. As one super is cleared so that becomes the receptacle for the next and so on.

    b) If the supers are sealed smoking has little effect on the bees; they are only subdued when they have gorged themselves with honey and when smoked they are not immediately subdued, only driven downwards. After the honey flow has ceased the colony is likely to be more aggressive and will defend their stores. It will be clear that it is not a method to be used by the uninitiated at the wrong time and certainly not in an urban situation.

    c) Where should all these bees be shaken? We like to shake them back into the hive rather than at the front, only the bees which we brush off land up at the entrance of the hive. The reason for this is that we keep the super covered with a cover cloth except when a frame is being shaken and if the bees are in the hive, we are in control of the situation and not the bees.

    d) The final consideration is when should this method be used? At a time when the bees are not flying to safeguard against robbing being started; this means early morning or late evening.

1.29.4 Other clearing methods. To provide an overall picture other methods of clearing should be noted:

a) Mechanical blowers usually powered by electric motor which in turn is powered by a portable generator. The super is stood on end and the bees are blown forcibly out of the super towards the hive entrance. Not for the small time beekeeper.

b) Chemical repellents. The three most commonly known are:

    Carbolic acid – not used these days.
    Butric anhydride – popular in USA.
    Benzaldehyde (smells of oil of bitter almonds) – used quite extensively in UK and works well. Should be kept in the dark. The residual crystals which dry out on the clearer cloth are a fire hazard, therefore the cloth should be kept in a sealed tin.

All the above chemical repellents are used by shaking a few drops onto a cloth which is put over the top super and covered with the crown board. When the bees are cleared (a few minutes normally) the super is removed and the cloth and crown board put over the next super below and so on.

1.30 How colonies are prepared for the winter period and give the principles underlying this preparation.

1.30.1 General. Preparations for winter should start in August after the main crop has been removed and extracted. There are reasons for this:

a) A colony of bees collects all the stores it needs for winter by the end of July under normal circumstances. If all these sealed stores are removed, sugar syrup has to be fed and this also has to be processed, ripened, stored and sealed; this is difficult for the bees to do on chilly days and nights in autumn, particularly the ripening and evaporating the excess water. It is as well to remember that unsealed stores are likely to ferment and fermenting stores are a cause of dysentery.

b) All colonies require sampling for the adult bee diseases before the colony settles down for winter. If Nosema is present, Fumidil 'B' can be fed with their winter rations. Fumidil 'B' is best fed in the first gallon of winter feed if this is required. If Acarine is present and the crop has been removed, the colony can be treated without fear of tainting any honey and the treatment (Folbex VA) can be given during good flying weather.

c) Colonies may require to be requeened and it is better to know that the new queen is accepted and laying before clustering starts at 57°F (14°C).

Those colonies that are destined for the heather are prepared before they go with a young queen and hopefully return with a full brood box of stores and a super of surplus honey.

1.30.2 Requirements for successful wintering are as follows:

A sound and weatherproof hive.
35lb of liquid stores.
A young fertile queen with plenty of winter bees.
The colony to be disease free.
Good ventilation while excluding mice.
No disturbance from October to March.

These will be examined to understand the importance attached to each.

1.30.3 A sound and weatherproof hive. The principle of this item is to keep the colony dry and must be self evident. However, it is quite surprising the tatty quarters some colonies get landed with; roofs in particular seem to be very often inadequate. Dampness in winter can spell disaster for a colony. Double walled hives have roofs that blow off and a secure method of roping or screwing them down is necessary. If a single walled hive roof has the right clearance between the brood box and the inside dimension of the roof, $\frac{5}{16}$in (8mm) it will not blow off; many do not meet this requirement. Weatherproofing means having the hive off the ground on a suitable hive stand so that the floor board is not permanently damp and can dry out when the weather allows it.

1.30.4 Stores – 35lb (16kg) minimum. The beekeeper who has to feed his bees before March should not be keeping bees; he has not prepared them adequately for their winter hibernation.

a) After the crop has been removed every frame has to be examined in August and the stores estimated. This is done by eye and by feel; it is surprising how quickly and expert one can become at this task. It is essential to know how much a full frame of stores weighs; eg. 5lb (2.25kg) for a BS and 7lb (3.2kg) for a Commercial.

b) Having totted up the total in the colony, a calculation is required to know how much sugar to feed. Honey contains 80% sugar and 20% water approximately. Suppose the colony has 25lb (11.4kg) of stores, then another 10lb (4.5kg) is required to meet the 35lb (16kg) criterion. 10lb (4.5kg) of honey is equivalent to 8lb (3.6kg) of sugar, the amount required to be fed in a suitable solution. It is frightening the number who keep bees and never do this examination and this simple arithmetic.

c) See section 1.14 for details on feeding and the strength of syrup to feed.

The principle involved in providing the right amount of liquid stores is to provide the fuel that the colony requires to stay alive during the low temperatures experienced during the winter period. This fuel produces heat when metabolised and converted into mechanical energy by the bee. 35lb (16kg) of honey is equivalent to 28lb (12.7kg) of sugar. It is equivalent to the energy produced by a 14 watt light bulb running continuously for 6 months. The arithmetic is as follows:

100g sugar is equivalent to 1700 kilo joules = 1700 kilo watt seconds
1lb = 454g is equivalent to 1700×4.54k watt seconds
28lb sugar is equivalent to $1700 \times 4.54 \times 28$k watt seconds = 216,104,000 watt seconds

For the winter period of year there are $182 \times 24 \times 60 \times 60 = 15,724,800$ seconds

∴ Size of the bulb = 216,104,000 15,724,800 = 14 watts.

1.30.5 A young queen. By observation over the years beekeepers have come to know that colonies winter better with a young queen compared with an older one. This sort of statement will be found throughout the literature but no explanation of why this should be ever seems to be forthcoming. Thus it is impossible to state the principle underlying this particular wintering requirement; the principle has been learnt, by trial and error, over many years by many beekeepers.

It is unlikely to be related to a quantitative problem of queen substance and the threshold amount available to each bee because the colony naturally reduces in size in the winter thereby allowing more queen substance per bee. Perhaps queen substance has other effects on colony well-being which are yet undiscovered. Young queens are likely to lay better than old queens and this could get the colony away to a better start in the early spring. The other point is what is young; a queen in her 1st, 2nd year etc? Brother Adam has always maintained that a queen lays better in her 2nd year particularly if she has not been stressed in the first year.

Requeening in the spring with queens bred the previous year and kept in over wintered nucs will go into winter at approximately 15 months old and carry the colony through winter before being replaced the next March. This system works well. Whether the queen is regarded as old is doubtful, but if she is not replaced at 21 months old, her efficacy thereafter may certainly be expected to taper off quite rapidly.

Our own feeling in the matter, as a result of experience, is to ensure that queens of 24 months old do not lead a colony into winter if this can be avoided. Good queens for breeding purposes can of course be kept in nucs for much longer periods. Nevertheless, the reasons why young queens are better for wintering do seem obscure and the fact will have to be accepted until a more scientific explanation is forthcoming.

1.30.6 The colony to be disease free. It is vital to sample all colonies for adult bee diseases in August so that treatment may be administered if found to be necessary. Before uniting, which is a common occurrence at the end of the active season, the check for disease is essential.

Examination for adult bee diseases now costs money if the samples are sent to Luddington, and the price per sample discourages beekeepers to use the service. Many counties have organised their own microscopy service and more individual beekeepers are doing their own (this must be good). On the other side of the coin more beekeepers are, for example, feeding Fumidil 'B' to all colonies before winter as a prophylactic against Nosema. Although there are rumblings that this is unlikely to be detrimental in the long run (development of strains resistant to this antibiotic) it would in our opinion be a wrong course of action until a definitive paper has been prepared on the subject by someone with the right scientific ability.

The principle involved here is that diseases are spread in the animal world by close contact one with another making it easy for the disease pathogens to be transferred. Anyone who regularly travels on the crowded London Underground in winter when the common cold is prevalent will readily appreciate the mode of transfer! In winter the bees are in a cluster and at very close quarters to one another for a prolonged period. The importance of the colony going into its clustering mode in a disease free state should now be very apparent.

1.30.7 Good ventilation while excluding mice. A colony during winter, if it metabolises 35lb (16kg) of honey, will be required to get rid of approximately $4\frac{1}{2}$ gallons (20.5 litres) of water. This can only be achieved by evaporation. The average rate is 5 pints (2.8 litres) / month or 3oz (84ml) / day. When the colony consumes its sugar stores carbon dioxide (CO_2) and water vapour (H_2O) are produced. The calculation of total water produced which must be dispersed by evaporation is as follows:

1lb honey has c. 18% water	= 3oz (84ml) water
1lb honey has c. 72% sugar	= 13oz (364ml)
To dilute the sugar 50:50 needs	= 13oz (364ml) water, 10oz (280ml) coming from other sources

Metabolising 13oz (364ml) sugar produces 8oz (224ml) water
∴ Metabolising 1lb (454 g) honey involves 21oz (588ml) water in the form of vapour
or 1kg honey involves 588 × 2.2ml water = 1.294 litres

20oz (560ml) = 1pint (568ml)
∴ 35lb (16kg) honey represents 35 × 21oz = 36.74pint = $4\frac{1}{2}$ gallons water.
or 16kg honey represents 13.6 × 1.294 litres = 20.7 litres = 4.5 gallons

In order to remove this amount of water it will be clear that the basic principle involved is good ventilation throughout the winter. It is more difficult for evaporation to take place in the damp western side of UK compared with the drier eastern side. These are the facts, the best configuration for achieving this evaporation is still being debated in the bee press and still no one seems to agree on the subject.

Our own method, which we have used successfully for many years after experimenting with various approaches, is as follows:

- Heat escaping from the cluster causes the movement of air, warm moist air moves upwards and is replaced by cold dry air at the bottom.
- All entrance blocks have nine $\frac{3}{8}$in (10mm) diameter holes drilled in them spaced equidistant apart across the length of the block. This gives a total cross sectional area of c. 1 sq.in (645 sq.mm) to limit the air flow. The block turned through 90° is a normal reduced entrance block with a 4in (100mm) wide slot. The $\frac{3}{8}$in (10mm) diameter holes form the mouse guard and are 'kinder' to the pollen collectors in the spring cf the perforated metal mouse guards.
- The crown board is raised about $\frac{1}{8}$in (3mm) with matchsticks at each corner. This gives an exit area for air to escape of c. 9 sq.in (5800 sq.mm). The feed hole(s) are covered so that the flow of air is round the outside of the cluster and avoiding the chimney effect directly above the cluster. The roof ventilators now play no part in the ventilation system.
- The mouse guards are put in, usually in September, before the ivy flow and the crown board is raised as late as possible to stop the gap being propolised. It is interesting to note that if there is no ventilation at the top of the colony, in the spring it is usually a mess with condensation and mouldy outside combs. One associated problem is that some of the stored pollen also develops mould and is then useless to the bees. Strains of bee that collect a lot of propolis will get themselves into this situation if crown boards are raised too early.

1.30.8 No disturbance during the winter period. Once the colony has settled down for winter it should be left undisturbed until the following spring. Experiments have been conducted and it has been found that the cluster temperature is raised quite a considerable amount, up to 10°F (6°C), by say just taking the roof off. Such increases in temperature shortens the life of the winter bee and this manifests itself in spring just when the colony requires all the bees it can muster. Hives should never be sited under trees where the drip of water from the branches can cause colony disturbance.

The principle involved here is quite simple. By alerting the colony it has to get itself into a state whereby it can defend itself by having bees which are capable of flying and attacking, by stinging, an intruder. For the indirect flight muscles to work they must be at a working temperature, the reasons for this do not concern us here. It will now be clear why the temperature of the colony is raised by disturbance at the cost of increased food consumption and shortening of the winter bee's life.

1.30.9 Other points of interest are:

a) The green woodpecker can spell disaster for a colony if they direct their attention to boring through the side of the hive. They are usually troublesome in very cold weather when they cannot find forage in the hard ground. There are two ways of protection:

- Surrounding the hive with chicken netting.
- Covering the hive with a plastic bag (but note this interferes with the ventilation).

b) It is desirable that a colony has stores of pollen which can then be used when brood rearing starts after the winter solstice. We have never found this to be a problem but there are probably parts of UK where there is a dearth of pollen. The final topping up of pollen stores occurs during the ivy flow in September / October (nb. winter bees are produced by large pollen consumption).

c) Plenty of bees are required for good wintering but making massive colonies by uniting can defeat the object as shown by some experiments done by Dr. Jeffree at Aberdeen University. For a synopsis of his work see appendix 8 'The size of the colony for winter'.
d) The old adage that bees do not freeze to death but starve to death is very relevant to the wintering problem.
e) The last thing to do is to remove the hive record card from the roof to bring the final years' records up to date and to prepare new cards for the next season.

1.31 The effect of honeybee stings and recommended first aid treatment.

We have included this item on bee stings as it appears to us to be an oversight on the part of the Examinations Board. It does not appear in the syllabi of any of the eight modules leading to the intermediate and advanced certificates. We consider that every beekeeper should at the very least have a rudimentary knowledge on the matter.

1.31.1 General.

It is the mature worker bee, 14+ days old, which is capable of injecting bee venom into its chosen victim. Queens only use their sting on other queens and drones have no stinging apparatus. It is a means of defence used by the honeybee, generally as a last resort. After stinging mammals, the honeybee leaves behind the stinging apparatus, including the 7th abdominal ganglion, thus terminating its own life.

Stings can be minimised as follows:

a) Beekeepers maintaining stocks of docile bees by culling the queens producing nervous bees and those with strong defensive traits eg. followers.
b) Handling colonies correctly ie. no jarring of frames, no fast movements, no squashing of bees or banging of hives. Bees are very sensitive to vibration.
c) Only open stocks under good weather conditions. Thunderstorms or approaching rain clouds definitely affect the temper of the bee.
d) Always wear a veil to protect the eyes, the nose, the mouth and ears where there is a proliferation of mast cells (mast cells are pharmacological 'time bombs'; when they rupture they release powerful chemicals that can effect various tissues nearby, such as blood vessels or smooth muscle).
e) Use protective clothing of correct material eg. cotton. It is said that woollen garments or garments dyed blue are best avoided. In our opinion the temperament of the bee is the predominant factor and not the clothing.
f) Dispersing the sting pheromone by the application of the smoker to the site of injection does discourage other guard bees being attracted to the site of the first sting. For stings on the hands, place a hot part of the smoker on the sting area to evaporate, as quickly as possible, the volatile pheromone and then smoke the area to mask any remaining smell. Better still wash the hands in plain water to dissipate the pheromone; we use the apiary water supply to rinse our hands. Beekeepers say that the first sting is the most expensive one!
g) Refrain from using perfumes, aftershave lotions, hair shampoos, nail varnish, hair sprays and other similar cosmetics prior to working with bees as these have been known to elicit a stinging reaction from bees due to the similarity in the chemical make up to

the isopentylacetate in the alarm pheromone of the sting chamber.

h) Site stocks as far away as possible from the general public.

1.31.2 The effect of stings.

1. Most beekeepers at the first sting may experience pain, reddening of the skin and swelling. The severity seems to vary depending on the site and the number of stings. But over the years a natural immunity will be built up and the discomfort and swelling will be minimal. The pain associated with a sting does not decrease with the years one keeps bees; it remains the same.

2. Extensive swelling may occur taking 12 hours to reach its maximum and 2 or 3 days to resolve. These symptoms may indicate an increasing sensitivity to bee venom.

3. A generalised reaction with symptoms of difficulty in breathing, skin rash, palpitations, vomiting and faintness occurring within minutes of a sting indicates a severe reaction (anaphylaxis) requiring emergency medical attention. **Do not attempt to take the patient to hospital you may get caught in a traffic jam. Call an ambulance which is equipped with bells and lights to get through traffic. Time is of the essence.**

1.31.3 First aid treatment.

- The barb should be removed as soon as possible by a scraping action of a knife, hive tool or finger nail, not by squeezing between the fingers. This will only inject more venom.
- Away from the stocks of bees, applying ice to the site of the sting, especially if it is situated where there is little spare skin for expansion eg. ear, nose or tip of finger, will bring some relief of pain.
- Application of calamine lotion, steroid creams or crushed leaves of the mallow plant, *Althaea officinalis*, has long been used to relieve inflammation and may give some relief. Antihistamine creams are best avoided as their repeated application can cause severe skin sensitization.
- Aspirin tablets may reduce pain and inflammation. Piriton tablets contain antihistamine and may lessen the symptoms. If in doubt consult a doctor.
- To the non-beekeeper a sympathetic attitude will often solve the immediate problem but should there be any severe reaction as may be the result of a sting close to or on the eye ball, in or around the mouth or neck then it is always safest to obtain medical advice.

1.31.4 Other points of interest.

- Most beekeepers expect to receive the odd sting and take no further action beyond removing the barb usually with their hive tool during a manipulation.
- About 15% of the population have an atopic constitution and roughly 50% of the children of two atopic parents will be similarly afflicted. This group includes individuals with a personal history of hay fever, eczema, asthma, allergic rhinitis and urticaria. They may show progressive worsening in their reactions to stings developing general symptoms such as nausea, skin rashes and respiratory difficulties. Medical aid should be sought immediately should anyone show these symptoms.
- Taking non inflammatory drugs eg. Aspirin, Triludan or Piriton under medical advice one or two hours before working in the apiary does reduce the reaction to stings. It should be remembered that antihistamines cause drowsiness so that driving the car is unwise after this kind of medication.
- For the hypersensitive person who wishes to continue beekeeping or for the members of the beekeeper's family who are exposed to the danger of being stung and are hypersensitive a

course of immunotherapy can be arranged through their family doctor. Recent NHS procedures require the treatment to be given where resuscitation facilities are available, ie a hospital. GPs actively discourage seeking the treatment and one has to be very insistent to obtain treatment. We understand that the cost to the NHS for treatment, lasting about a year, is about £100.

- Many give up beekeeping because of being stung and invariably say that they have developed a reaction. Bad tempered bees and inept handling are usually the truth of the matter.
- The alarm pheromone inducing the honeybee to sting requires a threshold amount to elicit this effect. In docile bees the threshold level is high and in aggressive bees the threshold level is low. In the latter case this can lead to mass attacks seldom occasioned in the UK but more often in other countries with Africanised bees. With mass attacks where 500 or more stings are recorded death can occur even though the patient is not hypersensitive, however, the chances of developing hypersensitivity, after recovery, are increased. One of the authors suffered a mass attack many years ago but did not become hypersensitive but it did take 4 or 5 days in bed to recover.

MODULE 2: HONEYBEE PRODUCTS AND FORAGE

The Candidate will be able to give detailed accounts of:

2.1 The main requirements of the current United Kingdom statutory regulations affecting the handling, preparation for sale, composition, labelling and weight of packs of honey.

2.1.1 General.

Statutory regulations regarding the sale of packs of honey are made by governing bodies to protect the consumer/customer from unscrupulous dealers. Beekeepers with surplus honey to sell should make every effort to be well informed on all the current legislation. This legislation appears to be constantly changing especially with metrication and other EC regulations. Satisfied customers will continue to purchase their favourite brand of honey from the same source ie. a producer of a good reliable product. This reputation, built up over many years can be easily lost by carelessness or ignorance. Bad labelling, sticky jars, poor packaging or semi-crystallised honey are not attractive to customers.

Adherence to all the legal requirements regarding the sale of honey will avoid prosecution by Trading Standards or Environmental Health Officers. A high standard of production, prepared with 'due diligence' will protect the beekeeper from a civil prosecution should any damage to the health of the consumers arise as a result of contaminated products. Honey produced by a hobbyist beekeeper and sold at the door should be prepared with the same care as that produced for the retail market. A look at the supermarket shelves with the attractive products of imported and home produced honey at very attractive prices should make the small time beekeeper realise that if he wants to sell his home produced honey at a premium price the presentation of his products must have equal or better characteristics.

From time to time regulations change. The 'BBKA News', produced 4/5 times a year and distributed to all members of the BBKA, reports on new regulations produced by MAFF or other regulatory bodies pertaining to the sale or production of honey for sale. Statutory Orders are obtainable from HMSO or can be viewed at public reference libraries. Copies of the Statutory Instruments are expensive and not easily obtained. At the reference library consult Sweet and Maxwell's Practical Food Law Manual, Halsbury Statutory Instruments and the Statutory Instruments (see numbers below). If the beekeeper is in any doubt about his obligations he should seek advice from the Local Authority Officers, LACOTS (Local Authorities Co-ordinating Body on Food and Trading Standards) responsible for supervising the regulations on sale of food. Obtain a copy of BBKA's Advisory Leaflet No 103 Leaflet, 'So you wish to sell honey?' which has been produced with the aid of Devon, Somerset and Warwickshire Trading Standards departments, Devon Beekeepers' Association and Mr. Derek Brown of Reading.

2.1.2 The statutory laws and regulations applying to the sale and supply of honey products:

- **The Honey Regulations 1976.** Statutory Instruments 1976 No. 1832
- **The Food Safety Act 1990**. Primary regulations 1976 Statutory instruments 1976 No 1832, amended S.I. 1980 No. 1849, S.I. 1982 No.1727, S.I. 1985 No. 67, S.I. 1991 No.1472 and S.I. 1992 No 2596. Ancillary regulations include Lead in Food 1984 S.I. 1984 No 1305
- **The Food Labelling Regulations 1984.** Metrication 1st October 1995 EC Regulations.
- **The Food (Lot marking) Regulations 1992.** Statutory Instrument 1992 No.1357
- **Food Premises Registration 1993.** Statutory Instrument 1993 No 2022.
- **Plastic Materials and Articles in Contact with Food Regulations Act 1992.**Amendment regulations 1994. Statutory Instrument 1994 No 979.
- **The Weights and Measures Act 1985. Primary regulations Weights and Measures (Miscellaneous Food) Order 1988** Statutory Instruments 1988 No.2040 as amended by S.I. 1990 No. 1550. Local working standard weights and measures testing equipment regulations 1986 S.I. 1986 No 1685.
- **Weights and Measures (Packaged Goods) Regulation 1986** Statutory Instrument 1986 No 2049.
- **Weights and Measures (Quantity marking and Abbreviations of Units) Regulation 1987**. Statutory Instrument. 1987 No.1538
- **Weights and Measures (Metrication) (Miscellaneous goods) (amendment) Order 1994**. Statutory Instrument 1994 No 2866
- **Trade Descriptions Act 1968.**
- **The Consumer Protection Act 1987.**
- **The Glazed Ceramic Ware (Safety) Regulations 1975.**
- **The Food Premises (Registration) Regulations 1991**. Statutory Instrument 1993 No 2022

The Honey Regulations, 2003. See Riches "Honey Marketing" which has a two-page update written in March, 2004.

Where a date and number for the Statutory Instruments has not been given it is because we have not been able to trace the necessary document at our reference library. The regulations are extremely complicated. The main requirements are explained in the following sections 2.1.3 to 2.1.5.

2.1.3. The main requirements of the current statutory regulations affecting the preparation of honey for sale.

The Food Safety Act 1990.

This act makes it an offence to sell honey which is not of the nature, substance or quality demanded by the purchaser. The most common use of this section relates to the sale of food containing foreign matter. In respect of honey it could be used where the description of the 'honey' was applied to products such as 'honeydew' and polymerised corn oil. It could be an offence to falsely declare the country of origin of honey as in the customer's view the quality of the honey is related to its country of origin. Section 21 of this act introduces a new defence which has not previously been available to food producers, namely the 'due diligence' defence. The effect of this provision is that if any producer in selling a product commits an offence he will not be liable for prosecution if it can be shown that all reasonable precautions were taken and all 'due diligence' was exercised to avoid the committing of the offence. Any product must not be harvested where unacceptable amounts of potential harmful substances are likely to be transferred to food.

The Food Premises (Registration) Regulations 1991.

These regulations require beekeepers who sell honey to register their premises with the Local Authority by 1st July 1991 ie. premises where the honey is extracted, bottled and stored. New businesses should register 28 days before trading. Amendments exempting hobbyist beekeepers as 'low risk' premises are as published in BBKA News, number 83 February 1992. These exemptions are quoted below:

'**Premises used irregularly or only occasionally.** Premises used for less than five days in any five consecutive weeks, the five days do not have to be consecutive and thus any premises used regularly once a week will be included in the exemptions.
Premises where only low risk activities take place, which are exempt unless the retail sale of food takes place there. This category includes places where fish is taken for food but not processed, where eggs are produced or packed and where honey is harvested.
Domestic premises. Used for the production of honey or subsequent preparation, storage, bottling or sale (whether wholesale or retail) of honey.'

Beekeepers should as far as possible conform to the requirements of the existing regulations concerning the preparation of food. Local Authority Inspectors are entitled to inspect a beekeeper's premises. The purpose of these inspections are:

• To identify potential hazards and assess the risks to public health arising from activities within the food business.
• To assess the effectiveness of management control to achieve safe food.
• To identify specific contraventions of food hygiene law.

If a beekeeper or trader applies to be registered the following basic requirements must be met (BBKA News No 77 November 1990):
a) All surfaces must be washable, they must be easy to clean and disinfect, this includes walls, floor and shelving i.e. made of stainless steel or tiles. It must not be possible to crack these surfaces. The ceilings must be constructed to prevent accumulation of dirt and to reduce condensation of steam.
b) Windows and doorways should be screened to prevent entry of insects. Doors must have a smooth, non absorbent surface. Doors should close automatically and be hermetically sealed. The premises should be free from vermin.
c) Two sinks with hot and cold water should be available, one for utensils and one for operators. There should be separate toilet facilities.
d) All equipment should be maintained to a high standard of cleanliness. All equipment must be impervious, resistant to corrosion and capable of repeated cleaning.
c) The operator should observe a high standard of personal hygiene. Clean overalls and hair cover are essential. Hands should be washed before commencing work. Nails should be kept short and clean. No cuts or abrasions present on the hands.
d) Where food is being prepared the area should be a 'no smoking area'. There should be no dust, smoke, no spitting or any unpleasant odour which may contaminate the product.
e) Good storage i.e. vermin free, exclusion of domestic animals and weather proof for supers awaiting extraction and storage of packed honey.

2.1.4 The main requirements of the current statutory regulations affecting the labelling and weight of packs of honey. The Food Labelling Regulations 1984 and the Food (Lot Marking) Regulations 1992.

The presentation of food shall not be such that a purchaser is likely to be misled to a material degree as to the nature, substance or quality of the food. The important points for labels are:

- The name of the product to be displayed. This may be:

  a) Honey   b) Comb Honey   c) Chunk Honey   d) Baker's Honey or Industrial Honey.
  e) The word 'honey' with a regional, topographical or territorial reference eg. Devon Honey, Honey from South Devon, Moorland Honey etc.
  f) The word 'honey' with a reference to the blossom or plant origin eg. Heather Honey, Lime Honey.
  g) The word 'honey' with any other true description eg. Honeydew, Pressed Honey, Set Honey.

- With wholesale transactions of containers of a net weight of 10kg or more, a separate document showing the required information is sufficient if it accompanies the container.
- The containers of honey for sale should be given a 'lot' mark. In the event of contamination all honeys of the same 'lot' number will be recalled from the retail outlets. The 'lot' mark should be easily visible, legible and indelible. The size should be appropriate to the operational pattern. The mark should be prefixed by 'L'. Records should be kept of the lot marks of all honey sold.
- There must be no misrepresentation in words or pictures.
- The producer's name and address to be displayed (telephone number optional).
- The net weight to be displayed in metric units. The size of the lettering for the weights is critical.
- The numerical value may be declared in words, in which case the unit of weight must be referred to in words.
- The numerical value may be declared in figures which in the case the unit of weight may be referred to in words or by means of an approved abbreviation.
- One type space between the figure and the unit used is not mandatory and presentation with the unit directly adjacent to the number may be used.
- All required markings should be clear legible, conspicuous and indelible.
- Honey weighing less than 50g, chunk honey and comb honey may be packed in any quantity.
- The units which may be used for declaring quantities are kilogram and gram. The permitted abbreviations are kg for kilogram and g for gram (lower case only). No other abbreviation should be used. The letter 's' may **not** be added to indicate the plural. Weight markings are subject to a minimum size requirement where the size is that of the number and not the unit as shown below:

Contents of pack	Minimum height of numerals
Not exceeding 50 gram	2 millimetres
Exceeding 50 gram but not exceeding 200 gram	3 millimetres
Exceeding 200 gram but not exceeding 1 kilogram	4 millimetres
Exceeding 1 kilogram	6 millimetres

Rules governing the declarations of quantity were changed on 1st October 1995 by a directive from the European Union (EU). This is the date when the Imperial weights were replaced by the metric system. The net weight of honey in the container should be 57g, 113g, 227g, 340g, 454g, 680g, or a multiple of 454g. The net weight of the honey in the container should comply with the following criteria:

Net weight of product	Maximum scale interval on weighing equipment
50g to not exceeding 200g	2g
200g to not exceeding 1kg	5g
1kg to not exceeding 25kg	10g

Labelling.
Labelling is very much a personal choice, we believe in simplicity and use Ablelabel (32mm x 63mm) black lettering on gold for all our honey. Once you have a label 'stick' with it if your honey sells well. The public quickly learn to recognise the label as a sign of a good product. Where a list of ingredients must be affixed to the product eg. Honey Mustard, Honey Fudge, Honey Linctus then the list must be preceded by an appropriate heading which consists of or includes the word 'ingredients' The listed items should be in descending order of weight.

Sales of home produced honey.
Sale of honey may take place at the beekeeper's door providing the goods for sale have been produced on the premises. It is therefore necessary for the beekeeper to have his hives in the garden or grounds of his home otherwise he will be contravening the retail licensing laws. If all your honey is sold to a retailer then the apiaries may be sited anywhere. The labelling requirements are identical in both cases.

Weights and Measures Act 1985.
Honey is a prescribed food and its packing is governed by the 'average weight' rules. This means that any production batch of honey must consist of packs, the average content of which is equal to the declared quantity. If these requirements are met then the packer is entitled to apply 'e' mark alongside the declaration of quantity. The advantage of this is that anyone exporting to another European country can do so with the knowledge that the product will have free access to the market without further checks.

Weighing of products for sale.
A small time seller of honey will not wish to purchase expensive scales as used by the retail trade because of the cost. Prices range from £200 to £500. Nevertheless the scales used for weighing products for sale should be regularly checked using stamped brass weights. We think for a small producer if the scales were checked twice a year and logged this action would demonstrate 'due diligence'. A commercial firm processing honey for the retail trade would be required to use scales which would meet the approval of the Weights and Measures Department inspectors who would mark the scales with a government stamp ie. crown and date if approved or a six sided star if rejected.

Containers.
Containers for honey should be made of materials which under normal and foreseeable conditions of use do not transfer their constituents to the honey in quantities which could endanger human health, bring about a deterioration in its aroma, taste, texture or colour or bring about an unacceptable change in its nature, substance or quality. This applies to

containers which are in contact with the honey and to the containers which are likely at some later time to be in contact with the honey. Certain ceramic materials may present particular risks. Packers are asked to obtain an assurance from their suppliers that containers comply with The Materials and Articles in Contact with Food Regulations 1987, Plastic Materials and Articles in Contact with Food Regulations Act 1992 and The Glazed Ceramic Ware (Safety) Regulations 1975. With ceramic containers difficulty arises with amount of honey a ceramic container will hold (see 2.1.4 regarding restrictions on the net weight of honey to be packed in a container i.e. 57g, 113g, 227g, 340g, 454g, 680g), whether the internal glazing is adequate and the efficiency of the lid to exclude the atmosphere in order to keep the honey in pristine condition until consumed. We have recently purchased pottery containers which would only hold 411g (14oz).

2.1.5 The main requirements of the current statutory regulations affecting the composition of honey for sale.

The Honey Regulations 1976 seek to regulate the compositional quality of honey. These regulations cover 10 pages and are available from HMSO, Statutory Instrument 1832. The following are summaries from the regulations.

Regulation 2 contains a number of definitions:

- 'Honey' means the fluid, viscous or crystallised food which is produced by honeybees from the nectar of blossoms, or from secretions of, or found on, living parts of plants other than blossoms, which honeybees collect, transform, complete with substances of their own and store and leave to mature in honeycombs.
- 'Comb Honey' means honey stored by honeybees in the cells of freshly built broodless combs and intended to be sold in sealed whole combs or in parts of such combs.
- 'Chunk Honey' means honey which contains at least one piece of comb honey.
- 'Blossom Honey' means honey produced wholly or mainly from the nectar of blossoms.
- 'Honeydew honey' means honey, the colour of which is light brown, greenish brown, black or any intermediate colour, produced wholly or mainly from secretions of or found on living parts of plants other than blossoms.
- 'Drained honey' means honey obtained by draining uncapped broodless honeycombs.
- 'Extracted honey' means honey obtained by centrifuging uncapped broodless honeycombs.
- 'Pressed honey' means honey obtained by pressing broodless honeycombs with or without the application of moderate heat.

Regulation 3 is an exemption clause for honey sold outside the UK or sold under contract to HM government for consumption by any of HM services.

Regulation 4 controls the composition of honey and in particular prohibits the addition to honey sold of any substance other than honey. It also prohibits the sale of honey unless it is as far as practicable free from mould, insects, insect debris, brood or any other organic or inorganic substance foreign to the composition of honey. It also prohibits the marketing of honey which has an artificially changed acidity.

Regulation 5 concerns the use of honey used as an ingredient in the preparation of food.

Regulation 6 deals specifically with the use of the description 'honey'. In simple terms it states that a product may only be called honey if it is honey as defined in regulation 2.

Regulation 7 lays down certain physical characteristics for honey and specifies the circumstances under which the descriptions comb, chunk, baker's and industrial must be used. In the case of baker's or industrial honey it lays down compositional criteria relating to moisture content, foreign tastes and odours, fermentation, reduced enzyme levels, diastase activity levels and hydroxymethylfurfuraldehyde (HMF) content. Note should be made of the standards set:

- Heather honey being derived wholly or mainly from the genus *calluna* or clover honey derived wholly or mainly from the genus *trifolium* may have a moisture content of no higher than 23 per centum.
- Any other honey must have a moisture content of no higher than 21 per centum.
- The diastase activity of the honey should not be less than 4, or if it has a naturally low enzyme content, less than 3. (*This may occur in Hungarian Acacia honey, Robinia and may be due to either the age of the foraging bee or the opulence of the flow of nectar. Enzyme activity is regarded as an indicator of careful processing and storage of honey. The diastase activity of honey can be measured by spectrophotometric test or using a more simple apparatus using degraded starch and iodine*).
- The hydroxymethylfurfuraldehyde (HMF) content should not be more than 80 milligrams per kilogram. A trace of HMF is always naturally present in honey though with adverse and prolonged storage or overheating the quantity can exceed 30-40mg/kg and rise even higher. (*Measured by Fiehe test or Winkler's direct colorimetric test see the book on 'Honey' by Dr E. Crane, reprinted 1979*).

Regulation 8 prohibits the use of a label which makes reference, either in words or by pictorial device, to the blossom or plant origin of the honey unless the honey is derived wholly or mainly from the blossom or plant indicated. The same prohibition applies where there is a reference to the regional, topographical or territorial origin of the honey unless it originated wholly in the appropriate place.

Regulation 9 provides that any statement required to be marked on a label must be clear, legible and indelible. It must be in a conspicuous position on the label in such a manner that it will be readily discernible and easily read by an intending purchaser or consumer under normal condition of purchase and use. The statement must not be interrupted by any other material where this might mislead the purchaser as to the nature of the honey, neither must it be hidden, obscured or reduced inconspicuousness by any other matter on the label. The height of the letters in any statement must not be such that, by giving undue prominence to any part of the statement will result in the purchaser being misled.

Regulation 10 lays down the penalties for contravening the regulations. The penalties range from a fine not exceeding £100 or 6 month imprisonment to a fine of £500 and a term of imprisonment not exceeding one year.

These Honey Regulations are somewhat daunting to the hobbyist selling a few pounds of honey in the local shop which are surplus to his family's requirements. The bees can produce the product in accordance with the regulations and the beekeeper should only extract it when completely capped (water content-OK), sell it without heating (diastase and HMF-OK) and show 'due diligence' straining and bottling (foreign bodies-OK). However, for examination purposes a knowledge of the regulations is necessary.

Schedule 1 gives a method of determining diastase activity.
Schedule 2 gives the compositional requirements for honey relating to apparent reducing sugar

content, moisture content, apparent sucrose content, water insoluble solids content and ash content. Summarised here:

- There should be no addition of substances other than honey.
- The honey should as far as practicable, be free from mould, insect debris, brood and any other organic or inorganic substance foreign to the composition of honey. Honey with these defects should not be used as an ingredient of any other food.
- The acidity should not be artificially changed. There is a legal maximum level of acidity ie.'not more than 40 milli-equivalents acid per kilogram'.
- Any honeydew honey or blend of any honeydew honey with blossom honey should have an apparent reducing sugar (invert sugar) content of not less than 60% and an apparent sucrose content of not more than 10%. Other honeys should have an apparent reducing sugar content of not less than 65% and an apparent sucrose content not more than 5%.
- Honey with a moisture content of more than 25% should not be supplied.
- The maximum water insoluble solid content is:
- for pressed honey 0.5%
- for other honey 0.1%
- The maximum ash content is:
- for honeydew honey and blends containing honeydew honey 1.0%
- for other honey 0.6%

Baker's or Industrial Honey.

Honeys of the following descriptions should be labelled or documented only as 'baker's honey' or 'industrial honey':

- Heather honey or clover honey with a moisture content of more than 23%.
- Other honey with a moisture content of more than 21%.
- Honey with any foreign taste or odour.
- Honey which has begun to ferment or effervesce.
- Honey which has been heated to such an extent that its natural enzymes have been destroyed or made inactive.
- Honey with a diastase activity of less than 4, or, if it has a naturally low enzyme content, less than 3.
- Honey with an hydroxymethylfurfuraldehyde (HMF) content more than 8mg/kg.

The Trade Descriptions Act 1968.

This act imposes a general prohibition on the sale in the course of trade or business under a description which is false or misleading. The falseness can relate to any physical characteristic of the goods such as quantity, size, composition or method of production. It is also an offence to give a false indication as to the place of production or false claim as to the county or country of origin.

The Trade Description Act 1972.

This act has been repealed. This act required any imported product which bore a UK name or mark had also to be marked with an indication of the country of origin. This means that imported honey blended/ and bottled in UK no longer has to declare the origin of the honey.

Organic honey.

The term 'Organic Honey' is misleading as the range of the honey bee when foraging cannot be strictly regulated. The use of this term would involve considerable risk and should be avoided.

2.1.6 Enforcement

Inspections are carried out by the local Environmental Health and Trading Standards Departments. These agencies would respond to any complaint from a member of the public. Government regulations are constantly changing and being updated. It is therefore important that beekeepers make themselves familiar with up to date information before processing packing and selling honey for retail sale. Operate within the law, litigation is always expensive. Should any customer complain to the producer beekeeper about the quality or quantity of honey or be dissatisfied in any way, the wisest action to take is to return the customer's money or replace the offending product or both. Always seek advice from either the County Secretary or General Secretary of the BBKA should there be any threat of prosecution.

2.2 How worker honeybees collect nectar and process it into honey.

2.2.1 The way nectar is collected and conveyed back to the hive.

- The factors which encourage nectar collection have, surprisingly, been little studied. It is not known whether the amount of nectar collected is related to the amount of honey stored; it is obvious that collection extends far beyond the colony's actual requirements.
- The presence of a queen and brood stimulates the collection of nectar in much the same way as it stimulates pollen collection. Unlike pollen which is deposited directly by the forager into a cell, nectar foragers pass their load to a house bee and can also do a wag-tail dance to recruit more foragers.
- Scouting and finding the source of forage occurs first. About 2% of the bees in a colony actually scout for forage. The scouts return with a load and communicate the source by dancing. The forage selected by the colony is likely to be the best in quality (highest sugar content) and quantity.
- Returning foragers are likely to repeat the wag-tail dances. The number of foragers in a balanced colony is about one third of the population (ie. two thirds of the adults are house bees).
- The bee collects nectar by sucking up the food canal of the proboscis (see section 4.9.1) and thence to the honey sac in the abdomen via the pharynx and oesophagus. Average load is 40mg. (cf. the weight of bee 90mg.) taking approx. 100 – 1000 visits to flowers on the one foraging trip. Foragers make c. 10 trips per day ranging in time from 30 – 60 minutes.
- The enzyme invertase from the hypopharyngeal glands gets added to the nectar as it transits the pharynx to the oesophagus and the conversion of sucrose (disaccharide) to fructose and glucose (monosaccharides) starts on the flight back to the hive. The process is continued after reception by the house bees receiving the load.

2.2.2 Conversion of nectar to honey including chemical changes and storage of the honey by the bee.

The conversion of nectar to honey involves two changes:

1. Chemical change (disaccharide to monosaccharides),
2. Physical change (evaporation of water).

Chemical change: A forager returning to the hive with a load of nectar transfers the load to a house bee which then undertakes the completion of the chemical change which was started by the forager as follows:

- A small droplet of nectar is re-gurgitated into the fold of the partly extended proboscis and then swallowed (time about 10 seconds). This process is repeated 80 – 90 times in about 20 minutes on the same droplet which is then deposited in an empty cell or $\frac{1}{2}$ full cell. This re-gurgitation process 'ripening'.
- Sucrose is converted to glucose and fructose by the enzyme invertase from the hypopharyngeal glands which is further added by the house bee during the ripening process. Note that the nectar will contain all three types of sugar in varying quantities depending on the floral source (see section 2.24).
- During the ripening process, the water content is reduced by approx. 15% as a result of evaporation when the droplet is exposed.
- Finally the house bee undertaking the ripening hangs the unripe honey (now honey not nectar) to dry in either empty cells or $\frac{1}{2}$ filled cells.

Physical change: is the process of evaporating the excess water in the unripe honey to bring the sugar concentration up to about 80%. This is done as follows:

- A large amount of space is required (see section 1.16) as the honey is hung in empty or partially filled cells in order to provide the maximum surface area for evaporation purposes. In the empty cells, the honey is deposited with a 'painting action' on the upper surface of the cell.
- Currents of air are distributed around the hive by the bees fanning bringing in dry air and expelling moist warm air (see sections 4.15.4 and 4.18).
- As the water content diminishes and the sugar concentration of the honey approaches 80%, the honey is moved and the partially filled cells are completely filled and capped with a pure wax capping with a minute air gap beneath the capping.

2.2.3 Other points for consideration:

- It will be clear from the above that plenty of space is required and there is much sense in the old adage 'over super early in the season and under super late in the season'.
- It is important to provide conditions in the hive to allow the bees to ventilate and ripen their honey easily. The authors believe that by providing top ventilation it assists the bees to ventilate via the hole in the crown board and roof ventilators. In a nectar flow if the roof is raised there are always bees fanning around the open feed hole; we notice many beekeepers keep this hole closed for no apparent reason. It must be hard on the bees to move the air from the 3rd or 4th super down to the bottom entrance.

2.3 The methods used to decap honeycombs and of separating the cappings from honey.

2.3.1 General.

There are a variety of methods for decapping combs, some for the hobbyist and others for large scale operation where a permanent installation is necessary. Some of the more common methods are as follows:

- Various types of knives used either hot or cold and with sharpened or serrated cutting edges. The common feature is the length of blade which requires to be about double the width of the super frame.
- Heating for the knives can range from the simple method of dipping into hot water to electric elements designed into the blade or steam being passed through the blade. The price for this last mentioned piece of equipment is over £100. The electric elements are usually controlled by thermostat.
- The electric carving knife with the two reciprocating blades adjacent to each other works well if cleaned after each cut in hot water. The movement of the blades immediately after cleaning and prior to uncapping throws any remaining drops of water off the blades. We have used this method for many years.
- Decapping machines based on a heated reciprocating blade in a fixed position, the comb being passed over the blade.
- Flailing machines which rip the cappings off are also very efficient for large scale operations. The latest type using rotating nylon brushes costs over £400.
- There are a variety of multi-pronged forks eg. 'Smith cutter/scraper' for scraping off cappings. Useful on badly drawn comb, heather combs or combs filled with granulated honey.
- The use of a propane torch passed rapidly over the comb face to melt the cappings has been used in Finland. The cappings form beads around the cell edges. Very little straining of the honey is required after extraction and all the wax is returned to the bees and no receptacle is required for the cappings.
- All other methods require some form of tray or receptacle to receive the cappings.

2.3.2 Uncapping trays

The essential feature of these trays is to provide a receptacle for the cappings to fall into in order to separate the honey from the wax capping. The two basic methods are cold straining through a suitable straining cloth or melting the cappings with the honey and allowing them to separate on cooling.

- The Pratley tray uses the heating principle. It is constructed in stainless steel with a water bath and heating element on the underside. It is expensive and probably one of the worst designed pieces of equipment available. There is no thermostatic control for the heater so one is continually switching on and off. The tray is built on a slope with the thin part of the wedge (and minimum thermal mass) at the place where maximum heat is required, with the result the whole thing clogs up and slows down the extracting process. The separated honey is heated to such an extent it is only good for cooking.
- Most of the devices make no provision for locating the frame over the uncapping tray and it is necessary to fix a bar across with a suitable hole, about $^1/_4$in (6mm) deep, in which to rest the lug of the frame while actually cutting the cappings off.

- An alternative is to hammer a nail through the centre of the wooden bar and use the exposed sharp end on which to pivot the lug of the super frame. Continual use of the spike method will damage the lugs of the frames. Super frames with drawn foundation are a valuable commodity. When well made with glue and non ferrous metal pins they will last for years. For this reason we prefer the wooden crossbar with central circular depression.
- The beginner to beekeeping should be warned of the pitfalls in this area before he parts with his money; unfortunately most of the experienced beekeepers have learnt the hard way.
- For a beekeeper with 3-5 colonies (9-15 supers) a large stainless steel bowl, 18in (450mm) or more diameter, a sharp bevel-edged bread knife and a wooden cross piece for supporting the frame would be adequate. The honey and cappings which collect in the bowl can be strained through a fine nylon filter.
- The cold straining method seems to be as good as any, the honey is not ruined and the cappings can be washed for mead making or given back to the bees to clean up.

2.3.3 The actual operation of removing the cappings.

The important thing is to arrange the set up so that the actual operation is undertaken comfortably with no strain, everything at the right height and everything to hand. It is as well to study the flow of the work from the full supers coming into the extracting room to the empty ones going out.

- Having two people working on the extracting makes life much easier, one decapping and the other operating the extracting machine.
- Most of the books recommend that the frame is held at an angle of about 30 degrees to the vertical and the cut made downwards away from the end of the frame which is being held. The other way is to cut upwards (which we find easier). In both cases the cappings fall away from the frame into the uncapping tray and do not stick to the uncapped comb.
- Again, most of the literature states that the cut should be made just under the capping (in the air space) to minimise the amount of honey removed from the comb. This also is considered to be a matter of preference. We do a straight and level cut across the face of the comb to end up with a set of even combs in the super ready for next year's operations. There are always likely to be some uneven combs and this is a good time to put these to rights.
- Manley type frames help to provide a straight cut, the uncapping knife being guided by the wooden bottom bars and the top bar of the frame.
- If the knife is heated in hot water it is as well to have a clean cloth close by to wipe the knife dry before making a cut, continual drops of water will increase the water content of the honey. This is not necessary with the reciprocating blades of an electric carving knife.

2.3.4 Separating the honey from the cappings.

Wax cappings should be separated from the honey and rendered down carefully using the minimum amount of heat. The wax can be moulded and used for showing, it is unadulterated with other hive products and requires little cleaning. High temperatures change the colour of the wax, deepening the shade. Wax for show should be pale, clean and with a delicate aroma. Iron containers should not be used.

- The cappings can be cleaned up by the bees in say a Miller type feeder with a grill to allow the bees to access both sides. They may require a stir after a couple of days to let the bees get to the inner sticky portions.
- Capping can be left to strain overnight through a fine filter into a settling tank. The almost

honey free cappings can then be washed in cold water. Then separate the water and wax using fine nylon strainer. The honey water so obtained can be used for making mead. The cappings when dried can be set aside for show wax, making candles, cosmetics or polish.
- Other methods of separation include using centrifugal force and spinning in a special cage in the extractor, using a purpose built decapping tank with inner mesh for straining the honey away, using a converted spin dryer or washing machine as recommended by DIY enthusiasts.

2.3.5 Other points.

- Extracting is a sticky thankless task and care should be taken to keep everything scrupulously clean and tidy.
- Store the supers awaiting extraction in a warm dry room. Warm honey is easier to extract.
- Any honey which has been heated in the Pratley tray should only be used or sold as cooking honey (baker's honey).
- Rape honey which has been allowed to granulate in the combs cannot be extracted by the spinning method. Heating the entire comb in a stainless steel tray, not unlike a jumbo size Pratley, will separate the honey from the wax, no uncapping required. Controlled heating of the comb to allow the wax to melt at about 147°F (63°C) followed by rapid cooling of the honey in order to prevent the level of HMF increasing and reduction of diastase activity requires specialised equipment. In order to avoid any unnecessary heating of the honey, the crop from the rape fields should be removed and extracted as soon as the honey is 'ripe'. Strain and store the honey, before it crystallises in air tight containers until it is required for bottling.

2.4 The extraction of honey from combs, including ling heather honey and the types of extractor used.

2.4.1 General considerations.

The principle involves two forces which occur when an object is rotated eg. a ball on a string. The first is the centrifugal force which acts away from the centre of rotation and the second is the centripetal force which acts towards the centre of rotation. In the case of the ball, the centrifugal and the centripetal force act on the ball and because they are equal the ball stays where it is on the end of the string. In the case of a honey extractor, only the centrifugal force acts on the honey and it moves outwards away from the centre, the droplets of honey hit the drum wall and trickle down to the bottom of the extractor under another force, gravity. The centripetal force, of course, is acting in the rotating frame of the extractor which being rigid does not move. Honey is hygroscopic. Extraction of honey should be undertaken in a warm dry atmosphere. Large commercial honey packers in USA or Australia use honey drying stores for supers awaiting extraction to prevent any increase in the water content of honey.

2.4.2 Types of extractor available.

Tangential extractors:

Generally have a cage whereby the frames for extracting can be inserted at a tangent to the circle of motion allowing only the honey on the outside face to be removed during operation of the extractor. The honey on the inner face is pushed on to the comb septum during operation thus necessitating the frame to be reversed in order to complete the extraction. The salient points of this type are as follows:

- With full frames the first side can only be partially extracted at slow speed otherwise the weight of honey on the inner face is likely to break the comb.
- The combs must be reversed to extract the second side and then reversed again to complete the extraction of the first side. This is time consuming.
- It is virtually essential to have wired combs for use with this type of extractor.
- The number of frames that can be extracted is limited by the size of the cage, 6 being the realistic limit.

Radial extractors:

These extractors are all very similar with a rotating framework designed to hold the frames radially with their top bars vertical and parallel to the sides of the drum and their side bars on a radius of the extractor's rotating framework. The salient points are:

- Honey on both sides of the comb is extracted simultaneously and there is no reversing of frames which makes the process that much quicker.
- Combs that are unwired can be easily extracted without damage.
- The design permits a greater number of frames for a given diameter drum compared with a tangential, 10 being a realistic size for a small model (or one super).
- Speed control is not as critical as the tangential but nevertheless it is necessary to start slowly.
- For a given speed and number of rotations, the radial is inferior on the amount of honey remaining in the comb.
- Unwired combs can be extracted by this method but care must be taken with new comb which is less strong and may be broken as a result of dynamic unbalance. This unbalance occurs when pollen or granulated honey is present in the combs. Extra care is necessary when increasing the speed to prevent damage to the combs. Only liquid honey can be removed by spinning.

Brinsea horizontal extractor.

Spins two frames horizontally in a plastic bowl with a honey gate. Works well for a small producer. Many small time producers like to produce sections or cut comb to avoid the necessity of extracting the liquid honey.

2.4.3 Other points of interest.

- Materials for construction range from tin plate, galvanised steel and polythene to stainless steel. These days only the two latter materials are used. Stainless steel costs more but is likely to prove the most economical in the long run.
- Both types can be either hand or motor driven. If the electric motor is used a speed control device is necessary to give a range of speed from 0 to about 400rpm. The problem arises in getting a device to give high torque at low speed when it is starting up from rest. The horse power (hp) required from the motor is quite small, a fraction of a hp being adequate.
- When purchasing a radial type, care should be taken that it will accommodate the frame the beekeeper intends to use. Many (most?) are designed for $^7/_8$in side bars and the full complement

of Manley frames (10 super frames) cannot be loaded because of their wide side bars ($1\frac{5}{8}$in).

- Most tangential types can take a reduced number of brood frames which is often useful; only some of the radial types can do this.
- Both types require to be loaded giving the best dynamic balance. No matter how carefully the frames are selected and loaded it will never be perfect and the extractor at top speed wants to move. There are two solutions, one to screw it down to a platform with castors and let it move or two, to bolt it securely to the floor. Our own is fixed in three places with rigging screws and chain from the top rim of the extractor.
- If a fixed installation is preferred then it is desirable to raise the extractor so that a honey bucket can be put straight under the outlet tap without any lifting.
- Never leave any rape honey in the bottom reservoir of the extractor. Strain and store in buckets as soon as possible.
- Never leave the extractor unguarded when the honey tap is open or the frames are being spun.
- Most enterprising beekeeping associations have an extractor for hire to its members for a small fee.

2.4.3 Extraction of Heather Honey.

Heather, *Calluna vulgaris,* or ling honey is thixotropic (property of becoming temporally liquid when shaken or stirred and returning to gel state on standing). When bottled after extraction its colour, aroma and typical aerated composition distinguish it from floral honeys. Because of its gelatinous nature ling honey cannot be extracted in the same way as floral honeys. The combs of heather honey can be processed in the following ways:

- Cut the sealed comb from the frame and place in a strong straining bag and press the honey out. For small quantities of honey the press can be made from two wooden planks hinged at the wide end or for larger quantities a wooden 'Peebles' type press (cost c.£400) which will press 3/4 combs at one time.
- Scraped back to the septum with a 'Smith' cutter. The honey and wax placed in a strong straining bag and spun in a metal cage in the extractor,
- After uncapping the cells of honey can be agitated by a 'Perforextractor. This is a roller, shaped like a rolling pin, with fine steel needles attached to the barrel in a pattern to match the honey comb. When the roller is passed over the uncapped comb of heather honey the needles enter the cells and agitate the honey. The action of the needles liquifies the heather allowing the comb to be extracted in a tangential extractor.
- Sold as cut comb honey.

Other points to note:

- Because of the higher water content (up to 23%) of heather honey there is a greater danger of the honey fermenting.
- Supers should be stored in a warm dry room prior to extraction.
- Ling heather honey makes very good cut comb and used to be sold in Scotland cut directly from the comb.
- Use a strong fine mesh straining bag when pressing the comb and collect the honey in clean containers in order to dispense with the necessity of any further straining.
- Brother Adam's hydraulic press at Buckfast Abbey in South Devon will press 2 tons of honey per day with a loss of no more than 1.2% of the crop.

- Honey from the bell heather, *Erica cinerea* is not thixotropic and can be extracted as for floral honeys.
- The honey collected by the bees moved to the moor to collect heather honey may not be 100% ling heather. If the heather is not yielding then the bees will look for other forage.

2.5. The straining and settling of honey after extraction.

2.5.1 The objectives of straining.

Is to remove solid matter down to a particle size determined by the strainer. There are three types of solids, those that sink to the bottom, those that float and those that remain in suspension. The solids can include wax, bees, grubs, propolis, sugar crystals, wood chips and other extraneous matter. All extracted honey must be strained and allowed to settle. The best time for this is immediately after extraction. Different strainers will remove different solids. Coarse and fine stainless steel strainers are usually used for the initial straining before storage in honey buckets. Before bottling. 'run' honey should be warmed sufficiently to pass easily through a fine nylon strainer, 80 mesh to inch, to remove any small particles of dust, wax, crystals of sugar etc. If these small particles are left in the honey the honey will remain cloudy and lack sparkle. The presence of the particles will encourage crystallisation. The particles act as a nucleus onto which the crystals of sugar will granulate and grow.

2.5.2 Methods of straining.

- **Single settling tank.**

The tap is at the bottom of the tank and only those solids that float will be strained out including air bubbles. The honey passes through a fine straining cloth as it is poured into the tank. Allow 24 hours in a warm room for settling of the newly extracted honey is usually sufficient to remove the air bubbles.

- **Sump tank with baffles.**

The input compartment is usually at a lower level than the outlet. The tank contains 3 or 4 baffles giving 4 or 5 compartments. The baffle openings are alternately top and bottom with the honey flowing alternately under and over the baffles. The surface can be skimmed as required to remove floating debris while the dense solids collect in the bottom of the tank. The tank can be double walled to provide a water jacket for heating if required. This method is used for large scale production of honey.

- **Filtering under pressure.**

Diatomaceous earth filters are used by commercial honey packers. The honey passes through the filters at a high temperature and is then immediately and rapidly cooled. Most of the pollen as well as the extraneous matter is removed by this method resulting in a very clear end product which has lost much of its flavour and colour.

- **Wire and cloth strainers.**

These can be in a variety of formats depending on the scale of the operation. Wire strainers should be made of stainless steel or monel metal. Cloth filters are usually made of nylon. The old fashioned use of 'cheese cloth' would leave small fibres in the strained honey. Commercial strainers such as the one designed by Ontario Agriculture College in Canada (O.A.C. honey strainer) incorporates a series of concentric metal strainers of different mesh size. The honey flowing through the coarse mesh first and the finest mesh last eg. 12 mesh/inch to about 80 mesh/inch.

• **'Strainaway'.**

Made by Garn Products. This is a fast method of straining honey by creating a vacuum in the honey collecting chamber. Figures quoted for straining 30kg of honey at 86°F (30° C) are 4 minutes compared to 120 minutes using a settling tank and a nylon bag filter. This equipment is light and easy to handle making it easier to clean. It is made from food grade polythene and stainless steel. The filters range from a basic 1,600 holes per square inch to an extra fine filter with 10,000 holes per square inch.

• **The most simple type.**

Small time beekeepers strain the honey as it goes into the settling tank. It has one major drawback; it produces a large number of bubbles which are formed when the honey drops from the straining cloth into the settling tank. If a long sausage shaped filter is used then the sealed end can be keep below the surface of the honey and air is not introduced during the filtering process.

2.5.3. Other points in relation to straining are:

• The higher the temperature the easier it is to strain with a fine mesh. A temperature of 95-100°F (35-38°C) is considered to be satisfactory. The viscosity of the honey increases rapidly with temperatures below 90°F (32°C).
• Well filtered honey will take longer to granulate.
• If a honey such as rape is to be stored in buckets and bottled later it is better to complete the fine straining before it is stored ie. while it is still in its liquid state. Later it only needs warming to a point where it will flow for bottling. This stage is reached well before all the crystals have melted. In this state it would be impossible to pass it through a strainer without bringing it back to the completely liquid state and thereby heating it unnecessarily. Using this method the honey is sold as 'soft set' honey.
• Long straining cloths can be an advantage. When clogged the cloth can be pulled across the tank to an unused portion. All straining is best below the surface of the honey to prevent bubbles of air forming.
• Large commercial honey packing organisations use very fine filters by pumping the honey under pressure at high temperatures and then cooling it quickly after straining. Such methods are not a practical proposition for small scale operators. This liquid honey has a wine like clarity which is very attractive to the buyer.
• Always avoid adding air to the honey during processing. Do not allow the honey to fall from a great height. Use an elongated filter bag which remains under the surface of the honey.

2.6 Storage of honey including the underlying principles of storage.

2.6.1 Principles of storage of honey is to prevent any deterioration taking place ie:

• Any increase in the HMF factor. This is a result of ageing and heating of honey.

- Any decrease in the diastase activity of the honey. This is also a result of heating and long term storage.
- Any fermentation of the honey. This is due to a water content higher than 20%, the crystallization process of honey and the presence of yeasts.
- Any contamination of the honey due to storage in faulty or inappropriate containers eg. used previously for storing strong smelling foodstuffs eg vinegar.
- Any loss of the aroma and taste of honey due to non air tight containers.
- Any destruction of comb honey due to the presence of wax moth or *Braula coeca*.

Honey should be stored in 30lb white polythene (food only) buckets with good fitting lids. Anything bigger becomes difficult to handle when preparing the honey prior to bottling. The old method used 28lb tins with lever lids with attendant problems of the lacquer and plating becoming faulty and the subsequent rusting. Full honey buckets should be stored in a clean, cold below 50°F (10° C), vermin proof store until required for bottling. Each bucket should be marked with date of extraction, source and type of honey. Comb honey can be stored in the freezer. This will kill off the wax moth and *Braula coeca* and keep the honey in a liquid state. First place the comb in airtight plastic bags or 'Tupperware' type boxes. This will protect the surface of the comb during the storage at low temperatures and when removed for use. Thus water condenses from the warm moist air outside the freezer onto the container not onto the comb. Honey is at its best when first taken from the hive.

2.6.2 Other points are:

- The buckets require to be as full as possible to minimise the amount of air trapped in the top.
- Before the lid is snapped shut, the centre of the lid should be depressed onto the honey to minimise the air content.
- Store at a temperature of 57°F (14°C) for rapid granulation and then at as low a temperature as possible after it has set. Don't open to check the granulation, do it by feeling the sides of the buckets. When honey is in the run state the sides are quite flexible but very solid when granulated.
- Long term storage should be below 50°F (10°C) to slow down any tendency to ferment and to minimise ageing of the honey (HMF and diastase content).
- Store honey for a maximum of 12 months. As honey ages the HMF value increases and the diastase activity decreases.
- Never extract unripened honey or allow the water content of honey to exceed 20% by careless handling and storage. Honey is hygroscopic and if left exposed will absorb moisture from the atmosphere. A refractometer will give an accurate reading of the moisture content of honey.
- Sugar tolerant (osmophilic) yeasts are present in all honeys. In honey with a moisture content greater than 20% the yeasts will multiply, secrete enzymes which ferment the sugars in honey creating alcohol, acetic acid and carbon dioxide. This chemical reaction will cause the storage buckets to expand and rupture giving off a foul smell. See section 2.12.
- Glucose is less soluble in water than the other honey sugars. Glucose dominant honey granulates faster than honeys with a high fructose content. During the crystallisation process molecules of water are released which increases the water content of the uncrystallized honey. If the honey already has a higher than average water content then any increase in temperature will encourage fermentation. Only extract and store ripe honey.
- Unripe honey should be given back to the bees before it ferments or pasteurised to kill off all the yeasts and then sold as 'Baker's Honey'.
When preparing stored honey for bottling keep the heating process to a minimum.

2.7. The preparation and bottling of liquid honey, including ling heather honey.

All 'run' honey should be heat treated before sale to delay granulation for 6 to 12 months. The honey needs to be raised to a temperature of 130°F (54°C) for about 45 minutes. If a higher temperature is used 160-180° F (71-82°C) there is a danger of the honey being burnt, the enzyme activity being destroyed and the HMF factor increased. Partially granulated run honey looks terrible and is a very common fault with the hobbyist beekeeper. There is much local honey on sale which should really be taken off the shelf and returned to the beekeeper as being unfit for sale. Many of these jars are labelled with a County Association label and thereby bring other beekeepers a bad reputation. We believe that a County organisation should take some responsibility for quality if their label is to be used. It is for this reason we don't use our County label.

2.7.1 Method of bottling liquid honey.

• Honey being an unstable solution of sugars will granulate after extraction. Depending on the origin of the honey this may be with a small or large crystal. Fructose dominant honeys are slow to granulate and produce a large crystal. When preparing liquid honey for sale it is these fructose dominant honeys which are warmed, strained and bottled.
• Starting with fully crystallised 28/30lb buckets from store. Remove from the surface of the honey in the storage bucket all the debris which has floated to the top using a small sharp knife. Clean and replace the airtight lid.
• Warm the containers of honey for 2-3 days in a thermostatically controlled heater at 90°F (32°C). The heater should have fan to minimise any hot spots occurring.
• An old refrigerator makes an ideal warming cabinet when fitted with a suitable thermostat, a small fan and a couple of 25 watt electric light bulb. Our's doubles up as an incubator for queen cells in the summer by resetting the thermostat. An 'Eco Micro' thermostat with its own heater is more expensive, sophisticated and reliable.
• Check the storage buckets after 24 hours by pressing the outside of the storage drum to assess the length of time necessary to convert the honey back to liquid state. Always use the minimum of heat ie don't forget you have placed the buckets of honey in the heater.
• Prepare containers to receive the honey. Most hobbyist beekeepers continue to use the squat glass jars. These can be purchased 'film' wrapped. Nevertheless the jars should be inspected for blemishes and washed in clean hot water to remove any dust. Here a dish washer is ideal as the jars are heat dried and warm for bottling. All lids should be checked that no dust is adhering to the under surface.
• Never use damaged glass containers.
• The bottling should take place in a warm, dust free, odourless room. Keep windows and doors closed to prevent entry of any insect or dust.
• The run honey from the buckets should be strained through a fine filter into a settling tank This will remove any fine crystals or specks of dust which will form a nucleus/focus for granulation if left in the honey. Allow the honey in the settling tank to stand in a warm bottling room for 12-24 hours to allow any air bubbles to come to the surface.
• When bottling, keep the empty jar close to the tap and allow the honey to run down the side of the warm jar.
• Cover the filled jar of honey with a lid immediately to prevent any dust being attracted to the surface of the honey.

- Make random checks for weight with an occasional jar of honey using calibrated scales, weighing the jar empty and after it is filled.
- Remember that when honey is warm the density is reduced and the volume increased. The jars should be well filled above the neck to allow for the increase in density as the honey cools. The test of holding the capped jars to the light to see if any gap is present is not fool proof especially if the honey is warm or contains air bubbles.
- At the end of a bottling session there is always a certain amount of 'scum' at the bottom of the tank. This is due to the presence of air bubbles. This honey should be drained out of the tank and used for home consumption.
- The 227g ($\frac{1}{2}$lb) hexagonal jars on sale from the bee suppliers are more expensive than the conventional one pound squat jars. but are attractive to the customer These jars can easily hold 256g (9oz) of honey. When filling the hexagonal jars air bubbles become trapped in the six upper corners. Use a sterilised curved probe of non ferrous metal to remove these air bubbles before closing with a clean lid.
- Lids should come clean and undamaged from the suppliers. We always make a habit of checking our deliveries and return any damaged lids for exchange. The lids should be checked for dust or foreign particles and applied as soon as possible to the filled honey jar. Tighten the lids after the honey has cooled to make a good airtight seal.
- The 'flowed in' lids make a better seal than the old type lid plus 'waxed wad'. The latter lid still has its uses for honey show exhibits or selling chunk honey to prevent the run honey coming into contact with the lid.
- After bottling heat treatment is required to prevent granulation for a further six months. Before labelling, the jars complete with lids are placed in a water bath for about 45 minutes. The water should be kept at 130°F (54°C). The level of the water should reach the neck of the jars. Commercial processors rapidly heat the honey to 160° F (54° C), pressure filter and rapidly cool the honey before bottling.
- Unfortunately the BBKA has not undertaken to give advice on the use of microwave ovens as a method of heating honey in order to delay granulation. Perhaps in the future we may see some authorised work done on this process where guidelines are given in order to maintain the diastase activity and prevent any increase in the HMF content.
- Fermenting honey due to poor handling eg. insufficiently air tight containers or the honey having been extracted in an unripe state, can be heated to a temperature of 200°F (94°C) for a short time to kill the yeasts but this will not reduce the water content sufficiently to make it completely safe from re-infection by other wild yeasts. It can then only be sold as 'bakers' or cooking honey or used to make mead.
- Beekeepers with only one or two hives will probably wish to bottle their 100 or more pounds of honey directly from the settling tank soon after extraction is finished ie. without storing the honey in 30lb storage buckets. Many beekeepers feel that heating the honey destroys its fine aroma and taste. They are probably right. But if the honey is to be sold heating the jars of honey is the only way to delay granulation taking place for about 6 months. Smokey or partly granulated honey becomes unattractive to the customer.
- Dust particles, air bubbles or pollen grains left in honey will encourage crystallisation.
- Once bottled in air tight containers the honey should remain in a warm atmosphere for 24 hours to allow any residual air bubbles in the honey to come to the surface. Then stored in a dark cool area at about 50°F (10°C).
- When supplying retail outlets ensure that:

    1. The honey stored on the shelves is not exposed to sunlight.
    2. Run honey once bottled has a shelf life of about 3 to 6 months. Supply your local outlets with reasonable quantities of honey at frequent intervals depending on the demand.

Avoid long term storage in jars. Always exchange any partly granulated 'run' honey.

3. Granulated honey should only be delivered to outlets after complete granulation has taken place. Any sudden drop in temperature in partially granulated honey will cause unsightly frosting around the neck and shoulders of the jar. The honey has shrunk away from the glass.

4. Avoid the use of the labels excusing the granulation/frosting as a natural phenomenon of honey.

5. A high quality unstable product like honey needs careful handling and storage.

2.7.2 Bottling Ling Heather honey

Much of the heather honey obtained by beekeepers will be sold as comb honey. Being thixotropic it is ideal as cut comb as after cutting the honey does not drain away from the cells in the comb after the initial draining. Heather honey commands a higher price compared with floral honey eg. Bottled in one pound jars £2.50 opposed to £1.80. Pure heather honey has a distinctive flavour described by Herrod Hempsall as 'bitter sweet', it is light to dark amber in colour with a pungent aroma of heather flowers. When bottled glistening air bubbles are present as a result of the pressing process of extraction. Some show judges regard the bigger the air bubbles the better the exhibit. Pure ling honey does not granulate but when it is mixed with floral honey partial granulation will eventually take place, star-shaped granules appear suspended in a jelly like medium. Ling honey has a higher protein and water content than floral honeys. If ling honey is over heated during processing much of the aroma will be lost and the thixotropic quality will be destroyed. Honey from bell heather honey, *Erica cinerea* is not thixotropic and can be extracted in the same way as floral honeys. The honey is a port wine colour with a distinctive flavour. The bell heather grows on the heathlands alongside the ling heather, it blooms in June earlier than the ling.

	Ling honey	Floral honey
Protein	1.8 - 2 %	0.2%
Water (sealed in comb)	Up to 24 %	17 - 20 %

2.7.3 Special care to be taken when bottling ling honey.

• After extraction ling honey should go straight into the settling tank and bottled whilst still warm.
• The honey in the tank should be stirred ready for bottling.
• The lower density of the honey due to the presence of air bubbles increases the volume of the honey. The honey jars should be well filled at the neck and weight carefully checked.
• Because of the higher water content ling honey is liable to ferment.

2.7.4 General points on bottling honey for sale.

• When bottling has been completed the outside of the jars should be free from stickiness.
• The lid should be well screwed down making an airtight seal.
• Suitable labels should be attached on each jar, many labels are too big for 227g (½lb) jars.
• Tamper proof labels enhance the look of the product but increase the cost of production. The design could include the 'lot' number.
• At some time in the future EEC regulations may require all beekeepers producing, processing and selling honey to be registered. Most beekeepers undertake the processing in the family kitchen. It prompts the question whether it is suitable? Are there two sinks ? Are the walls

and floors washable surfaces? It is likely to be taboo if there is a washing machine installed where soiled linen is washed despite the fact that all the family food is prepared every day in the same room. Beekeepers must be vigilant of current legislation, it is all too easy to transgress unwittingly.
- Prevent partial granulation of run honey by careful preparation.
- Prevent fermentation by storing honey in airtight containers at a temperature below 50°F (10°C). Honey with bubbles on the surface indicate fermentation. At an advanced stage fermenting honey has a characteristic unpleasant smell and the surface of the honey heaves!
- Do not use scratched lids and unclean wads.
- Always keep the surface of the honey free from impurities.
- Never sell under weight jars of honey.
- Always ensure the labelling is correct.

2.8 The preparation and bottling of naturally granulated, soft set and seeded honey.

2.8.1 General.

Some types of honey will granulate more quickly than other types. Fast granulating honeys produce a fine grain crystal, slow granulating honey produce a larger crystal which is gritty to the tongue. Glucose is much less soluble in water than fructose. If there is a higher percentage of glucose than fructose in the honey then there will be fast granulation eg. rape, *Brassica napus* (immediately after extraction). If rape honey is left on the hive too long the honey will granulate in the comb causing further complications.

2.8.2 Naturally granulated honey.

Types of honey that are likely to granulate quickly with a fine texture should be strained immediately after extraction. If naturally granulated honey is required then the honey should be bottled directly from the settling tank. This will produce a 'hard set' honey. Sometimes the surface is difficult to penetrate with the honey spoon. Pure rape honey will have a lard like colour. After bottling the jars of honey should then be stored at 57°F (14°C) to allow granulation to take place. If moved too soon to a cold store frosting will occur. This a particularly difficult fault to avoid with honey that granulates rapidly and is associated with low temperatures. It is caused by shrinkage, generally at the neck of the jar, as the honey granulates. Honey that granulates slowly or granulates at higher temperatures, greater than 57°F (14°C) seldom exhibit this fault. During the granulation process water molecules are released as the sugar crystallises increasing the total water content of the remaining honey. This may cause fermentation to take place. A vertical streak on the side of a jar of granulated honey with a rough surface texture will indicate that fermentation is taking place. Always avoid scratched lids and unclean wads, under-weight products and incorrect labelling.

2.8.3 Soft Set Honey.

- To obtain a soft set honey the extracted honey should be fine strained immediately after extraction, then stored at 57°F (14°C) until granulation has taken place, and then stored at the coolest temperature possible below 50°F (10°C).
- When preparing to bottle 'soft set' honey warm the buckets of granulated honey in the

warming cabinet for 24/36 hours or until the honey attains a pouring consistency.
- For 'soft set' honey only use honey which has set with a fine grain. This can be determined when cleaning off the surface layer before heating the buckets of crystallised honey. Honey containing rough or large crystals will need to be seeded before bottling for 'soft set' honey.
- The clean warm honey when at a pouring consistency can be poured into a settling tank. Stirred thoroughly and allowed to settle for a few hours in a warm room. The stirring breaks up the formation of the sugar crystals in the honey giving a smooth creamy texture. This honey is sometimes referred to as 'creamed' honey.
- The creamer or stirrer must be kept below the surface of the honey to prevent introducing any air bubbles.
- Electrical heating coils can be used to wrap around the tank to keep the honey warm allowing the air bubbles to come to the surface.
- Bottle after careful preparation of jars.
- The last pound or so of honey in the settling tank may be filled with air bubble sometimes called 'scum'. The last jars may not contain the correct amount of honey owing to the presence of air bubbles. Underweight jars should not be sold.
- This honey which has granulated in the storage bucket and then rewarmed for bottling and stirred will not return to its previous rock like state. It is a 'soft set' or 'creamed' honey.
- Be sure that the honey jar lids are tightened after the honey has cooled in the jars.

2.8.4 Seeded Honey.

This honey should be of a fine texture. Honey should be seeded with 10% rape or similar honey which granulates with a fine grain eg. clover. With so many fields of oilseed rape planted every year unless the beekeeper makes a special effort to extract the spring honey before the rape fields come into bloom much of the spring honey will be seeded as it is extracted. Rape honey is ideal for seeding, producing a very attractive granulated honey with fine crystals. If the beekeeper is not in an area where rape is grown then in order to produce a granulated honey which is not too hard, does not contain large crystals, is quick to granulate with an overall consistency and produces an attractive product he will need to seed his honey. Honey was first treated in this way by a Canadian called Dyce in 1931. Much of the Canadian honey had been lost due to fermentation. He found that honey was less likely to ferment if it granulated rapidly with a fine crystal. The process is known as the 'Dyce Process' and full details may be found in Chapter 10 of 'Honey' by E. Crane.

2.8.5 Points to observe.

- The honey to be seeded needs to be returned to its liquid state by using the warming cabinet, 90°F (32°C) and filtering to remove any dust particles or crystals of sugar. This honey is allowed to cool in the settling tank.
- Honey is damaged if heated above 95°F (35° C).
- The crystals in the 'seed' the honey must not be dissolved. This honey should be in a soft state.
- Both the honeys should have been strained at the time of extraction ie. when in the liquid state.
- If 45lb (20kg) of honey is placed into a settling tank then 5lb (2.3kg) of the 'seed' honey is added and stirred carefully and thoroughly.
- Avoid adding any air to the blend of honey by keeping the mixer below the surface of the honey.
- Allow the honey to settle in the bottling tank in a warm room for 2-3 hours.

- Prepare all the jars with care as previously stated.
- Bottle the honey while it is still in a warm state.
- Once bottled keep the jars of honey in a warm room for 24 hours to allow any air bubbles to come to the surface. Then move to a temperature of 57°F (14°C) to allow granulation to take place. This will keep frosting to the minimum.
- Once granulation is complete the honey can be stored at a low temperature.
- 'Frosting' is a particularly difficult fault to avoid with honey that granulates rapidly. It is caused by the air bubbles present in the honey. When placed too soon into a cold store the honey shrinks away from the shoulders and neck of the honey jar forming white irregular patterns. As stated before honey that granulates slowly or granulates at higher temperatures, greater than 57°F (14° C) seldom exhibits this fault.
- Fine granulation minimises the water content between the crystals and thereby minimises fermentation.
- A vertical streak in granulated honey with the surface texture rough indicates fermentation. At an advanced stage fermenting honey has a characteristic unpleasant smell.

2.9 The preparation of section, cut-comb and chunk honey for sale.

2.9.1 Preparation of Sections.

- The sections must be fully sealed (capped in wax by the bees). If open half filled cells are present, the section is not suitable for sale. Honey is hygroscopic and these cells will absorb water.
- The woodwork should have been treated with paraffin wax before the sections were placed in the hive. This will protect the woodwork leaving it unstained when the propolis and paraffin wax is scraped off.
- Each section should be held up to the light and any with cells of pollen should be rejected.
- All sections should be put into the freezer (minimum 10° C) for a period of 24 to 48 hours to ensure that any *Braula coeca* and wax moth eggs are killed. If this is not done, it is possible for the section to be ruined while on the shelf awaiting sale.
- Pack the sections into 'Tupperware' type containers to avoid damage to the surface of the comb whilst it is in the freezer. During the thawing process (on removal from freezer) first allow the container to reach room temperature before opening and removing the sections. This prevents water condensing on the surface of the comb.
- Before packing and after cleaning, the section should be weighed and the net weight of honey comb noted for labelling.
- The packing should be in specially made cardboard boxes with a built in cellophane window on one side to display the sealed comb. These boxes are obtainable from the equipment supplier.
- After packing into the container it must be labelled correctly in accordance with the regulations.
- The special cardboard containers usually describe the product adequately and the only addition required is the name and address of the producer (telephone number may be included) and the net weight.

2.9.2 Preparation of Cut Comb

- The combs of honey from the supers are selected for thickness, good cappings and freedom from pollen and granulated honey. Any combs that do not meet these criteria should be used only for extraction.

- A flat board or 'formica' surface larger than a super frame is required for preparing the cut comb. The tools required are a Price cutter (the size to suit the clear plastic container nb. two sizes of container are now available) or a large sharp knife and a template as a guide for cutting the comb and a kitchen spatula for moving it after cutting.
- The comb in the frame is inspected and placed in the middle of the board with the best side upwards. The knife is run around the inside woodwork of the frame cutting the whole comb free from the frame which then simply lifts off. This can be returned to the bees for cleaning up with the rest of the wet supers.
- The comb is then cut into pieces to exactly fit the containers. A piece of comb approx 4in×3 in×1$\frac{1}{2}$in is needed to fill a 227g (8oz) cartoon. This is easily done with the Price cutter which not only cuts it to size but provides a tool to place it accurately in the container all in one operation. If a Price cutter is not available the comb can be cut by knife and placed in the container by using the spatula. A fair degree of expertise is required to not only cut it to the right size but then to get it into the container without damage to the comb. Before the cut comb is put into the container, it should be drained for a few minutes to allow the honey to run off the cut edges. Using the Price cutter does not allow this to be done easily. There should not be a line of honey in the bottom of the container after it is filled with comb.
- The surface of the comb should be immaculate and free from drips of honey and any damage.
- The packed cut comb should be frozen for a couple of days to kill off any *'Braula coeca'* present.
- The label placed on the outside after any condensation has evaporated.
- The labelling requirements are the same as for sections. Cardboard sleeves are now available, but add to the cost of the product. The minimum description must be 'COMB HONEY' followed by net weight. A black on white 'Ablelabel' with a space to put the actual weight in by hand is acceptable. A second label with the producer's name and address and lot number is necessary. There must be more illegal labelling in cut comb than in any other honey product on the market.
- There is a certain amount of wastage from one BS shallow frame when used for cut comb; the surplus can usefully be used as chunks for 'chunk honey' and it is advisable to have some 454g(1lb) jars handy for the chunks, the jars to be filled later with honey when extraction has been completed.
- To prevent granulation if the comb honey has to be stored for long periods, it should be kept in the freezer at low temperatures. Honey granulates fastest at 57°F(14° C). Above and below this temperature granulation is slower. Higher temperatures are not good because of the ageing effects (diastase and HMF) on the honey. Low temperature storage is the best.
- Heather honey is an ideal honey for cut comb because it is thixotropic (in a jelly form until stirred when it will become liquid and flow for a short time reverting back to jelly) making it easy to cut up with no waste of the actual honey.
- Rape honey granulates rapidly in the comb. It is better to extract this honey while it is still in the run state. Cut comb from the rape blossom does not sell well. Honey show judges prefer the exhibits of comb honey which contain liquid honey.
- All comb honey should be produced in wire free super frames which have been fitted with extra thin foundation or 'starters'.
- Drone or worker foundation can be used. When pulling out drone comb the bees use less wax than pulling out worker foundation. The disadvantage of drone comb is that should the laying queen find her way into the supers she will fill the supers with drone brood.

2.9.3 The preparation of chunk honey for sale.

- One piece of sealed comb approx. 1in× 1½in× 3in for the traditional squat (454g) honey jar. Straight sided jars with a wide neck are sometimes used making it easier to introduce the piece of comb honey.
- The comb must be surrounded with a heat treated liquid honey otherwise granulation takes place and the product becomes unsightly.
- Fill with heat treated liquid honey. The liquid honey needs to be well filtered and 'bright' to show off the comb in the jar.
- Hold the jar close to the honey tap and run the liquid honey down the side of the jar to avoid introducing air bubbles.
- The major fault is to provide too small a piece of comb. Do not use comb honey containing pollen.
- The total weight should be carefully checked. The honey comb tends to rise above the level of the liquid honey.
- The labelling must observe all current regulations.
- Prepare small quantities of chunk honey and supply it to the retailers in small quantities. Chunk honey has a short shelf life, the run honey tends to granulate and the appearance of the comb is spoilt.

2.10 The constituents expressed in percentage terms of a typical sample of U.K. honey and an outline of the normal range of variation of its main constituents;

2.10.1 A typical sample of U.K. honey will contain the following:

18% water
35% glucose (dextrose)
40% fructose (levulose)
4% other sugars (eg. maltose)
3% other substances:
-about 15 organic acids (eg. acetic, butyric, malic, etc),
-about 12 elements (eg. potassium, calcium, sulphur, etc),
-about 17 amino acids (proline, glutamic, lysine etc.),
-about 4-7 proteins (c.0.2% for floral honeys and c.1.2% for heather honeys).

2.10.2 An outline of the normal range of variations of main constituents.

Honey is an unstable solution of sugars and other substances. These 'other substances' are either collected by the bees when gathering nectar from the flowers eg. pollen, enzymes, yeasts or added by the bees as the nectar is elaborated into honey in the hive. The composition of honey will vary depending on the soil, weather, type of plant producing the nectar and pollen or species of aphids producing the honeydew. Bees show a preference for collecting nectar which is well balanced ie. a mixture of glucose and fructose and sucrose. Most of the research work done on the composition of honey has been carried out in the USA by Dr J. W. White jr and can be found in Dr Eva Crane's book on' Honey' published in 1975.

Water.

The percentage of water in honey can be ascertained by using a refractometer. These are expensive to purchase c.£100 but very simple to use. A hydrometer can be used but it is rather a messy process. Both readings require correction according to the temperature of the honey. Wedmore states that the water content in sealed honey can vary from c 14–22%. Variations to note are:

- With < 17% of water the honey is unlikely to ferment. Heather and clover honeys have a higher water content than that of floral honey, up to 23%. Honeydew honeys generally have a low water content. The humidity of the atmosphere during the honey flow will cause the variations in the water content of the honey stored, it could be as low as 16.4% or as high as the 23%.
- When the honey is ripe the bees will seal the honey in the storage cells with wax cappings. When the beekeeper removes and extracts this honey these cells are opened. Honey being hygroscopic will absorb further moisture if left exposed to a damp atmosphere during extraction and storage.
- During the crystallisation process water molecules are released into the remaining liquid honey increasing the water content and the risk of fermentation. Osmophilic (sugar tolerant) yeasts present in honey will multiply and turn the sugars into alcohol and carbon dioxide → acetic acid and water. The rate of fermentation will be increased with temperatures over 50° F (10°C) and below 80° F (27°C).

Glucose.

The flowers of the plants belonging to Cruciferaceae family yield a nectar which is high in the monosaccharide sugar, glucose. Glucose is less soluble in water than other sugars. It has the same empirical formula as fructose, $C_6H_{12}O_6$. Honeys with a dominance of glucose will granulate rapidly with a fine crystal eg. Rape, *Brassica napus*. This honey, because of its high glucose content, will granulate in the comb and cause problems for beekeepers during extraction and later with fermentation during storage.

Fructose.

Fructose is a monosaccharide. It is twice as soluble in water than glucose. The darker honeys usually contain more fructose than glucose. When the honey has a fructose dominant composition the honey will granulate slowly forming large crystals. These crystals are gritty to taste. Honey produced from nectar collected from the Blackberry, *Rubus spp* has been recorded as having 37.8% of fructose with 25.9% glucose present.

Other sugars.

- Sucrose is a disaccharide and is found in the nectar collected from the long tubed flowers eg. clover. During the ripening process the bees convert most of the sucrose using the enzyme '*invertase*' into monosaccharides.
- Maltose is a disaccharide ie. made up of two glucose molecules joined together. It occurs in honey as a secondary sugar when the sucrose is inverted by the enzyme invertase.
- Trisaccharide sugars eg. melezitose, erlose and raffinose are found in honeydew honey. The sugars found in honeydew vary with the species of plant sucking insect producing the exudate. Melezitose is less soluble in water than other sugars causing honey to granulate rapidly. If the sugar erlose dominates then the honey will not granulate.

Pollen.

Honey when extracted from the comb is an aqueous dispersion of material covering a wide range of particle size. The largest particles are the pollen grains. Unless the honey has been passed through a very fine filter grains of pollen are found in all floral honeys.

Acids

The pH of honey is about 3.9, it can range from c.3.42 - 6.10. Formic acid, acetic, butyric, citric, gluconic, lactic malic, succinic are amongst the acids to be found in honey. Gluconic acid is produced by the action of the enzyme glucose-oxidase on glucose producing gluconic acid and hydrogen peroxide when the honey is diluted. Honey dew honey and honeys rich in ash are particularly rich in acids.

Elements.

As a rule the more mineral elements present in the honey the darker the colour, traces of iron are know to darken honeys. These minerals are derived from the soil on which the nectar producing plants grow. Hence there must be great variations in the honeys produced in the UK. The ash content may vary from 0.02% - 1.2%. Potassium, sodium, calcium, magnesium, iron, copper, manganese, chlorine, phosphorous, sulphur, silica have all been found in honey.

Amino acids.

These are the building blocks of proteins. 18 free amino acids are know to occur in honey, all in very small amounts. Proline is the major amino acid found in honey. Others found include glutamic acid, leucine, tyrosine, glycine lysine etc. Glycine is the simplest of all amino acids and is found in most proteins.

Proteins.

The thixotropic properties of heather honey, *Calluna vulgaris* are due to the 'gel-sol-gel' transformation of a protein. Honey contains small amounts of colloidally dispersed material. The nitrogen content of this material may show a protein content as high as 55-65% and as low as 15 -25%. The colloids produce a state midway between a suspension and a true solution. The liquid properties are classified as 'sol' and the more solid like properties as the 'gels'. Enzymes are proteins, five are found in honey ie. catalase, glucose-oxidase, diastase, acid phosphatase and invertase. The enzyme activity of diastase is reduced in honey by heating or storage.

Vitamins.

Small amounts of thiamine (B_1), riboflavine (B_2), ascorbic acid (C), pyridoxine (B_6), niacin and pantothenic acid are found in honey.

Colour.

Floral honeys can range from a pale yellow to a deep amber. Honeys containing iron usually have deeper shades of yellow. Carotenoids are a group of red and yellow pigments which occur widely in living organisms may contribute to the differing colours of honey. Honeydew honeys are usually darker than floral honeys ranging from a darkish green to black. The darker colour may be due to the higher mineral (ash) content of honeydew honeys, c.0.736% compared with 0.26% of floral honey. The green tinge may be due to the presence of algae. Age and heating will darken honey.

Flavour and aroma.

The lighter the honey the less flavour present. Even this subtle flavour may be lost when the honey granulates. An almost infinite number of aroma and flavour variations of honey exists. These subtle differences are most powerful immediately the honey is removed from the hive. They range from the strong rather unpleasant aroma and taste of the honey obtained from ivy, privet or ragwort, the characteristic smell and flavour of heather and lime tree honey to the very light flavour and aroma of the pale honeys. The flavouring and aromatic constituents (oils and gums) come from plant sources.

The optical rotation of honey depends on its component sugars, their types and relative proportions. Using a polarimeter the axis of the light passed through the jar of honey will be rotated to the right ie dextrorotary when the percentage of glucose present exceeds that of fructose.

2.11 Methods of determining the moisture content of honey

Before removing any honey from the hive for extraction the beekeeper must first make sure that the honey is 'ripe'. Honey sealed in cells is considered ripe and suitable for extraction but any unsealed cells should first be tested by holding the comb horizontally over the top bars of the open stock and vigorously shaking the comb. Should any nectar fall onto the top bars from the comb then the 'honey' is considered unripe. These combs of unripe 'honey' should remain on the hive for the bees or until the cells have been sealed over by the bees. Once the honey is extracted the specific gravity of the honey can be taken using a hydrometer or an easier method is to use a refractometer. With this last method honey could be tested before extraction ie. taking a sample directly from a sealed cell, to test samples of honey at a honey show or prior to storing or bottling. A correction scale is supplied with the instrument to adjust the reading for the ambient temperature. The scale is calibrated to read correctly for 68°F (20° C) eg. for 59° F (15° C) deduct 0.29 from the % of sugar or at 69.8° F (21° C) add 0.06 to the % sugar. This instrument can also be used for testing the sugar content of solid substances such as apples and grapes. The water content of honey affects the density and viscosity of honey see section 2.13

2.12 The spoilage of honey particularly by fermentation (including the effect of water content, storage temperature and the presence of yeast).

Honey can be spoilt by:

• The presence of foreign particles carelessly added during extracting or straining eg. small amounts of oil used to lubricate the rotating parts of the extractor or the draining tap, dust particles etc.
• Unpleasant odours that have been absorbed during storage or extraction. All storage buckets

must be absolutely clean and free from any odour. All lids must fit to prevent any air being absorbed ie. air tight.
- Poor presentation eg. unclean jars, lids and sticky containers.
- Misuse of medicaments by treating bees at the wrong time of the year ie. whilst the supers are in place.
- Feeding of sugar syrup to the bees at inappropriate times so that the sugar syrup is stored with the floral honey.
- Illegally mixing high fructose corn syrup to the honey. HMF is formed during the process of producing invert sugar from sucrose by acid hydrolysis. A high level of HMF can be an indication of adulteration with invert sugar.
- Fermentation of the honey.

2.12.1 Fermentation of honey:

All honeys contain yeasts derived from the bees or the flowers. These yeasts are osmophilic yeasts ie. tolerant to high concentrations of sugar. Unripe honey in the hive will ferment and cause dysentery in the bees if not processed and sealed with wax in the cells. Section 2.11 explains the varying levels of water found in different honeys. Fermentation in extracted honey is associated with the granulation process. Any small particle left in the honey after straining will provide a nucleus on which the sugar crystals form. When honey crystallises water molecules are released into the ungranulated honey increasing the water level. Any increase in the storage temperature above 50° F (10° C), such as happens in the spring, will help to initiate the fermentation within the storage buckets. Pressure will build up inside the buckets. Fermentation also occurs in bottled honey. Bottled honey prepared as 'set' honey should be sealed with an air tight lid, stored at 57° F (14° C) until the crystallisation is complete. Then store below 50°F (10° C) to prevent any fermentation taking place. The chemical changes which take place when fermentation occurs can be expressed as:

$$C_6H_{12}O_6 + YEAST = 2CO_2 + 2C_2H_5OH$$

2.12.1.2 The risk of fermentation is increased by a high moisture and yeast count:

Moisture level	Yeast count.
<17.1 %	No fermentation regardless of yeast count
17.1 - 18%	Safe if yeast count < 1,000/g
18.1 - 19%	Safe if yeast count <10/g
19.1 - 20%	Safe if yeast count < 1/g
>20%	Always in danger.

- Numerous osmophilic yeasts have been isolated in honey including *Zygosaccharomyces spp, Torula mellis, Schwanniomyces occidentilis, Schizosaccharomyces occidentilis, Saccharomyces spp. etc.*
- To destroy yeasts honey is heated to 145°F (63° C) for 30 minutes or raise to 160°F (71° C) for 1 minute followed by rapid cooling. This will prevent fermentation occurring.
- If fermentation is established then the honey must be heated to a temperature of 200°F (94°C) to destroy the yeasts.
- Heating honey destroys the subtle aroma, darkens the honey, increases the HMF and decreases the diastase activity.
- Signs of honey fermenting are:

Sour/flavour and unpleasant aroma due to the presence of ethanoic acid (vinegar).
Streaks appearing at the side of the jar. This can be confused with the white mottling at the neck of the jar due to frosting.
A layer of air bubbles on the surface of the honey caused by the presence of CO_2.
A heaving surface.

2.13 The physical properties of honey including specific gravity, viscosity, hygroscopicity and reaction to heat.

2.13.1 Specific Gravity and Density.

The density of substance is its mass per unit volume. The density will vary with the water and solid contents found in the honey. The relative density or specific gravity is the ratio of the mass of a given volume of a substance, at a stated temperature, to the mass of the same volume of water at a stated temperature. This is shown simply below:

Weight of $1cm^3$ water = 1g   and weight of $1cm^3$ honey = c. 1.4g(varies with T)
$\therefore SG_{honey} = 1.4 \div 1 = 1.4$

The higher the water content the less dense is the honey. The specific gravity of honey with a water content of 18.6% at 68°F (20° C) is 1.4129. This property of honey should be remembered when preparing honey for sale ie. honey expands when warm. The higher the water content of the honey the lower the reading measured on a Baumé hydrometer. The reading will vary with the temperature of the honey as shown in the table below taken from Wedmore.

Water %	Density, g/cc at 68°F (20°C)	Density at 60°F (16°C)
16	1.445	1.448
18	1.425	1.428
20	1.412	1.414
23	1.392	1.395

2.13.3 Viscosity.

Viscosity causes liquids to resist flowing. Anyone filling the storage buckets from the reservoir of an extractor cannot but help noticing the differing rates of flow of the honey from varying sources. The viscosity of honey is highly temperature sensitive, it is also affected by its water content and the quantity of colloidal materials (non sugar materials). When the temperature of the honey is increased the viscosity is decreased ie. warm honey runs more freely than cold honey. It can be measured by a viscometer ie. measuring the time taken for a steel ball with a diameter of $\frac{1}{16}$in (0.16cm) to fall 200mm through the centre of a 25mm standard wall pyrex tube of honey at a known temperature. Or it can be expressed as:

Proportional to 1/Temperature and is also proportional to 1/Water content with no appreciable decrease over 86°F (30°C)
Some honey judges invert a jar of honey to note the speed of the air rising to the top of the honey. The quicker the rise the less dense the honey.

2.13.3 Hygroscopic Nature of Honey.

This is the ability to remove moisture from the air. When honey is exposed to air, a gain or a loss in its moisture content will take place, depending upon the temperature, the moisture content of the air and the vapour pressure of water in the air (usually expressed as relative humidity). For each honey a relative humidity exists at which no gain or loss of moisture takes place. This is the equilibrium relative humidity. Because of the high viscosity of honey moisture is absorbed at the surface, water can only diffuse very slowly throughout the mass. The approximate equilibrium between the relative humidity of air and the water content of honey is:

Water Content of Honey	Relative Humidity of Air
16.1%	52%
17.4%	58%
21.5%	66%
28.9%	76%

2.13.4 Reaction to Heat.

2.13.4.1 Warmth is a great ally to honey processors, it can also be a great enemy. Honey should be heated as little as possible for as short a time as possible in order to:

• Allow particles to be strained from the honey to give a clear end product.
• Allow air bubbles to rise to the surface of the honey.
• Return crystallized honey to a fluid state in order to bottle, blend or seed the honey.
• To reduce the water content. In humid areas eg. Sri Lanka, commercial firms have large drying rooms to reduce the water content of honey in sealed cells or extracted honey from as high as 25% to a level where there is less risk of fermentation. The liquid honey is passed over a series of heated metal trays.
• To delay granulation and to kill off yeasts before any fermentation has taken place prior to selling.
• To kill off yeasts once fermentation has begun.

2.13.4.2 When honey is heated care must be taken to limit:

• The loss of aroma and flavour by driving off the volatile oils and other substances of plant origin.
• Any increase in hydroxymethylfurfuraldehyde (HMF). There is a little HMF in fresh honey produced by bees. The Honey Regulations 1976 state that the HMF content should be no higher than 80mg per kg of honey. HMF is formed during the normal industrial method of producing invert sugar from sucrose by acid hydrolysis. A high level of HMF could be a indication of adulteration or overheating. Work carried out by White, Kushnir and Subers 1964 shows a rise of 3.0mg HMF per 100g of honey under the following conditions:

    300 days at 68°F (20°C)
    60 days at 90°F (32°C)
    3 days at 125°F (52°C)
    4 hours at 160°F (71°C)

• Any loss of diastase activity. The Honey Regulations state the diastase activity should not be less than 4 or if the honey has a naturally low enzyme content not less than 3. Diastase activity is destroyed by heat as demonstrated by the work of White et al who calculated the half-lives of enzymes in honey under differing temperatures. Two of the well known enzymes are shown below:

C°	F°	Diastase	Invertase
10	50	12,600 days	9,600 days
20	68	1,480 days	820 days
25	77	540 days	250 days
30	86	200 days	183 days
32	90	126 days	48 days
35	95	78 days	28 days
50	122	5.38 days	1.28 days
71	160	4.5 hours	39 minutes
80	176	1.2 hours	8.6 minutes

• Any darkening of the honey through overheating or long term storage.

2.13.4.3 Other points:

• Any over heated honey should only be sold as 'Baker's honey'.
• Honey should be stored below 50°F 10°C. Below 52°F (11°C) yeasts do not grow. Above 50°F (10°C) darkening of honey and increase in HMF occurs.
• When heating honey care must be taken not to exceed recommended temperatures. Honey should be rapidly cooled after heating. Commercial firms have the ability to rapidly heat to a high temperature (flash) and rapidly cool honey prior to bottling.
• Levels of diastase below 4 indicate over heating of honey.
• Heat transmission in solid crystallized honey is slow.
• Caramelization occurs in heather honey when the temperature exceeds 150°F (66°C) because of the high protein content.
• Many small time beekeepers sell their honey with out heating.
• Honey is degraded if heated over 95°F - 104°F (35°C - 40°C)

2.13.5 Optical Properties of honey.

The optical rotation of honey depends largely on its component sugars, the types and relative proportions. Honey has the property of rotating the plane of polarization of polarized light. Most floral honeys are laevorotatory (left hand rotation or anti-clockwise) and honeydew (or adulterated) honeys are dextrorotatary (right hand rotation). The preponderance of fructose in floral honeys has a negative specific (− 92.4°) rotation over glucose (+ 52.7°). Honeydew honeys give a rotation of + 88.2° when melezitose is present or + 121.8° when erlose is present, together with glucose usually results in giving a positive net rotation. Modern analysts have largely abandoned this method of detecting sugars in honey for more precise methods eg. mass spectrometry.

2.14 The main constituents and physical properties of beeswax.

Beeswax is a water repellant substance of firm but plastic consistency with a low co-efficient of friction. It has an agreeable honey-like odour and a faint characteristic taste. Beeswax is produced by the bees from esters of fatty acids and synthesised sugars in the four pairs of abdominal wax glands after consuming pollen and large quantities of honey. Bees collected from a swarm are energetic wax makers. Within the hive it is the young bees aged 12-20 days, whose wax glands have become well developed after a diet of honey and pollen whilst performing their duties within the brood nest, who produce the wax for comb building. Beeswax is insoluble in water, slightly soluble in alcohol and completely soluble in fixed or volatile oils at 86°F (30° C). When liquid wax cools and becomes solid it shrinks by c.10%. Beeswax stored at a cool temperature develops a powdery bloom on the surface. This bloom has a crystalline structure and has a melting point of 102°F (38.8 °C) far below that of beeswax. Little is known about it.

The average chemical properties of beeswax are:

Hydrocarbons (C_{21} - C_{33}) odd numbers	16%
Monohydric alcohols (C_{24} - C_{36}) even numbers	31%
Diols (C_{24} - C_{32})	3%
Fatty Acids (C_{12} - C_{34}) mostly C_{16}	31%
Hydroxy acids (C_{12} - C_{32}) mostly C_{16}	13%
Other substances eg. plant pigments, propolis etc	6%

The physical properties of beeswax are:

Melting point	c 147°F (63.8°C)
Solidifying point	c 146°F (63°C)
Flash point	c 468° - 482°F (242° - 250°C)
Specific Gravity	0.95
Density at 68°F	0.963
Insoluble in water	
Slightly soluble in alcohol	
Soluble in chloroform, ether, benzine	

2.15 Methods of recovering saleable beeswax from used comb and cappings.

See Section 1.3 During an average season a beekeeper will expect to collect about one pound of wax from each stock of bees during the year. This wax will include the cappings from the sealed combs of honey, the brace and burr comb removed from the frames during inspections, any wild comb built by the bees and old brood combs which are discarded. The cappings are of high quality and need very little treatment to clean them for use. They should be used solely for show wax, making cosmetics, candles or high quality wax blocks for sale. Quite a considerable amount of brace and burr comb is collected during colony manipulations and inspections. This wax should be lumped in with the old combs for rendering. These last mentioned sources contain wax contaminated with propolis (which cannot be removed) it is only suitable for re-use as foundation, candles, etc. after rendering and cleaning. There is no way of cleaning wax at home that is comparable with large scale commercial operations with heated pumps and filters.

2.15.1 Small scale methods of recovering beeswax from cappings.

- The cappings will be initially separated in a decapping tray or similar device with a mesh basket to allow the honey to drain off or spun again in the extractor using a fine mesh basket or nylon bag.
- The cappings can be given back to the bees to clean up in an Ashforth type feeder (only do this in the evening after the bees have finished flying), washed to make mead with the washings or washed with soft water and drained, dried and set aside for making show wax.
- For show wax remove any discoloured pieces of wax.
- The cappings, free from honey, are melted and filtered first through lint and then filter paper as a final cleaning process. The wax should not be heated above 194° F (90° C) to prevent discolouration. To save the natural colour of the wax iron containers should not be used. The containers for moulding should be kept solely for this purpose. See Section 2.18.3.1

2.15.2 Processing old comb

When the wax in the old combs melts it adheres to and saturates the old larval skins and except by pressing or centrifuging at high temperatures some wax will inevitably be lost. These two methods are generally unsuitable for home operation. There are two suitable methods for home use. These are the solar wax extractor and the steam boiler. Old comb contains very little wax. If only a few combs are involved or there are disease pathogens present then the combs are best destroyed by burning. See Section 1.3 and Appendix 2

The steam wax extractor.

This is a stainless steel boiler with a mesh cage suspended inside with a drain at the bottom for the wax to run off and the steam to escape. The device has a water reservoir which is converted to steam which melts the comb and wax inside. The boiler has an air tight lid. It can be driven by gas or electricity. The largest steam wax extractor seen by the authors is at Buckfast Abbey. Here the wax steamer takes an entire brood box and frames.

The solar wax extractor (see 1.3.2.4)

This is probably the best wax recovering device. Later a second melting of old comb wax is usually necessary. Heat the broken wax in a saucepan of soft water until all the wax has melted. Leave the wax to cool and solidify ontop of the water (Specific Gravity of beeswax c 0.95). Any dross, 'slumgum' can be scraped off the bottom of the cold block of wax. Further cleaning by filtering may be necessary if cleaner wax is required. See Section 1.3.2.4

The M & G extractor.

This piece of equipment is still offered for sale by the commercial appliance suppliers at about £110. It works well with care and controlled heating. It consists of a metal drum, old comb is put inside and filled up with water. A filter (fine nylon) is tied across the open top. The water and wax are heated. Around the outside and as part of the device there is a large rim to catch the contents as they are pushed through the filter. The rim has a spouted outlet for the wax. The wax is forced out through the filter onto the rim by hydraulic pressure when water is poured into the high spout, the bottom end of which is connected into the lower part of the drum. If care is not used it is claimed that the ceiling is likely to receive a wax treatment. This method is definitely an outdoor activity.

Using an old 44 gallon oil drum The old beekeeping books show this outdoor method. The tank is filled with water and heated by wood/gas. All the old combs are place in a sack which is kept below the surface of the boiling water with a strong stick. As the wax melts it passes out of the sack and rises to the surface of the water. Rainwater is usually recommended! When all the wax has passed out of the sack the wax is allowed to cool and solidify on top of the water.

Other points:

- Most appliance suppliers will purchase rendered beeswax or exchange it for equipment or foundation.
- When handling small amounts of wax especially on domestic appliances it should be remembered that wax is very inflammable. Use double saucepans made of aluminium or stainless steel. Should any wax spill wait until the wax has solidified before attempting to remove it. Covering the top surface of the oven with aluminium foil is a wise precaution to take before undertaking any wax melting.

2.16 The range of uses for and preparation of beeswax.

Some of the earliest evidence of uses of wax and honey date from c. 1450 BC. Encaustic paintings were found in ancient Egypt. In Greek mythology it is said that Icarus made his wings with beeswax and feathers. He flew too close to the sun, the wax melted and he fell back to earth. The present day cost of beeswax is high. Most of the church candles or candles for domestic supply are made from paraffin wax, a by-product of the petroleum industry. Beeswax candles will give a good light, retain their shape in warm weather, burn with little or no smoke and no unpleasant aroma. Paraffin wax candles melt at a temperature 118° -154°F (48°-68°C) The present day uses of wax are many and various because of its water repellant, insulating, malleability and low frictional qualities. Most of the beeswax used for commercial purpose is imported into the UK from New Zealand, Australia, Canada and China. Other waxes from vegetable or mineral sources may be mixed with beeswax as an 'extender'.

Examples of the usages of beeswax:

- An ingredient of cosmetics. 'Brylcream' the hair lotion of the 1950s was one of the last mass produced products using beeswax. Wax is used in the manufacture of lipstick, mascara, eye shadow, epilation, camouflage for commandos etc.
- Polishes made with beeswax are used by owners of antique furniture eg. The National Trust has some magnificent examples of furniture treated with beeswax polish. Wax is used by wood turners to enhance and protect the surface of wood.
- Dental impressions are now made using a plastic derivative where previously beeswax was used.
- Long before electricity or gas were discovered candles from beeswax were used to illuminate the night hours. Candles would be marked to denote the hour of the day or night.
- Traditional patterns are dyed on material with wax eg. the 'batik' sarongs of Indonesia in South East Asia.
- In the 16th Century Benvenuto Cellini used the ancient technology of 'cire-perdue' or lost wax casting to make his famous statue of Perseus. This statue can still be seen in the National Museum of Florence.
- Waxed thread is still used by the sailing fraternity for whipping ends of rope. The Victorian

needlewomen would keep a piece of wax in their work boxes to wax the linen thread used for sewing on buttons.

- Ornamental moulds, seals and artificial flowers are still made. The National Honey show has several classes for exhibitors to show their artistic talents in moulding and colouring wax to represent flowers, fruit etc
- Madame Tussaud used beeswax for her death masks and models.
- Beekeepers can recycle their own wax by producing their own foundation.
- Primitive tribes used wax for casting gold ornaments eg. Incas of South America.
- For insulating cables used in the electrical and telecommunication industries. This use has now been superseded by other materials.
- A long list of uses and recipes appear in Ron Brown's book called 'Beeswax' reprinted in 1995.

2.16.1 The preparation of beeswax for making polishes, candles or cosmetics.

If the wax is to be used in a cosmetic or polish it should be free from impurities eg. minute slithers of wood or pieces of bee may cause abrasions, propolis will make the wax adhere to the wax moulds or the flame of a candle to splutter. Beeswax imported from China is renowned for its adulterated state. As the beeswax is collected during the year it is best to keep the clean wax apart from the old combs. Cappings are best kept for moulding into blocks for exhibits at the annual Honey Shows. The darker coloured pieces of wax are only suitable for recycling as foundation or trading in at the 'Bee Equipment' centres. See section 1.3.

Prepare clean wax for making polish, candles or cosmetics by refiltering the wax:

- Use an old coffee tin (catering size) and remove the bottom. Attach four metal hooks around the brim.
- On to the bottom secure a piece of plain lint with clean string, smooth side to the bottom, fluffy side to the inside and fill the tin with pieces of broken clean wax.
- Into a large pyrex bowl place 1-2in of soft water. This water could be water saved when defrosting the fridge or strained rain water ie. it should not be hard water containing salts.
- Set the oven at a low temperature ie. a thermometer placed on the top shelf should not read higher than 194°F (90°C) other wise the colour of the wax will darken. The colour is not so important for the cosmetics or polish but it is important for the candles and pieces of wax for exhibits for show.
- Place the bowl of water in the bottom of the oven.
- Hang the can of wax over the pyrex bowl in the oven. Use the metal hooks to suspend the tin of wax from the top shelf.
- As the wax drips onto the water in the bowl the wax in the tin can be replenished.
- This is a long slow process. When all the wax has filtered through the lint, turn out the heat and leave the bowl in the oven until the wax has solidified. Then remove and place the bowl under a cold running tap. The wax will float to the surface of the water. You will now have a clean piece of wax for moulding for show, for making candles, cosmetics or polish.
- Aim to clean 2-3lb of wax at each operation.
- Or use a double saucepan to melt the wax. The wax will melt at about 147°F (64°C). When all the wax has melted pour it through a paper filter (wine filter paper) or fine nylon strainer (use several layers) into a clean glass jug or bowl. Always keep all utensils used when processing wax scrupulously clean and use only for the sole purpose of refining wax.
- See Appendix 12 for recipes for making cold cream and polish.

2.17 The uses of other bee products such as pollen, royal jelly, venom and propolis.

2.17.1 Pollen.

The nutritional value of pollen varies with the species of the plant which produces it. The protein value can range from 7-35%. The amino acids found in pollen are also very variable. Pollen grains contain lipids 1-14%, carbohydrates or sugars 25-48%, minerals 1-5% and vitamins. Pollen pellets can be collected by means of a pollen trap fastened over the entrance of a strong colony when the bees are busy foraging. As the pollen foragers return the metal grill ($^3/_{16}$ inch square mesh) is across the entrance to the hive. The wire knocks the pollen loads off the legs of the returning foragers. The pollen is collected on a tray below after falling through a metal grill ($^1/_8$ inch square mesh). The trap should not be used continuously as this will deprive the colony of this valuable source of food. The design of the pollen trap should allow the grill to be easily removed allowing the foraging bees to bring pollen loads into the brood nest and to allow for the drones to pass out of the hive. Australian beekeepers leave the pollen trap on for 3 weeks and then remove the trap for one week. This will result in a loss of c.24% of the expected honey harvest. The length of time the trap is in position will depend upon the strength of the colony, the forage available and the amount of pollen required. The pollen should be removed from the tray each day cleaned, dried and stored otherwise it becomes contaminated with debris and deteriorates. The uses of this pollen are mainly:

Pollen patties.

Beekeepers who maintain apiaries in areas where there is a scarcity of pollen eg. the grain growing areas of South East England will collect and preserve pollen to be used in pollen patties in times of dearth or as a spring stimulant to brood rearing in preparation for pollination contracts or queen rearing. Other sources of pollen are available in a commercially produced packages eg. 'Early Start'. Here as with bees from unknown sources, pollen from unknown sources should be treated as 'suspect'. Has it been collected from a diseased colony? See section 1.25.3.2.

Medicinal use.

Pollen is collected to sell as dried pollen or mixed with honey. Health food shops sell these products as a food supplement. Hay fever sufferers are keen to buy local honey and pollen in the hope that it will provide some immunity during the hot dry days of late spring and summer when their allergy is at its most sensitive owing to the high pollen content of the air. The following passage is taken from a book called 'Honey and Hay Fever' by Dr L.R.Croft of University of Salford '*it is well known that the bee before sealing the honey comb injects a small amount of venom into the honey cell. It is possible that due to the unique chemical nature of the bee venom that it could be specifically absorbed into the pollen grains that occur in the honey. In this way it would be protected from exposure to the human digestive enzymes. Ultimately the venom would be released from the gut into the blood, where it would induce the release of natural corticosteroids*'.

2.17.2 Royal jelly

This is the name given to the proteinaceous food produced from the mandibular and hypopharyngeal glands of the worker bee. Royal jelly is fed by the worker bees to the developing larva in a queen cell or to a queen bee during the whole of her life. A cell with a 3 day old queen larva will yield about 250mg of royal jelly. The larva is removed and the jelly aspirated out. The exact composition of royal jelly is not known but it contains a large amount of the hydroxylated fatty acid 10-hydroxy-trans-2-decenoic acid and of the nucleic acids RNA (ribonucleic acid) and DNA (deoxyribonucleic acid) together with c.35% hexose sugars, proteins, vitamins, amino acids, cholesterol and water. It has been recorded as a cure for morning sickness during pregnancy, giving protection against viral infection, slowing down the ageing process and acting as a tonic to improve one's general well being. It can be purchased in capsule form (at an inflated price), in honey or combined with ginseng. It can be purchased at 'Boots' in capsule form. Most of the royal jelly found in these highly advertised products originates in China. The taste of royal jelly taken directly from a queen cell is bitter in flavour. Because of the presence of 10HDA it will keep well in the fridge. Queen breeders may use it in a dilute solution to prime queen cups before grafting. It has been reported that it can be successfully used in a diluted form to coat a queen before introduction to a queenless stock of bees.

1.17.3 Venom.

It is thought that 10% of the population of UK are stung by a bee or a wasp each year. About 4 or 5 of these individuals may die as a result of a severe reaction to the insect sting. Multiple stings can be lethal but this is a rare occurrence, every beekeeper can tell a story! A small number of people are hypersensitive to bee venom. Sensitivity can develop after long periods of apparent immunity to bee stings. Bees are capable of stinging after 15 days from emergence. The total capacity of the venom sac is c. $50\mu g$. Once this is used by the bee no further venom is produced by the venom gland. The venom contains enzymes phospholipase A*, hyaluronidase* and acid phosphatase*as well as allergen C*, mellitin-F, mellitin*, apamin, mast cell destroying peptide, secapin and tertiapin (* denotes the main allergens). Anaphylactic shock, a severe reaction to an antigen eg. wasp sting or bee sting is a very dangerous condition and requires emergency medical treatment, call for an ambulance immediately. De-sensitising treatment can be given to people who are at risk. Some beekeepers fall into this category. The purchase of the bee venom prepared for this purpose costs about £80.00. Bee venom is collected by giving the bee a small dose of an electric current as it returns to the hive. A grid of parallel wires of alternate polarity is stretched over a wooden frame, a glass plate is underneath the wires and some fine material is stretched over the wires. The bees can withdraw their stings from this material after depositing c.0.02mg of venom. The apparatus is fixed at the entrance to the hive so that the returning foraging bees receive a mild electric shock from the wires, the bees sting the cloth, the venom falls onto the glass plate and dries. No information can be found on the source of this electrical stimulus (AC/DC or voltages involved). This apparatus cannot be left on a hive for longer than five minutes because of the reaction from the bees. Another use of bee venom is as a treatment for rheumatoid arthritis. The authors have known a patient who on the recommendation of his GP regularly induced bees to sting around his inflamed knee joint. This treatment is less popular now there are other anti-inflammatory drugs eg. Voltarol and Brufen available. There is anecdotal evidence that if beekeepers are taking this kind of anti-inflammatory drug the body's response to a bee sting maybe exacerbated. See Section 1.31.

2.17.4 Propolis

Propolis is a resinous substance collected by the bees from trees. It has anti-microbial properties. It consists of 30% waxes, 55% resins and balsams, 10% ethereal oils and 5% pollen. Some races of bees are particularly prone to collecting propolis eg. Caucasians. The bees use propolis to fill up any empty space within the hive where the rule of bee space has been ignored. Propolis makes inspection of the hive by the beekeeper difficult ie. sticky when it is warm and the propolis is soft or annoying to the bees when the propolis is hard and the crown board and frames are not easily removed without a sudden crack. One beekeeper in 2,000 is hypersensitive to propolis, contact with propolis causing dermatitis The bees not only fill all the gaps within the hive with propolis but paint each brood cell with propolis in preparation for the queen to lay, build curtains to reduce the entrance, encase unwanted visitors eg. slugs, mice and reinforce the wax comb with propolis. Propolis is only soluble in alcohol, acetone or petrol. Because of its antibactericidal qualities it has been attributed with many healing properties. It has been used as a veterinary aid in Russia for many years. It is recommended by a supplier in Yorkshire who advertises in the national press as a miracle cure. Propolis products like capsules, tincture or cream may improve the mobility of arthritic joints, reduce stress, heal surface wounds, reduce asthma. attacks etc. The capsules cost £3.50 for a 30 day supply and £9.50 for a 90 day supply. The medical journal, 'The Lancet' has published papers on successful treatment for gastric ulcers using small daily doses of propolis in milk. Lastly, Stradivarius used to mix propolis with the varnish he applied to his violins.

You could make your own 'Tincture of Propolis' by dissolving a small amount in alcohol (vodka). The authors always keep a supply of this tincture for treating small ulcers. It is especially useful for banishing ulcers on the lip or in the mouth.

2.18 The preparation of bee products for the show bench.

Each year the National Honey Show and Beekeepers' Convention is held in London usually in November. The BBKA Honey Show part of the Royal Agricultural Show is held annually at Stoneleigh in July. Around the UK, Welsh, Scottish and most county Associations have their own Honey Shows, even the branches of the Associations have their own small shows. It is interesting and instructive to go and support these shows where exhibits of honey, wax and other related interests are displayed. Showing is the best way to improve one's products for sale. The number of exhibits seem to be decreasing year by year, even in good seasons when there has been a good honey flow. Would be exhibitors are unable to spare the time to prepare and organise some way of getting the exhibits to the show. Time, means of travel, parking problems and finally the collection of the entries after the show deter many a would be exhibitor. Both the BBKA and the National Honey show have their own sets of show rules. The county associations and the branches within the associations may have their own rules and regulations. Each schedule denoting the classes available for exhibits should inform the exhibitor which rules he/she should adhere to when preparing their entries. Usually an entry form needs to be completed and returned together with any entry fee to the organisers of the show before a given date. Lastly, it is most important that the exhibits are entered for the correct class. Unfortunately each year some exhibitors fail to grade their honey correctly. Light and dark honeys are entered in the medium class. The judge will automatically disqualify any item entered in the wrong class. Honey grading glasses should be used when preparing entries. Always read the show regulations carefully. It is the bees which collect the nectar from the flowers and convert it into honey which is stored in the honey combs. It is the beekeeper who removes this honey, extracts and prepares the exhibits. If a judge considers that the exhibits do not come up to the standard appropriate to the show he is at liberty to award only 2nd or 3rd cards or none at all! Honey Shows are good advertisements for beekeepers. Members of the public come to buy and admire the exhibits, others who are interested may take the first steps towards taking up beekeeping. Every competitor should aim for the best award. Rule 5 of the National Honey Show states that all honey and wax must be the bona fide produce of the exhibitor's own bees except in the candle classes. Points to observe when preparing honey exhibits for show are:

2.18.1 Preparation of jars of honey for show.

- Set aside blemish free jars and lids of identical manufacture for use for show items with each delivery of jars. Clean these jars in the dish washer ready for use.
- Always prepare three items if the class asks for two. Enter the two best matching exhibits.
- The honey must be free from any foreign bodies, check the bottom of the honey jar, any dust particles are likely to fall to the bottom of a jar of honey. The honey jars should be well filled, the surface of the honey free from scum and dust particles, the lids clean and unmarked and finally no stickiness around the neck or outside of the jar. The entry numbers should be stuck on the jar according to the schedule, usually $\frac{1}{2}$in (10 -15mm) from and parallel to the bottom of the jar.
- 'Run' or clear honey classes must be free from any sign of granulation. The judge will use his torch to show up the tiniest crystal. The honey may need to be gently heated in a water bath at about 145° F (62°C) just before the show.
- Naturally crystallised honey should have only slight frosting on the surface of the honey. There should be no frosting at the shoulders of the jars. To avoid frosting occurring allow the honey to settle in the tank for at least 24 hours in a warm room prior to bottling. This allows the air bubbles to come to the surface. Run the honey whilst still warm into clean warm bottles. After bottling keep the honey at 57°F (14°C) until well crystallised then store at 50°F (10°C) or below. Keep the lids well screwed down to avoid any absorption of moisture. In this class the judge is looking for a fine granulation, good colour and aroma with no trace of fermentation or foreign bodies.
- 'Soft set or 'creamed' honey exhibits should not be full of air bubbles. When mixing the honey with the creamer, which resembles a long handled mixer, it should be kept below the surface of the honey. After bottling the surface of the honey should show signs of movement when the jar is tilted. The crystalline formation of the sugar particles have been broken up by the action of the creamer. This honey will not return to the hard crystallised state.
- Once the honey is bottled keep the lids tightly sealed in order to preserve the volatile oils which give the honey its distinctive aroma. Prior to the show check the lids for cleanliness. The tinned surface of the lids should be free of honey, dents or scratch marks. 'Flowed in' lids are now generally used but some judges may prefer the waxed wad. The acid in honey will cause corrosion if it comes into contact with the metal lid.
- Heather honey contains air bubbles introduced during the pressing process. The jar should be well filled. As with all the paired exhibits both should be identical. This class usually refers to ling honey ie. nectar collected solely from ling, *Calluna vulgaris*. Heather honey if overheated during extraction and bottling will become caramelised, this is caused by the solidifying of the protein colloids. Overheated honey has an uncharacteristic appearance and unpleasant flavour. Care should be taken not to heat the honey over 145°F (63°C). Any heating should be followed by rapid cooling.
- The judge will test the viscosity and flavour of the honey with his glass rods. He may use a refractometer to check the moisture content before making his awards.

2.18.2 Preparation of a comb exhibit.

All comb exhibits should be placed in the freezer for 24 hours at –10° to –18°C this will kill any form of the *Braula coeca* and prevent the fly damaging the cappings. All comb exhibits should be free from brood, pollen or granulated honey. The wax cappings should be level, dry and free from any staining.

Cut comb exhibits.

The piece of comb should fill the container. The surface of the wax should be level and without blemish. There should be little or no run honey in the bottom of the container. It should be just one piece of comb cut from a wire and pollen free comb of sealed honey at least $1\frac{5}{8}$in (40mm) thick. Both exhibits should be cut from the same comb. With so many rape fields in bloom throughout the flying season much of the comb honey is spoilt by granulation, clover fields produce the best 'cut comb' honey. Judges prefer liquid honey in the comb. Two labels are usually supplied for each exhibit, one for the lid and one for the container. Both exhibits should be of equal weight. A good judge will remove the comb from the casing to examine the underside. Cut comb containing ling honey is usually entered in a separate class.

Round or cabana shaped sections.

The paired exhibits should both weigh the same and be completely sealed on both sides. A good round section weighs c. 283g (10oz). Clear covers are usually requested for both sides. The inside rings should be free from propolis.

Sections

Sections are usually displayed in white show boxes with narrow white lacing. The sections will be removed for examination by the judge. All the propolis and wax should have been removed from the soft wood (bass) surround. This is made easier if, before the section boxes are fitted with extra thin worker/drone foundation and placed on a hive, all the white bass wood has been painted with paraffin wax. When completed by the bees the woodwork will be propolis stained, this staining is easily removed with the paraffin wax before finally packing for show. On sections and combs for extraction the labels are usually placed one on the top of the horizontal bar and the other on the top right hand corner of the vertical transparent face of the case. Good sections will weigh c.454g (1lb) or more.

Combs for extraction.

These exhibits should be placed in a show case which when closed does not allow entry of any insect. This exhibit should be chosen for its depth of comb, evenness and good cappings on both sides of the comb. It should look as if the uncapping knife would run easily over the surface with one sweep. When held up to the light no granulation or pollen should be revealed. It is a good idea to select several combs as probable items for exhibition as soon as they have been sealed. First scrape the wooden parts of the frames clean of wax and propolis then return them to the super for a further 24 hours for the bees to tidy up before removal. If left in the hive too long the surface of the cappings may become marked by the bees.

2.18.3 Wax exhibits.

See Section 2.16.1. In all classes of wax the judge is looking for cleanliness, purity, good colour, shape and aroma. The wax should not be chemically treated to improve the colour. All the wax exhibited must be the bona fide produce of the exhibitors own bees.

2.18.3.1 The wax mould.

The late Mr F.Padmore remarked in his monograph on preparing wax for show that there is no use for a perfectly moulded piece of wax. However he goes on to say that the production of a perfect cake of wax is a real challenge of the exhibitor's skill. The authors have used the

'Padmore' method of moulding wax for the last 20 years and after much practice can now produce an almost perfect piece of wax. One of the most difficult items to find is a good mould, free from blemishes with slightly sloping sides from which the wax mould will easily release itself when immersed in cold water. An idea of the shape to look for can be seen when examining the moulds of wax which have been made for the National Honey Show. A show case is an advantage as it protects the exhibit during transport and when on display. The majority of the exhibits these days are protected only by a paper plate and a plastic bag. Showing the wax mould on a piece of velvet gives good contrast to the colour of the wax but may also be the cause of minute pieces of fibre adhering to the mould. A plain piece of wood or paper doily on a paper plate is sufficient to protect the edges of the mould. Light polishing of the mould with a 'soft' piece of silk may improve the lustre of the finished mould. Removing blemishes with methylated spirit requires a good deal of skill. See Appendix 12 for a method of preparing the wax cappings and casting a wax mould. 'Gelflex' made from polymerised P.V.C. can be used to make moulds of small objects, flat plaques or seals which can be entered in the ornamental mould classes.

2.18.3.2 Candles.

Mr. B. Reynolds, director of Poth Hille a firm which imports and refines wax, gave a talk at the 1995 National Honey show. He reminded us that burning beeswax candles was like burning five pound notes. Nevertheless some magnificent candles are made every year. Candles can be made by moulding, dipping, pouring or rolling warmed sheets of foundation. The wick for a beeswax candle should be thicker than that used for a paraffin candle eg. no 5 wick for 1 inch (44mm) diameter candle. The wick should be plaited and round in shape so that as it burns the tip becomes bent and is burnt off in the hottest part of the flame. All wicks should first be primed with mineral salts and then wax to improve the burning qualities. The candles entered for show should be identical in all respects. The judge will test the candle exhibits by lighting and allowing the candle to burn for as long as an hour! 'Beeswax Candles' by Clara Furness published by The British Bee Journal publications offers helpful advice on making candles. Like making the wax mould one will improve with experience. The experts seem reluctant to give detailed advice. The moulds on the market made from a soft flexible material (latex) or a rubber mould are easy to use and produce elaborate moulding on the sides of the candles.

2.18.4 Home made frame and foundation for exhibition. See section 1.3 and 1.4.

2.18.5 Mead.

Mead can be made from the 'washings' from the cappings or extracted honey. Served chilled either dry or sweet these wines make a very pleasant addition to a light meal on a summer's day. Meads improve with age but like most homemade wines are drunk far too early. They should be left to mature for 5 years or longer. For the show bench the mead must be shown in clear colourless punted bottles of round section, with rounded shoulders holding approximately 26oz (728ml). There should be no lettering or ornamentation of any kind on the glass bottle. Only cork stoppers with white flanges must be used. No alcohol may be added to the exhibits. The only additions allowed are acids, nutrients and tannin. The finished mead should be free from any sediment, crystal clear, have a pleasant taste reminiscent of honey, a good aroma and an alcohol content of 7-10%. A well matured mead when twirled around in the glass will show 'curtains' clinging to the sides. Any alcoholic drink may not be sold without a licence from the Customs and Excise Department. A small book written by S.W.Andrews, a past Chairman and President of the National Association of Wine and Beer Judges, published by Northern Bee Books called 'All About Mead' is a useful guide for a novice. It has several recipes for mead, metheglin and melomel as well as useful tips for preparing exhibits for show.

2.18.5.1 Making mead. See Appendix 12. for mead recipe. Brother Adam has a chapter on making mead in his book 'Beekeeping at Buckfast Abbey'. We may not be able to mature our mead in oak barrels but we can produce a very enjoyable wine for the table and for the Honey Shows.

2.18.5.2 Metheglin is made with spices eg ginger, rosemary, coriander, aniseed, cloves etc.

2.18 5.3 Melomel is made with the addition of fruit or fruit juices.

2.18.6 Miscellaneous, photographic, confectionary etc. classes.

Much time, imagination and trouble has been taken by exhibitors in these sections. Where a recipe or instruction as to size and presentation have been given these restrictions should be followed assiduously. One year all the cakes were rejected at the NHS by the judge as the weight of the entries did not correspond to the recipe given in the schedule!

2.19 A list of 10 major nectar and/or pollen producing plants of the U.K. and their flowering periods together with detailed knowledge of those in his/her own locality.

2.19.1 The candidate should familiarise himself / herself with the classification of the plant kingdom in appendix 15. Scientific names are in a constant state of flux and under review, reflecting the latest studies in the genetic relationships between and within different plant categories eg. Bluebell or wild hyacinth, *Scilla non-scripta,* was first described in 1753 by Linnaeus as *Hyacinthus non-scriptus,* in the nineteenth century it was transferred to the genus *Endymion* by the Belgian botanist B.C.Dumortier and then to *Scilla* by the Germans, J.C.von Hoffmannsegg and J.H.L.Link. Some established English common names often have no connection with the divisions of modern scientific taxonomy and these names may vary within the British Isles eg. Fireweed or Rose Bay Willow Herb, *Epilobium angustifolium.*

2.19.2 Terminology.

Aggregate (agg): used to indicate a number of very closely related species. It is often difficult to identify the exact species without specialised knowledge eg. blackberries over 250 species.
Cultivar: This is an abbreviation of 'cultivated variety' (only grown in cultivation) shown in quotation marks eg. *Erica carnea 'Springwood White'.*
Genus, Plural – *genera*: a category in biological classification consisting of one or more closely related and morphologically similar species. The name of the genus and the species together form the scientific name of an organism.
Hybrid: This is a plant derived from the crossing of two varieties often of the same species or genus. A first generation hybrid is known as F1 (Filial one) hybrid. Hybrids are distinguished formally by a multiplication sign in the plant's scientific name eg. The common lime tree, *Tilia x europaea.*
Species (sp), Plural – *species (spp)* is used for a group of organisms, minerals or other entities formally recognised as distinct from other groups. Where a genus has many species it is very often defined as the genus followed by spp (many species).

Latin specific epithets common in cultivated plants.

Albus - white
Angustifolius - narrow-leafed
Arvensis - growing in cultivated fields
Campestris - of the fields
Cerasus - cherry bearing
Fragrans - sweet scented
Glabrus - hairless
Hortensis - of gardens
Luteus - yellow
Maritimus - of the sea

Officinalis - used in pharmaceutics
Repens - creeping
Ruber - red
Sativus - cultivated
Spinosus - spiny
Sylvestris - of forests, woods
Viciifolius - with leaves like vetch
Vulgaris - common
Vulnerarius - healing

2.19.3 A list of plants whose flowers produce nectar and pollen and their flowering periods.

The syllabus asks for a list of ten 'major' nectar and pollen flowers of the British Isles and their flowering periods. We have given in this list those plants which we know to be valuable to honeybees in the south of England. Sixteen plants/trees are given in the table below from which a beekeeper may expect a surplus of honey under favourable weather conditions and an abundance of flowers. Most candidates, no matter where they live in the United Kingdom, should be able to identify 10 of these plants/trees.

Name	Family	Genus	Species	Nectar	Pollen	Colour
Willow (3-4)	*Salicaceae*	*Salix*	*caprea*	√	√	yellow
Cherry (4-5)	*Rosaceae*	*Prunus*	*cerasus*	√	√	brownish
Horse Chestnut (4-5)	*Hippocastanaceae*	*Aesculus*	*hippocastanum*	√	√	red
Sycamore (5)	*Aceraceae*	*Acer*	*pseudoplatanus*	√	√	grey
Field Beans (6)	*Leguminosae*	*Vicia*	*faba*	√	√	grey
Rape (5-6)	*Cruciferae*	*Brassica*	*napus*	√	√	yellow
Dandelion (4-5)	*Asteraceae*	*Taraxacum*	*officinale*	√	√	orange
Currents (4)	*Glossulariaceae*	*Ribes*	*spp*	√	√	grey
Raspberry (5)	*Rosaceae*	*Rubus*	*idaeus*			grey
White clover (6)	*Leguminosae*	*Trifolium*	*repens*	√	√	grey
Rose Bay Willow Herb(7)	*Onagraceae*	*Epilobium*	*augustifolium*	√	√	blue
Lime (6)	*Tiliaceae*	*Tilia*	*platyphyllos*	√	√	yellow
Hawthorne (5)	*Rosaceae*	*Crataegu*	*smonogyna*	√	√	whitish
Ling (8)	*Ericaceae*	*Calluna*	*vulgaris*	√	√	grey
Blackberry (7)	*Rosaceae*	*Rubus*	*fruticosus*	√	√	grey
Ivy (9)	*Aralaceae*	*Hedera*	*helix*	√	√	yellow

Other points are:
- The approximate flowering periods are given in brackets in the first column after the common name. 1 = January, 2 = February 3 = March etc.
- Flowering times will vary with changes in weather patterns.
- The yields of nectar and pollen, from each plant or tree will also be influenced by the type of soil, geographical location, rainfall and range of temperature which varies from year to year.
- The flowering time of some of the field crops will vary depending on the time of sowing. eg. *Brassica napus* and *Vicia faba* may be autumn or spring sown. The autumn sown crop will bloom about April to May and the spring sown crop about July depending on the weather.
- The colour given in the last column is the colour of the pollen load. This colour will vary in shade depending on differing growing conditions of the plant, weather and soil.
- The colour of the pollen is different from the colour of the anther which produces the pollen grains.

2.19.4 Other plants visited by bees include:

Name	Family	Genus	Species	Nectar	Pollen	Colour
Snowdrop (2)	*Amaryllidaceae*	*Galanthus*	*nivalis*		√	brown
Crocus (2)	*Iridaceae*	*Crocus*	*spp.*		√	yellow
Gorse (most of the year)	*Leguminosae*	*Ulex*	*europaeus*		√	yellow
Hazel (2-3)	*Corylaceae*	*Corylus*	*avellana*		√	yellow
Yew (2-3)	*Taxaceae*	*Taxus*	*baccata*		√	yellow
Blackthorn(4-5)	*Rosaceae*	*Prunus*	*spinosa*	√	√	whitish
Bluebell (5)	*Lilliaceae*	*Endymion*	*non-scriptus*	√	√	blue
*Top fruit (5)	*Rosaceae*			√	√	yellow
Laurel (5)	*Rosaceae*	*Prunus*	*laurocerasus*	√	√	yellow
Holly (5)	*Aquifoliaceae*	*Ilex*	*aquifolium*	√	√	green
Poppy (6-8)	*Papaveraceae*	*Papaver*	*rhoeas*		√	black
Thistle (6-8)	*Asteraceae*	*Cirsium*	*arvense*	√	√	grey
Hogweed (6-8)	*Umbelliferae*	*Heraculeum*	*sphondylium*	√	√	yellow
Lavender (6-7)	*Labiatae*	*Lavendula*	*spp.*	√	√	grey
Charlock (6-8)	*Cruciferae*	*Sinapis*	*arvensis*	√	√	yellow
Runner bean (6)	*Leguminosae*	*Phaseolus*	*multiflorus*	√	√	grey
Evening primrose (7-8)	*Onagraceae*	*Oenothera*	*biennis*	√	√	yellow
Bell Heather (6)	*Ericaceae*	*Erica*	*cinerea*	√	√	grey
Old Man's Beard (7-8)	*Ranunculaceae*	*Clematis*	*vitalba*	√	√	grey
Michaelmas daisy (7-9)	*Asteraceae*	*Aster*	*novi-belgii*	√	√	yellow

* Top fruit includes apple, pear, cherry, plum, etc. all belong to the Rosaceae family.

2.19.5 Detailed account of the wild and cultivated nectar and pollen producing flowers of the beekeeper's own locality.

Students should obtain a large scale map of his/her locality, say 2 inches to 1 mile. Draw a circle showing a three mile radius around each apiary. This will demonstrate the area over which the bees are foraging. A beekeeper's knowledge of the local flora is acquired by observation of the gardens, fields, parks, woodland, avenues of trees, hedgerows, nurseries, soft fruit farms, orchards, coastal areas, riverbanks, wetland and heathland within the three mile radius. Particular attention should be paid to the appearance of *Brassica spp.*, field bean or any other crop which may need to be sprayed by the local farmer. Moving stocks of bees directly onto a crop for pollination or nectar yield is more profitable to the beekeeper. Before moving stocks of bees onto the crop make contact with the owner of the land or better still have a written contract with the farmer or landowner so that they are aware of the presence of stocks of bees thus minimising any damage due to spraying.

Below is a list of recommended books which will assist students identifying sources of nectar and pollen. An accurate identification of the source of pollen and nectar can only be made by microscopic examination of the honey or pollen loads.

Author(s)	Title	Publisher
Howes, F. N.	Plants and Beekeeping	Faber and Faber
Hodges D.	The Pollen Loads of the Honeybee	IBRA
Sawyer, R.	Pollen Identification for Beekeepers	University College Cardiff
Hooper, T. & Taylor, M.	The Beekeeper's Garden	BBNO formerly A&C Black
Keble Martin, W.	British Flora Illustrations	Ebury Press & Michael Joseph

2.20 Illustrated descriptions of the floral structure of apple, oil-seed rape, heather (ling and bell), lime, dandelion, white clover and salvia (bee pollinated species) including plant family names.

See 2.21.8 for glossary of botanical terminology.

2.20.1 Apple, Malus spp.

Apple trees belong to the *Rosaceae* a family of over 2,000 species in 100 genera. Nectar can easily be washed out from the open type flower by rain or diluted with dew. Each flower consists of 5 white or pinkish petals, 5 sepals, 5 styles and c. 20 stamens, the nectaries are on the receptacle. Insects are necessary for successful cross pollination, fertilisation and formation of well shaped fruits. Flowering commences in April or May varying with the many different varieties. Most apple trees are self sterile and require pollen from a compatible tree to provide cross pollination. The apple flower remains open for c. 5 - 6 days before the petals fall. About day 7 or 8 the flower aborts if fertilisation has not been completed before this time and no fruit will set. The critical time is up to petal fall. The stigma of the apple flower is receptive to the pollen grain from the time the flower opens until about day 3. Pollination must occur during this time. After germination on the stigma it takes about 5 days for the pollen tube to grow and fertilisation to take place. It is for this reason that the deadline for pollination is day 3 because adding 5 days for the pollen tube growth brings the time to day 8 the flower aborting time. In warmer climates eg. the Mediterranean the pollen tube grows faster, typically 2 or 3 days making the fertilisation process more reliable. The honeybee is the only insect available in sufficient numbers at the time of the apple trees flowering to provide this service. In good weather bees will work the apple blossom avidly providing they are not distracted by another source of nectar eg. dandelion or rape flowers providing a nectar with a higher sugar content. Apple is superior to the pear, cherry and plum blossom in providing nectar and pollen early in the spring. In good years there may be a surplus of light coloured honey. This early supply of nectar and pollen stimulates brood rearing within the colonies. Modern methods of spraying apple trees to prevent infestation by parasitic insects should only be carried out after the hives of bees have been removed from the apple orchards. The pollen loads on the bees legs appears light yellow to green. Diagram 2.2

2.20.2 Oil seed rape, *Brassica napus*.

B. napus like the other mustard plants belongs to the Cress family, *Cruciferae* with over 2,000 species in 220 genera throughout the world. Rape, black mustard and wild cabbage are placed in the *Brassica* genus whilst the charlock and white mustard are placed in the *Sinapis* genus. The flowers of the oil seed rape are bright yellow in colour are in racemes, each flower consists of 4 sepals, 4 petals all separate and 6 stamens. Nectar is secreted by the 4 nectaries at the base of the flower. There is an inner ring of 4 stamens and a shorter outer pair. When a field of rape, *B. napus* is in bloom on a warm sunny day the yellow carpet of blossoms fill the air with a distinctive sweet odour attracting honey bees, flies, bumble bees and other nectar feeding insects. The period of blooming will last for about a month. The sugar content of the nectar is high and with good weather a surplus crop of honey can be obtained. In good years as much as 50–100lb/ hive. The nectar has a high glucose content and will granulate rapidly in the comb. This causes problems when the beekeeper comes to extracting the honey. Honey when obtained solely from the rape flowers is very light in colour. Pure rape honey when granulated looks rather like lard. It has a very fine crystal and is useful for blending and seeding with other honeys. The pollen loads on the bees legs are large and bright yellow. See diagram 2.3.

2.20.3 Heather: Ling, *Calluna vulgaris* and Bell Heather *Erica spp.*

Calluna vulgaris and *Erica spp.* belong to the *Ericaceae* family which has over 1,200 species in 50 genera. *C. vulgaris* is the dominant plant in the heathlands in the South of England. There are more extensive moors in Scotland and Yorkshire. The name 'Ling' comes from the Anglo-Saxon 'lig' meaning fire. Ling, *C. vulgaris* is usually in bloom in August. It is a deep rooting plant and prefers an acid soil. It is an evergreen plant with minute leaves. The flowers are usually pale purple but some white heather is occasionally found. The flowers are in slender racemes, forming loose spikes at the tops of the stems. The flowers have 4 - 5 petals with twice as many stamens as petal lobes. The sepals are longer than the petals and similar in colour and structure. The corolla tube is 2–3mm long. The nectar is secreted by 8 tiny swellings which alternate with the bases of the stamens. As the flower ages the nectar secretion ceases and the stamens elongate. The honey is thixotropic, amber in colour with a characteristic smell. The pollen loads on the bees legs are slate grey in colour.

Bell heather, *Erica cinerea* blooms earlier than the ling heather, July to September, and grows well on lime free, well drained sandy soils. The sepals are shorter than the petals which form a bell shaped flower, the corolla tube is about 5mm long. Bumble bees pierce the lower end of the petals to obtain nectar and honeybees sometimes use the same route. The flowers grow in racemes or compact clusters. The leaves have very short stalks and grow in whorls of three Today there are many cultivars of the Ericaceae family eg. *Erica carnea Springwood white*. These cultivars bloom in early spring and are lime tolerant. The colour of the flowers range from ruby pink to white. The leaves vary from green to bronze. Heather gardens are planted to give colour all the year round. Bees will visit these cultivars but it is the heathers of Scotland, New Forest, Yorkshire Moors, Dorset, Derbyshire, Bodmin, Dartmoor and Ireland from which the bees obtain a crop of honey. Regular burning, say every five years as is carried out in Scotland is said to improve the growth of heather. Only the ling honey is thixotropic. The colour of pure bell heather honey will be a shade of ruby red. The small pollen loads on the bees legs are grey in colour. See diagram 2.4.

2.20.4 Lime, *Tilia spp.*

There are some 30 different species of lime native to the northern latitudes all belonging to the *Tiliaceae* family which has over 300 species in 35 genera. These deciduous trees have either been planted in parks, avenues, streets and gardens or grow wild. Three lime trees commonly found in the UK. are:

- *Tilia x europaea* may grow to a great age and over 100 feet in height.
- *Tilia platyphyllos* mainly found in Hereford, Radnor and Yorkshire.
- *Tilia cordata* the small leaf lime which flowers later than the two other species occurs in the west of England.

The flowers of the lime tree have 5 boat shaped sepals containing the nectaries, 5 petals and numerous stamens. The nectar is retained in the sepals by means of hairs on the inner surface aided by surface tension. The pale yellow flowers hang in small pendulous clusters with a large single bract towards the base of the cluster of flowers. This bract becomes detached with the fruits of the blossom and aids dispersal of the seed by the wind. The individual flowers open at night and last for about a week, turning to a darker shade of yellow by the third day. Nectar is secreted during the whole of the time the flower is open, most nectar being secreted during the 'female' stage of the flower. The flowering period usually late June to July, will last for 2–3 weeks depending on the weather. The intense fragrance of the lime blossom is well known. The nectaries secrete their nectar before midday; honeybees have been observed working the blossoms early in the morning. On warm mornings the nectar can be seen glistening in the flowers and can easily be dislodged by shaking the flower bearing branch. In a hot summer the nectar will crystallise on the flower. Poisoning of bees foraging on lime blossoms is reported from time to time. It is thought that this is due to the sugar mannose present in the nectar which the bees are unable to metabolise. The honey has a distinctive minty flavour and is a pale yellow in colour, it will granulate with a fine crystal. The lime trees also produce honeydew. In a hot dry season the insects producing this sweet sticky exudate multiply very rapidly (see section 2.27). The honeydew honey produced may vary in colour from olive green to almost black. The pollen loads of the bee appear greenish yellow. See diagram 2.5

2.20.5 Dandelion, *Taraxacum officinale.*

The dandelion, *T. officinale* belongs to the daisy family, *Asteraceae* previously known as *Compositae* which contains over 14,000 species in 900 genera. It is a perennial herb with a rosette of leaves sprouting from a tap root. The bright yellow flower heads are solitary, borne on a hollow scape, flat topped when opened, florets are all rayed (like the spokes of a wheel) the inner florets shorter than the outer. The florets are tubular, 5 toothed and fused together around the style. There are between 100–200 individual florets in a single dandelion head. The floret tubes vary from 3–7mm in length. At night and in dull or wet weather the heads close up protecting the pollen and nectar from damage or dilution by dew, wind or rain. The time of the opening of the flowers in the morning varies with the time of the year viz. earlier in the warm summer mornings than early spring or autumn. It flowers throughout the year but most freely just before the appearance of the fruit blossom, late April/May. It grows well on chalky soil, particularly on the Cotswolds and Chilterns soil where beekeepers may harvest a spring crop of honey from the dandelion blossom. The ovules in the carpels of the dandelion and the hawkweeds, *Hieracium spp* can develop into seeds without pollination or fertilisation. This is a vegetative process called, *'apomixsis'*. The offspring all inherit the exact genetic make up of the parent plant. In cross pollination the offspring inherits half the genetic material from each parent. The deep orange coloured, oily pollen loads on foraging bees returning from the dandelion blossom stains the wax within the beehive with a characteristic yellowish glow. The honey is a golden yellow in colour, it will granulate with a coarse crystal. The large pollen loads of the honeybee are bright orange. See diagram 2.6.

2.20.6 White clover, *Trifolium repens*.

Clovers, *Trifolium spp.* belong to the pea family, *Leguminosae,* the third largest family of flowering plants (exceeded only by the *Asteraceae* and the *Orchidaceae)* with over 16,000 species. The leaves of the clovers are trifoliate with stipules at the base. Each flower head consists of 50-100 flowers or florets. These florets are typically pea shaped, calyx tubular with 5 petals i.e. upper 'standard', 2 lateral 'wings' and the lower 2 fused together to form a keel. Enclosed in the keel are 10 stamens, a style and an ovary. The florets do not open simultaneously but in a sequence of circles from the outer ring. As the florets become pollinated nectar secretion ceases and the florets wither and droop. The roots bear root-nodules with bacteria, *Rhizobium.* These bacteria fix atmospheric nitrogen and help to improve the fertility of the soil.

Clovers worked by the honey bee include:

• **White Clove / Dutch clove** *Trifolium repens.*

Low plant, more or less hairless with creeping stems rooting at nodes. Flowering starts in June, the flowers are white or pale pink, sweetly scented in dense globose heads. The outer florets open first and when pollinated droop. Leaflets are bright green with a pale or dark mark in the centre. Clover grows on a wide variety of soils but does best on well drained calcareous soils. Yields of nectar are best when daytime temperatures reach 72°F (22°C) i.e. when the meniscus of nectar in the staminal tube rises within reach of the proboscis of the honey bee. The honey is of a very light colour and will granulate to a hard consistency with a fine crystal. Fifty years ago this was the main honey produced in the UK c. 75% of the honey produced. Agricultural patterns change but now some of the clover forage is reappearing. The pollen loads of the honeybee are grey brown. See diagram 2.7.

• **Red Clover**, *Trifolium pratense.*

Red clover, a hairy perennial is grown for cattle fodder. The flowers are similar in structure to *T. repens.* Flowers are a pale rose colour. Nectar yields are reduced when nitrogen has been applied to the soil resulting in vigorous leaf growth at the expense of the flowering heads. It is reported that after the first cut of clover for silage the second crop of flowers have a shorter staminal tube which enables the *Apis mellifera* to reach the nectar. Again, a daytime temperature of 72°F (22° C) is required for the nectaries to yield.

2.20.7 Salvia (bee pollinated species), *Salvia spp*.

This group of flowers belongs to the mint family, *Labiatae* with over 3,000 species in 170 genera. A group of aromatic herbs of shrubs which usually have a square stem. The flowers form a lax raceme. Both the calyx and the corolla are two lipped, the upper lip of the corolla forming a hood. The lower lip is 3- lobed. There are only two stamens. The anthers and style are versatile, can move around in any direction and ripen at different times. When a bee visits these blue violet coloured flowers for nectar when in the male stage, pollen from the ripe anthers will become trapped in the hairs of the bee's exoskeleton. On visiting another flower in the female stage pollen on the dorsal or ventral side of the bee is attracted to the ripe stigma. The meadow clary, *Salvia pretensis* and the wild clary, *S. verbenacea* are close to becoming extinct as the hedgerows and grasslands are ploughed. *S. pretensis* produces flowers of two sorts on different plants, one has female flowers only the other plant has both male and female organs in the same flower. The culinary herb sage, *Salvia officinalis* does not grow so well in this country as in its native Mediterranean regions. May be this is why despite a grand display of blue violet flowers it is hardly ever visited by the honey bee *Apis mellifera* in our garden but is visited by the bumble and solitary bee. The best salvia for attracting honey bees is *Salvia x superba*, a hybrid originating from Eastern Europe. It flowers in June and will continue until September. This hybrid does not produce viable seeds, it is propagated by root division. Honey from *Salvia spp.* is honey water white and slow to granulate. The authors have not been able to ascertain the colour of the pollen loads. See diagram 2.8.

2.21 An outline account of the process of pollination and the fertilisation in a typical flower.

2.21.1 Pollen, the male sex cell of seed plants, is produced in large numbers in the anthers of flowering plants and in the pollen sacs of gymnosperms. See diagram 2.9.

2.21.2 Pollination is the transfer of compatible pollen grains from a ripe anther of a plant to the receptive stigma of the same plant or of another plant of the same species ie. self pollination or cross pollination. Transfer may be by wind, *anemophilous,* by insects, *entomophilous* or some other agent eg. water, birds, bats. Many species have one or more mechanisms to prevent self pollination including spatial arrangement, differential ripening of the floral parts and chemical compatibility systems which prevent pollen of the wrong sort fertilising the ovules. The ripe powdery pollen adheres to the exoskeleton of the visiting insect eg. the plumose hairs of the *Apis mellifera*. Entomophilous flowers are so arranged that a ripe stigma will receive pollen as the insect collects the nectar provided by the nectaries. Recent research shows that the pollen is attracted to the stigma by an electrical charge. When compatible pollen is deposited onto a mature/receptive stigma of the same flower or another flower of the same species pollination takes place. The following terms should be noted:

• self pollination - same flowers of identical genetic material,
• cross pollination - transfer of pollen which is not identical genetic material,
• self fruitful - capable of fertilisation with its own pollen,
• self unfruitful - do not become fertilised when self pollinated,
• cross fruitful - become fertilised when cross pollinated,
• cross unfruitful - non compatible when cross pollinated.

Bees pollinate, they do not fertilise. When the flowers open and the stigma is receptive (female stage) nectar is secreted as an attractant to the pollinators. The aroma, colour shape and nectar guides of the flower also attract insects. There are a wide range of estimates of the number of pollen grains that can be collected and carried on the plumose hairs of the honeybee ranging from 50,000 to 5,000,000 depending on which source is quoted.

2.21.3 Differences between wind pollinated and insect pollinated flowers:

Wind pollinated	Insect pollinated
Inconspicuous flowers.	Flowers large, brightly coloured some with 'nectar guides'.
Male flowers numerous eg. pendulous catkins.	Compact inflorescences to attract pollinating insects.
Never scented.	May be scented to attract insects.
Nectaries not present.	Nectaries produce sugary nectar collected by insects.
Stamens numerous or with large anthers.	Stamens fewer in number.
Male flowers more numerous than female flowers.	Smaller amount of pollen produced.
Large amounts of pollen produced.	Filaments often short and so situated to come into contact with visiting insects.
Pollen easily dislodged and dispersed by air.	Pollen grains often large with sculptured walls.
Pollen grains smooth walled, small dry and light.	Stigmas capitate or lobed, usually on short styles remaining enclosed by the perianth.
Stigmas branched and feathery, borne on long styles, often extending outside the perianth to trap airborne pollen.	Entomophilous flowers often have highly specialised mechanisms, adapted to the type of visiting insect eg. Bee orchid, *Ophrys apifera*
Anemophilous flowers are characteristic of trees eg. oak, elm where they are produced before the foliage leaves.	There are mechanisms to prevent self pollination and promote cross pollination eg. Lords and Ladies, *Arum maculatum.*

2.21.4 Development of the female gamete.

Each *carpel* consists of an *ovary* surmounted by a slender *style* which terminates in a small swelling called the *stigma*. The ovary is hollow and contains one or more *ovules*. Each ovule begins as a protuberance projecting into the cavity. Initially the ovule consists of a uniform mass of cells, called the *nucellus*. In the centre of the ovule an embryo sac develops from a single cell. This cell undergoes meiosis to form four haploid cells. Three cells disintegrate leaving a single cell to develop rapidly into the *embryo sac*. The single haploid cell undergoes three mitotic divisions making eight daughter nuclei. Four at each end of the embryo sac. One nucleus will move from each group to the centre to form the *polar nuclei*. One of the cells at the micropyle end becomes the functional egg cell, **the female gamete,** the remaining two are called *synergids*. The three cells at the other end of the embryo sac are called the *antipodal* cells. See diagram 2.10.

2.21.5 Development of the male gamete.

Each *stamen* consists of an *anther* borne at the end of a slender flexible *filament*. The anther contains four pollen sacs in which the pollen grains develop. Initially each pollen mother cell within the pollen sac is diploid. Each of these mother cells undergo meiosis making a tetrad of four haploid cells. Each of these haploid cells will develop into a pollen grain with a thick outer wall or *exine* and a thin inner wall or *intine*. The exine is very resistant to decay, it may be pitted and sculptured depending on the species. Within each pollen grain the haploid nucleus divides mitotically into two nuclei one of which is called the *generative nucleus* and the other the *tube nucleus*. When the pollen is ripe the outer layers of the anther dry and burst, *dehisce*. See diagram 2.11.

2.21.6 Fertilisation.

The stigma cells produce a sugary solution in which the pollen grains germinate. Incompatible pollen may germinate but will abort. From the compatible pollen a tube pushes its way through a pore in the exine, penetrates the stigma and style tissue. It will grow towards the micropyle of the ovule. The pollen tube nucleus, which is usually positioned near the tip of the tube, enters the pollen tube followed by two nuclei formed from the generative nucleus. As the pollen tube penetrates micropyle it disintegrates and the first male nucleus fuses with the egg nucleus in the embryo sac to form a *zygote*. The second male nucleus passes further into the embryo sac and fuses with the two polar nuclei. ***This double fertilisation is a unique feature of the angiosperms.*** After fertilisation has taken place nectar secretion is discontinued and the petals fall from the flower. See diagram 2.12.

2.21.7 Germination is the onset of growth of a seed or spore following successful fertilisation.

2.21.8 Glossary:

Androecium. The male organs of the flower. Generally consisting of filament, anthers and pollen.
Anther. The upper part of the stamen which contains the pollen grains.
Apomixis. The production of seed without fertilisation eg. Sweet violet, *Viola odorata* produces apomictic flowers during the summer.
Bract. A leaf like structure immediately below a flower and located where the flower stalk joins the stem.
Calyx. The outer whorl of floral organs in many flowers (the sepals).
Carpel. One of the units or compartments making up the ovary or gynoecium
Clone. One of a group of identical plants all raised from a single parent by vegetative propagation.
Corolla. The second whorl of petals located inside the sepals. Petals are present in the majority of flowers and are often large and coloured. The petals may be as small as sepals or absent altogether.
Cotyledon. The initial leaf or leaves of a seedling plant, borne above or below the soil surface. Flowering plants are divided into two main divisions - those with a single leaf (*Monocotyledons*) and those with two seed leaves (*Dicotyledons*).
Deciduous. Losing leaves in the autumn.
Dehisce. Splitting open to release the seed.
Dioecious. Having separate male and female flowers on separate plants.
Diploid. Cell having chromosomes in homologous pairs.
Filament. The stalk of the stamen that connects the anther to the receptacle.
Filial. Resulting from cross breeding.
Gametes. Simple unisexual organisms.
Globose. Globe like, rounded.

Gymnosperms. Plant have bare seeds ie. unprotected by seed vessels.

Gynoecium. The female organs of the flower. Usually the ovary, ovules, style(s) and stigma(s).

Haploid. Cell having a single set of unpaired chromosomes.

Hermaphrodite. Having both male and female organs in the same flower. Majority of flowers are of this type.

Hybrid. A plant originating from a cross between two distinct species ie. genetically dissimilar parents.

Keel. A petal which has a sharp keel like edge.

Ligule. A small flap of tissue, often located at the base of a leaf or petal.

Monoecious. Having separate male and female flowers on the same plant.

Mycorrhiza. An association of roots and fungi dependent or partly dependent on one another.

Ovary. The female organ containing the ovules.

Ovule. The organ containing the egg.

Perianth. A collective name for all the floral leaves.

Petiole. The leaf stalk.

Phloem. Part of the vascular tissue of higher plants, composed of living cells, through which organic substances are transported.

Pinnate. A leaf composed of more than three leaflets arranged in two rows along a common axis.

Pistil. Pistil = carpel.

Pollen. Tiny particles produced by the anthers containing the male gametes.

Raceme. A spike like inflorescence in which individual flowers are clearly stalked.

Ray floret. The outer florets of a flower head such as a daisy or cornflower, which are often elaborated into a distinctive strap like or lobed, partly tubular, structure (ligule). Ray florets generally surround a central disk of shorter florets, disk florets.

Receptacle. The part of the stem from which all the floral organs arise.

Rhizome. An underground or surface stem, often thickly swollen and lasting a number of years. Rhizomes like stems bear nodes and buds.

Stamen. The male organ of the flower consisting of a stalk, the filament and the anther.

Subspecies. A subdivision of a species generally separated from the typical plant on several characters eg. colour and hairiness.

Standard. The upper petal of a pea flower, often showy and larger than the other petals.

Sterile. Not producing fertile seeds or pollen.

Stigma. The receptive tip of the style to which pollen grains attach themselves.

Stipules. A leaf like or scale like process at the bottom of the leaf petiole.

Style. The part of the gynoecium that links the ovary with the stigma.

Trifoliate. A leaf composed of three distinct leaflets.

Variety. A subdivision of a species or subspecies differing from the typical plant.

Whorl. More than two organs arising at the same point on the stem. Usually leaves or petals.

Wing. The lateral petals in various flowers.

Xylem. A composite tissue in higher plants with a water-conducting function. It also contributes to the mechanical support of the plant.

2.22 The genetic and evolutionary importance of cross-pollination and the methods used by plants to favour cross-pollination.

2.22.1 A gene is a theoretical unit of inheritance, theoretical in the sense that the word was coined long before chromosome structure was investigated in detail or the DNA theory of inheritance put forward.

2.22.2 Mendel's work carried out with the garden pea during the 19th century showed that an organism's characteristics are determined by internal factors which occur in pairs. Only one of a pair of such characteristics can be represented in a single gamete. Mendel knew nothing about genes and chromosomes. For over 3,500 million years that life has been present on earth there has been a continual changing of forms of life as new types have arisen and old types improved or became extinct. This process of change is known as *evolution*. All organisms produce variable offspring. Those that are best fitted to overcome a hostile environment will survive. To achieve the maximum variation of any offspring cross pollination is preferable for survival. In general offspring resulting from self fertilization are less vigorous and less productive than those resulting from cross fertilization. In flowering plants this means having mechanisms that encourage cross pollination and prevent self pollination. The different devices that have evolved include:

- Brightly coloured petals or sepals, nectar guides, nectar and the emission of a potent scent for attracting insects.
- Stamens and carpels being located in different flowers or plants, or maturing at different times (stamens first, carpels later).
- Some plants are self sterile ie. The plant's pollen fails to germinate on its own stigmas.
- The stigma may be higher than the surrounding stamens, making it impossible for the pollen to fall onto the stigma. If an insect such as a bee visits a flower its body will brush against the stigma before it reaches the anthers. Any pollen that the bee has picked up from another flower will be deposited on the stigma. In such flowers self pollination is by no means impossible but cross pollination is more likely.
- Wind pollinated flowers produce millions of small light pollen grains which are easily moved by air currents which may lift the pollen many miles away. Much will be wasted but some may find a receptive stigma. See section 2.21.3
- A single apple blossom may produce as many as 100,000 pollen grains but less than 10 are needed to pollinate one flower. The male gamete is always overproduced (each gamete is haploid ie it has undergone meiosis which involves a reshuffling of genes).
- Highly specialised mechanism in some plants eg. the arum lily, *Arum muculatum,* more commonly known as 'lords and ladies' bears separate male and female flowers which ripen at different times. Attracted by the pungent odour from the base of the shoot small dung flies crawl through a ring of stiff hairs in a tube to get to the base where the nectar is secreted. The female flowers at the base will be pollinated if the insects are carrying pollen from another plant. The dung flies are prevented from leaving the plant for 12 hours ie. until the ring of hairs has withered. The upper male flowers with ripen stamens are now exposed and attract the insects which crawl out carrying the pollen to the next flower.

2.22.3 Some plants are capable of producing viable seeds without fertilisation, this is called 'apomixsis' both the bramble, *Rubus fruticosus,* and the dandelion, *Taraxacum* are examples of apomictic plants.

2.22.4 For hundreds of years man has altered the evolution of species by artificial selection, known as animal or plant breeding. Plants like wheat, barley and potatoes have been bred for higher yield and greater resistance to disease. During the 20th century plant scientists are busy adding genes to create tomatoes that keep their ripe condition longer or rape plants which are resistant to weed killing sprays. Plant breeders create black tulips, blue roses, double cherry blossom etc. Some of these cultivars like the mule created by man from a donkey and a horse are sterile.

2.22.5 A mutation is a spontaneous change. A chromosome may produce an alteration in the characteristic under its control. Gene mutations occur when a section of the DNA in a chromosome is not copied exactly at cell division. Mutation rates are low and few are beneficial.

2.22.6 The environment in which a plant lives will effect its development and its ability to survive. Changes in the plant's structure may be due to temperature, water supply, type of soil, quality of light, humidity, wind and air currents.

2.22.7 Honeybees as pollinators.

- Bees are able to over winter as a cluster and are available in sufficient numbers in early spring to act as efficient pollinators for early fruit blossom. Poor pollination will result in misshapen fruits.
- Bees remain faithful to one flower type whilst foraging ie continues to visit same flower type whilst nectar is available. Honeybees are polytropic *cum* constancy.
- *Apis mellifera* has a distinct sense of time foraging only when the flowers are open and secreting nectar. It has the ability to remember plant forms, odour and colour.
- Bees continually look for food to feed the brood within the hive whilst weather is favourable. It has the ability to navigate using polarised and UV light from the sun.
- The bees ability to recognise UV light reveals the 'nectar guides' of flowers.
- It is thought that bees will mark suitable forage with secretion from the Nasonov gland facilitating further visits. Similarly it is thought that bees mark the flowers they have visited.
- Scout bees recruit other bees to a profitable source of food by communicating the distance, direction, odour and quality of nectar and pollen available by dancing on the comb, offering samples of nectar and vibrating the thoracic muscles.
- The hoarding instinct of the honeybee is of great importance for the effectivity and assiduity as pollinators.
- Stocks of honeybees can be moved directly onto the crop for pollination. Large numbers of stocks of bees can be moved onto crop and provide rapid distribution over crop. The best time to place stocks in orchards or fields of beans etc is when the flowers are producing nectar. This will prevent the bees being attracted to other sources of nectar and pollen which may be growing in a nearby field.
- Stocks of bees required for pollination can be fed sugar syrup when in position on flowering crop. This will result in an increase in brood and more bees foraging for pollen providing better pollination. This may be a necessity if flowers are not yielding nectar eg. the Kiwi fruit in New Zealand.
- Efficient pollination ensures good formation of fruit eg. apples, strawberries, pears, rape seeds etc and a good set of seed for commercial use.
- Honeybees forage for nectar and pollen cf. wasp are omnivorous. A small proportion of the hive bees will forage for propolis
- The honeybee's exoskeleton is covered with plumose hairs. 5 million pollen grains enmeshed in these hairs may be carried on its exoskeleton.
- Honeybees only forage during daylight hours when the temperature is over 57°F (14°C). Spraying or other work can be carried out on crops whilst bees remain in the hive eg. in the evening or early morning.

2.23 An illustrated description of the extra-floral nectaries of broad bean, cherry laurel, cherry and plum.

2.23.1 Extra floral nectaries consist of patches of glandular tissue found on the cotyledons, on the trunk, leaves, stipules, bracts, petioles etc. of certain species of plant. Sometimes they are barely distinguishable with the naked eye from the surrounding plant tissue. The sugar content of the secretion from the extra floral nectaries depends on the composition of the plant 'sap'. Plant nutrients are absorbed by the roots from the soil and converted by photosynthesis to sugar and starch which are stored in the leaves and stem of the plant. The extra floral nectaries may function as 'sap valves' to regulate sap pressure within the plant. If the sap in the phloem tubes, the transport system within the plant, becomes too concentrated with nutrients eg. sugar, amino acids, hormones etc. a reduction in 'osmotic pressure' within the vascular system of the plant is achieved by the release of nectar from the extra floral nectaries. Another school of thought suggests that it is a defensive mechanism attracting and rewarding ants which will deter other animals from eating the plant. The formation and secretion of nectar is an active process in the cells of the glandular tissue of the nectaries.

2.23.3 The broad bean, *Vicia faba*.

The broad bean belongs to the pea family, *Leguminosae*. *Vicia faba* has pairs of triangular stipules at the base of the petioles. These leaf like outgrowths have black spots which secrete nectar which is collected by honeybees and other insects. See diagram 2.13.

2.23.3 The cherry laurel, *Prunus laurocerasus*.

The cherry laurel belongs to the *Rosacea* family. Two pairs of extra floral nectaries are found on the back of the leaf, on either side of the central leaf vein close to the leaf stem. If attacked by a fungus they appear as 4 black spots. Pick a small branch with well developed leaves, place the stem in water and leave standing in a warm room near a sunny window and note the secretion from nectaries. Honeybees have been noted visiting these nectaries on warm sunny days. See diagram 2.14.

2.23.4 Cherry, *Prunus spp.*

P. cerasus, plum *P. domestica,* almond *P. dulcis* all belong to the *Rosacea* family. Like the cherry laurel the leaves of these trees have on the underside pairs of nectaries close to the leaf petiole. The authors have noted wasps but not honeybees visiting these nectaries on their own trees. It maybe that the variety of tree, soil, temperature and water levels in the garden were not conducive to activating these extra floral nectaries or that there is more rewarding forage elsewhere. The bee will visit the blossoms of *Prunus spp.* during February to May. The flowering period will vary with each variety of tree. See diagram 2.15.

2.23.5 Bracken, *Pteridium aquilinum*.

Pteridium aquilinum belongs to the *Polypodiaceae* family (Ferns). *Aquila* (an eagle) alludes to the bird like vascular structure apparent in the cross section of the rhizomes. Bracken is widespread from the Arctics to the Tropics. The fronds (large leaves, usually pinnately divided) push up from the ground in early spring becoming fully expanded by June. The young fronds are coated with 'chaffy' brown scales and a dense coat of soft hairs which fall off. When the lobes of the fronds unroll the glands at the base where it joins the main stem, secrete a sugary liquid which is much sought after by ants and bees. Bracken prefers acid, humus rich soils, it is usually absent from chalky or limestone areas. The rhizomes are deeply buried and tend to spread rapidly. *Pteridium* is poisonous to grazing animals if eaten in large quantities, therefore it is considered a nuisance by farmers. See diagram 2.16.

2.23.6 Salicaceae, *Salix fragilis*.

The Crack Willow, *Salix fragilis* has extra floral nectaries at the base of the leaf on the underside. These have been recorded by W.Herrod-Hempsall. The authors have found difficulty in locating these nectaries.

2.24 An account of the composition of nectar and its variations.

Bees tend to prefer a balanced nectar but the nectar with the highest overall sugar content is usually collected in preference to one with a lower sugar percentage. Nectar is an aqueous, sugar-containing secretions of plant glands called nectaries. Nectaries can be found on any part of a plant which is above ground, occurring in ferns as well as flowering plants. Floral nectaries may be situated on the receptacle of the flower, on the sepals, petals, stamens or carpels. Extra-floral nectaries may occur on the cotyledons, trunk, leaves, stipules, bracts or petioles. The sugar content of the nectar depends largely on the type of innervation of the nectaries. Those directly connected to the *phloem* part of the vascular bundles of the plant will produce nectar with a higher sugar content than those nectaries which obtain nourishment from the *xylem* (woody part).

2.24.1 Nectar may contain varying amounts of water and sugar.

The amount of sugar present will depend on the type of flower, prevailing weather conditions and the condition of the soil in which the plant grows. The sugar content of nectar may be as high as 60% or as low as 5%. The sugars are principally sucrose, fructose and glucose. The nectar types are discrete to each plant species which are generally in three categories, namely:

• sucrose dominant sugars or only sucrose eg. Alpine rose *Rhododendron ferrugineum* found in eastern France and southern Germany or long tubed flowers such as clover, or alfalfa (lucerne).
• equal parts of sucrose, glucose and fructose (balanced nectar) *eg. Leguminosae* family.
• glucose or fructose dominant sugars with only small quantities of sucrose. Sucrose is almost completely absent from the nectar of most *Cruciferae* eg Rape, *Brassica napus*. Nectar from *B. napus* is glucose dominant. Glucose is less soluble in water than fructose. Honey derived from the glucose dominant nectars granulates early. Fructose dominant nectars from plants such as Blackberry, *Rubus fruticous,* Sweet chestnut, *Castanea sativa* and many of the *Labiatae* family when collected by honeybees and processed into honey granulate slowly. Fructose tastes sweeter than other sugars.

2.24.2 The vascular tissue of plants is concerned with transport. There are two types of tissue, *xylem* and *phloem*. Xylem tissue conducts water and minerals from the roots to the leaves. Phloem tissue conducts food materials from the leaves to other parts of the plant. Phloem sap is a clear colourless liquid, the sugar content will vary throughout the day and during the season. The movement of sap through the phloem tubes is probably brought about by a *pressure difference* set up between regions of comparatively high sugar concentration and regions where there is a lower concentration because of utilisation. Sugar and water are used by the nectary glands leading to a fall in osmotic press within the vascular system of the plant so that sugar rich sap is directed to the points where it is required. Most of the sugar in the nectaries comes from the leaves close to the flower. Some sugar is produced from stored carbohydrates eg. Lime trees, *Tilia* spp. Plant leaves use the energy of the sun to build up sugars from carbon dioxide of the air and water in the presence of chlorophyll. This process is called **photosynthesis.**

$$CO_2 \quad\quad + \; H_2O + \text{sunlight and chlorophyll} \quad \text{converts to} \quad CH_2O + O_2$$

or

carbon dioxide from the air + water + energy   carbohydrate + oxygen

Most plant nectaries have a characteristic rhythm of secretion throughout the 24 hours. Diurnal in insect pollinated flowers but nocturnal in flowers that are pollinated by moths or bats.

2.24.3 Composition of nectar. The process of nectar secretion is complex and not entirely understood. It is an active secretion of the glands of the nectaries which using *enzymes* convert the phloem sap into nectar. The composition of nectar varies from plant to plant and flower to flower, it contains:

- sugars varying in concentrations 5–80%
- traces of nitrogen compounds, minerals, organic acids
- traces of vitamins: thiamine, riboflavin, pyridoxine, nicotinic acid, pantothenic acid, folic acid, biotin and ascorbic acid
- pigments and aromatic substances
- the ash content ranges from 0.023–0.45%
- nectar has a pH 2.7–6.4

Most floral nectaries cease secreting nectar once pollination has taken place. In some plants the nectar yield can be increase by repeated removal of nectar by visiting insects, this may be due to the negative pressure set up in the 'transport system' when the nectar is removed. Nectaries have a high rate of oxygen utilisation consistent with the high concentration of mitochondria (energy producing organelles of the cells) embedded in the cytoplasm. Some nectars contain substances which may be harmful to bees, humans or both.

2.24.4 Environmental variations. The variations in nectar secretion of plants is extremely complex with a large number of variables. Sunlight is very important as this is necessary for photosynthesis (hydrocarbons to nectar). With plenty of sunlight temperatures increase. A minimum temperature is required for the enzymes causing nectar secretion to operate. Rain may wash the nectar from the flower or dilute it or wind may dry the nectar evaporating some of the water and increase its sugar content; both conditions can sometimes be found on the same tree.

Variations in the amount of nectar available in a given area is important to the beekeeper; only a finite quantity is available. An area can be over stocked with bees to the detriment of the beekeepers concerned.

2.24.5 Total availability of nectar.

A few figures on foraging areas and colony density:

- Dr. Bailey considers that colony density should be no higher than 1 colony per 10 sq. kilometres to minimise disease (or 1 colony / 4 square miles approx.).
- The foraging area of 1 colony = $\pi 3^2$ = 28.3 square miles (r = 3 miles).
- Therefore 7 colonies/apiary is about the maximum (28 ÷ 4).
- cf. 1 colony/acre for pollination purposes or on a concentrated nectar crop such as rape. Note that 1 square mile = c.640 acres or c.260 hectares.

It is important that the beekeeper should get to know his area; the flora, the micro climates, other beekeepers and where each keeps his bees all in relation to available nectar supplies.

2.25 A list of floral sources of undesirable nectar in the UK and a brief description of the characteristics of these nectars.

Toxic substances and organic compounds are synthesised by various plants some with marked pharmacological activity. For example:

- Deadly Nightshade, *Atropa belladonna.* The juice of the berries causes dilation of the pupil of the eye.
- Foxglove, *Digitalis purpurea.* Digitalis can be extracted from its leaves, in its fresh state this can cause drowsiness, convulsions and even death. Where foxglove is grown extensively, honeybees bees foraging for pollen have been poisoned.
- Common Ragwort, *Senecio jacobaea,* designated an injurious weed in the Weeds Act 1959, is poisonous to cattle and horses causing damage to the liver with *pyrrolizidine alkaloids.* Bees work ragwort blossom and obtain both pollen and nectar with no toxic effects. The honey is bright yellow with a strong unpleasant odour. After granulation much of the strong aroma disappears.

2.25.1 Some nectars, honeydews or pollens collected by honeybees are poisonous to the bees while others appear to be acceptable to bees but toxic to man or livestock. Those toxic to bees can contain toxins in the nectar or pollen or both. With toxic nectar bees die in front of the hive. Toxic pollen will affect brood and bees. Brood can die in the cell. Some toxins can affect the queen. 'Toxic' means poisonous and practically any substance can be toxic if taken in large enough quantities. There is a toxic level for almost any substance. Below this level, a material is safe, above it becomes harmful. Incidences of poisoning have been poorly documented. Sometimes abnormal environmental conditions produce effects that look like poisoning. As in cases of spray damage, the colonies affected should be fed sugar syrup in order to dilute the toxins and compensate for loss of foraging bees. The authors understand that some French beekeepers feed a sample of honey to a dog as a test for toxicity before human consumption is contemplated.

2.25.2 The syllabus calls for undesirable nectars in the UK only. However, there are so few that we considered it desirable to provide a wider view of this restricted subject.

2.25.3 List of known plants which produce undesirable nectar and pollen or act as hosts to insects which produce toxic honeydew.

- In 1955 an incident of poisoning was reported in colonies of bees on the island of Colonsay off the west coast of Scotland. The bees had died out completely in 2–3 days after starting to collect nectar from Rhododendron blossoms, *Rhododendron thomsonii.* The death of the bees had been caused by the poison *andromedotoxin or acetylandromedol.*
- Other hearsay evidence includes reports of bees found dead or dying under lime trees, *Tilia petiolaris* and *T. tormentosa,* these incidents may have been due to the honeydew present on the trees or to the presence of mannose in the nectar. It has been reported that the casualties vary from season to season and affect the bumble bees more than the honeybee.
- Spring dwindling or '*May disease*' caused by the pollen from the *Ranunculaceae* family (buttercup) was reported in 1944 from Switzerland, probably due to the toxin *protoanemonin.* Nurse bees appeared at the hive entrance trembling and unable to fly, excitedly moving on the landing board, losing control of their legs, rotating violently on their backs, becoming paralysed and dying. The leaves of most species of buttercup are poisonous and avoided by

livestock. The presence of *protoanemonin* in the sap gives the leaves a bitter taste. Each spring the stocks in the authors garden forage on the buttercup, *Ranunculus ficaria,* no ill effects have been observed over the last 10 years.

- The silver fir, *Abies alba,* is a source of honey dew which is toxic to bees. In Switzerland in 1951 thousands of returning foragers, with a waxy black appearance, were reported dying outside hives. Insects feeding on the plant sap of the silver fir convert the sap into simple sugars and synthesise new sugars by means of group transference eg. raffinose, rhamnose, stachynose, melibiose and mannose. Some of these sugars may be the cause of toxicity in bees foraging for honeydew which varies in composition depending on the species of sap sucking insect present on the tree.

- In the United States of America the 'California buckeye' chestnut tree, *Aesculus californica,* produces poisonous nectar and pollen. The bees become black and shiny, trembling and paralysed. Non-laying queens, dying brood and infertile eggs have also been reported. As this species covers 14 million acres in North America its effects on honeybees are well known to local beekeepers. The mountain laurel, *Kalmia latifolia* found in the Appalachian Mountains contains the same toxins as Rhododendrum. *Andromedotoxin* accumulates in honey and can be poisonous to man, bees and cattle.

- In Asia Minor, the earliest account of poisonous honey was recorded by Xenophen in the year 40 BC. It was thought that his troops were poisoned by eating the honey from hives of bees that had been foraging on *Rhododendron ponticum.* Around Trebizond today bees are kept not for honey but for wax production .

- New Zealand where bees were introduced to pollinate the clover crops has two trees which are dangerous to bees or mankind. The Karaka tree, *Corynocarpu laeigata* produces flowers which are very attractive to bees. The nectar probably contains *karakin* which poisons the foraging bees, the colonies die out due to loss of foragers. The Tutu tree, *Coriaria arborea* in Northern New Zealand does not yield nectar but bees collect pollen and honeydew exuded by the leaf hopper, *'Scolypopa australis'.* The honey produced contains *picrotoxin tutin* which was thought to be responsible for an outbreak of poisoning amongst local inhabitants, the honeydew was not toxic to bees.

- If beekeepers do not follow the instructions given by the producers of chemical medicaments used in the treatment of Varoosis, Acariosis etc. then in time toxic residual amounts of these chemicals may be found in both wax and honey.

Further details on undesirable nectars can be obtained in 'Honey Bee Pests, Predators and Diseases' edited by R.A.Morse and R. Nowogrodski and published by Cornell University.

2.26 An account of the factors affecting nectar secretion and the variations in the composition of nectar in different flower species and differing weather conditions;

2.26.1 Variations in the production of nectar due to internal influences:

- Innervation of the nectary.
- Size of the flower.
- Nectary surface.
- Age, sex and maturity of flower eg. *Tilia* spp secrete twice as much nectar and sugar at the female stage of the flower than at the male stage of development. Where there are separate male and female flowers on the same plant (monoecious) eg. *Curcubitaceae,* the female

cucumber and marrow flowers produce 3 or 4 times as much nectar as the male flowers. The willows, *Salicaceae,* where there are separate male and female plants (dioecious) the male catkins produces more nectar than the female catkins.

- Position of flower or plant eg. Flowers at the top of *Tilia platyphyllos* secret less nectar than those on the lower branches but the sugar value is higher at the top flowers.
- Species or variety to which the flower belongs. The production of nectar may start in the closed bud, may cease after fertilisation or continue eg. lavender flowers, *Lavandula* spp cease secreting nectar soon after they have been visited by bees whereas rape flowers, *Brassica napus* are stimulated to produce more nectar after a visit by bees.

2.26.2 External influences on nectar secretion.

- Soil humidity. Light sandy soil will dry out more quickly than heavy clay soils. In times of drought plants on light sandy soil are more prone to stress than plants on clay soil. Clover will yield better on well aerated sandy soil with sufficient moisture.
- Type of soil. Certain crops will yield best on limestone soil eg. lucerne, mustard. Heathers grow best on acid to neutral soils. Excessive nitrogen fertiliser will stimulate too much leaf growth with less flowers. Lack of potassium will reduce nectar supply. The best nectar plants are grown on a well balanced soil containing potassium, phosphorous, calcium and nitrogen.
- Temperature. The combination of low night temperatures and high temperatures with clear skies during the day are thought to promote nectar secretion. A minimum temperature of about 64°F (18°C) is thought to be necessary in order to activate the enzymes in the nectaries. Photosynthesis is likely to be reduced with low light intensity eg. Dandelions, *Taraxacum* spp. close up in dull weather as well as at night. Clovers yield best when there is a high temperature during the day and night between 75°- 65°F (24°C - 18°C). Excessively high temperatures with little or no rainfall will cause stress particularly to the herbaceous plants. This is when the water loss is greater than the water uptake by the plant roots, which will cause a reduction in photosynthesis, sugar transport and nectar production. The nectar production of trees may not be so effected as the production of plant flowers. Nectar production of trees is thought to depend on the rainfall of the previous year.
- Winds have a drying effect on open flowers increasing the sugar content. This is particularly noticeable with apple or cherry blossom due to the open structure of the flowers. The nectar of flowers on the windward side may have a higher sugar content, bees may prefer working only one side of a tree. This will result in a better set of fruit on the side of the prevailing wind of the trees in an orchard.
- Humidity of the air. This is likely to affect the sugar content of the nectar more than anything else. Low humidity will result in water evaporation increasing the sugar content of nectars but low humidity can also create moisture stress in the plant resulting in a decrease in nectar secretion. High humidity will result in the nectar equilibrating with the vapour pressure of the air.

2.27 An account of the origins and typical composition of honeydew with a brief description of the characteristics of honeydew honey.

Honeydew is the name given to the exudate of insects which feed on the sap (contents of the phloem tubes) of plants. These insects, are true bugs and belong to the order *Hemiptera* of which there are 50,000 species. 1,650 occur in the British Isles. All these bugs possess piercing mouthparts adapted for sucking juices of plants or other animals. There are three sub-orders *Coleorrhyncha, Heteroptera* and *Homoptera*. All the homopterans are plant feeders and the sub-orders contains serious pests. In the sub-order *Homoptera* there are two distinct divisions *Auchenorrhyncha* and *Sternorrhyncha*. It is the Sternorrhyncha that are the major producers of honeydew.

2.27.1 Sternorrhyncha.

These insects, mostly less than 5mm long, cause a vast amount of direct and indirect damage to plants by taking large amounts of sap, injecting toxins which may destroy chlorophyll, blocking the phloem tubes and transmitting viruses. Most of the bugs multiply rapidly in favourable conditions. Eggs overwinter and hatch the following spring, producing apterous (wingless), viviparous (producing living young), parthenogenic females. Several generations will be produced during warm weather, at the end of the summer male and female individuals will be produced, pair and produce eggs for the winter stage. The honeydew is exuded in small droplets from the anus during all the feeding stages of development but more especially during the larval stages. The exuded liquid is colourless, sweet and wholesome, it quickly solidifies in air and dries to a sticky, light brown, gummy like substance which will collect and retain pollen grains of wind pollinated plants, fungal spores, algae, soot and dust particles. The plant may develop a shiny black appearance due to the growth of the fungal spores on the honeydew. Honeydew may be produced so copiously that it can be seen falling from aphid infested trees. This may happen in urban areas where cars parked under trees will become covered in a sticky exudate.

2.27.2 The sub-order Sternorrhyncha is divided into five superfamilies, *Coccoidea, Aleyrodoidea, Psylloidea, Aphidoidea and Cicadoidea*.

The manna of the bible story (Exodus Chapter 16 verse 3) is thought to have been the syrupy honeydew exuded by certain species of the family *Coccidae* (mealy bugs) belonging to the superfamily *Coccoidea*. In warm dry climates honey dew quickly solidifies into sugary lumps as the water evaporates and falls from the trees as *'manna'*. The bugs such as the aphids, greenfly and plant lice are especially characteristic of the northern temperate region belong to the superfamily *Aphidoidea*. There are over 3,600 species. They have a complicated life cycle and a highly developed polymorphism. The champion plant suckers are the aphids of which there are hundreds of species, 500 species occurring in U.K. The other three super families are of little importance to honeydew honey in temperate climates.

2.27.3 Honeydew.

Honeydew attracts honeybees when there is no other forage available usually between the months May to August. Many floral honeys contain a small percentage of honeydew. The honeydew also attracts ants, for whom the honeydew may be the main item of diet. Some species of ant have a permanent relationship with a number of the aphid species. The best producers of honeydew are always attended by ants. Honeybees collect the honeydew in the morning whilst it is still moist from dew. Later in the day it becomes sticky and gummy and more difficult to collect. This may be the cause of 'bad temper' reported whilst honeybees are collecting honeydew. In the northern temperate zone bees may collect honeydew from lime, oak, sycamore, beech, elm, ash, chestnut, hawthorn, fruit trees and various conifer trees. Modern farming techniques and the use of pesticides has greatly reduced the production of honeydew collected from aphids feeding on cereals and beans. Sections of honey, or cut comb can be spoilt by bees collecting honeydew.

In the U.K. the collection of honeydew by honeybees varies from year to year. Rex Sawyer reports in his book 'Honey Identification' that in the years 1970, 1976, 1983 and 1984 crops of red to brown honey containing honeydew were harvested in the UK. Pollen analysis of honeydew honeys may show grass pollen and other airborne pollen of non-nectiferous plants, characteristic square crystals, fungal spores, green algae, soot particles and mineral dust. Fifty or more years ago the lime trees in the cities were blamed for the sticky deposits which would fall on to the pavements or parked cars. In recent years either these trees have been removed, died from old age or been so severely pruned the honeydew is no longer a problem.

2.27.4 Toxic effect of honeydew on honeybees.

Sometimes dead or dying bees thought to have been poisoned by honeydew are found around lime trees. In 1908 the Earl of Ducie reported many dead bees lying poisoned beneath a lime tree, *Tilia petiolaris,* at Tortworth and the following autumn a very green rich turf beneath the tree was noted. In Switzerland in 1951 thousands of dead bees with waxy black appearance accumulated in front of hives. These toxic effects were correlated with the presence of aphids on silver firs, *Abies alba.*

2.27.5 Definition of honeydew honey.

Honeydew may contain both the exudate of insects and the secretions of the extra floral nectaries of a plant. It is usually collected when there is no floral nectar available. Honeybees collect both these sugary liquids and transform it into honey within the hive. 'Honeydew honey' *means honey, the colour of which is light brown, greenish brown, black or any intermediate colour, produced wholly or mainly from the secretions of or found on living parts of plants other than blossoms.* Definition taken from The Honey Regulations (1976).

2.27.6 Production of honeydew honey outside of UK.

In Germany, honeydew honey, 'Waldhonig', is popular. Beekeepers move their stocks up into the mountains for the bees to work the pines trees particularly *Abies alba* and larches, *Larix decidua.* 'Tannenhonig' comes mainly from the Norway spruce, *Picea abies.* In Hawaii much of the honey produced is from insects which feed on sugar cane.

2.27.7 The constituents of honeydew honey.

As the basic raw material of the phloem tubes vary in content between species and at different times of the year so will the honeydew honeys vary in colour and taste eg. nitrogen content is high in the spring and low in autumn when the leaves change colour. The colour of the honey may vary from light brown, reddish or greenish brown to darker shades of brown. The taste may be anything from bitter, treacly, malty, like figs or toffee. The honeydew flow is determined by many complex factors including the population dynamics of the insects producing the honeydew.

Comparison of the constituents of average floral honey with honeydew honey

	Honeydew honey	Floral honey
Water	16–17%	18%
Fructose	31.8%	40%
Glucose	26.08%	35%
Other sugars	14%	4%
Undetermined	10.1%	
Ash	0.736%	(0.26%- 0.17%)
Nitrogen	0.10%	
Other substances		3%

2.27.8 Other characteristics of honeydew honey are:

- Honeydew honey is generally more acid than floral honey c. pH 5.1–7.9 cf. floral honey 2.7–6.4.
- The colour of honeydew honey is usually darker than floral honey and may have a distinct aroma.
- More enzymes are present, those from the secretions of the salivary gland of the honeybee and gut of the plant sucking insect eg. invertase, diastase, proteinase and a peptidase.
- As many as 22 amino acids and amides eg. glutamic acid, leucine, histidine, glycine have been found.
- Organic acids present include citric, malic, succinic and fumaric acids.
- Other sugars found include mannose, rhamnose, stachynose, raffinose, melezitose, maltose, galactose, xylose, earlose and melibiose. Bees like sweet tasting sugars like melezitose and maltose. Galactose, raffinose and xylose do not taste sweet. Mannose is toxic to honeybees.
- Bees do not collect honeydew containing sugar alcohols eg dulcitol, sorbitol, inositol.
- Bees do not winter well on honeydew honey. This is thought to be due either to the presence of mineral salts eg. potassium or melezitose and dextrins.
- Honeydew containing melezitose may granulate in the comb and will cause problems when extracting.
- Honeys containing honeydew will form long hair like threads when a glass rod is dipped and lifted from the surface of the honey. The viscosity is higher cf floral honey.
- Honeydew honeys are usually dextro-rotatory, slow to granulate and have a higher ash content than floral honeys. If melezitose is present the honey will granulate rapidly, if erlose is present little or no granulation takes place. The slow granulation will produce large crystals.
- When examined for pollen content under a microscope there is a marked lack of nectiferous pollens. The presence of wind pollinated plant pollens as well as fungal spores, characteristic square crystals, hypae, green algae and soot indicates the source of the honey ie. honeydew.

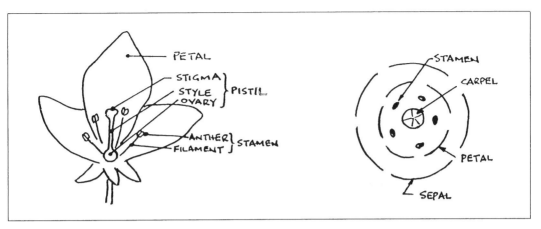

Diagram 2.1.   Parts of a flower   Floral diagram of a hypothetical flower.

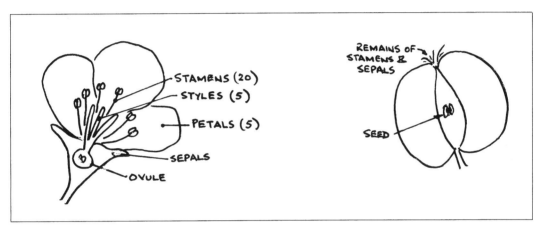

Diagram 2.2.   Apple (Malus spp.) × section   Well pollinated fruit.

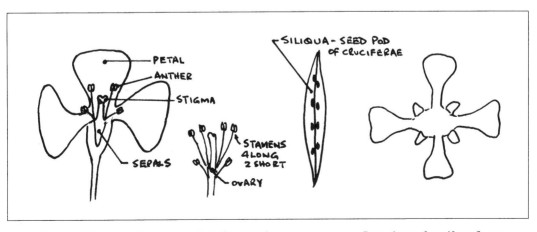

Diagram 2.3.   Oil seed rape (Brassica napus)   Cross shape of cruciferae flower.

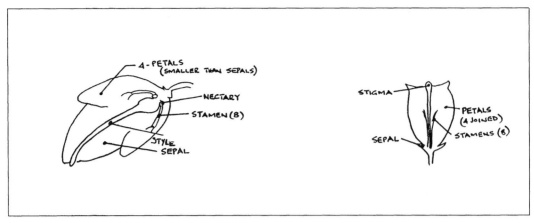

Diagram 2.4.   Ling (Calluna vulgaris) × section   Bell-heather (Erica cinera).

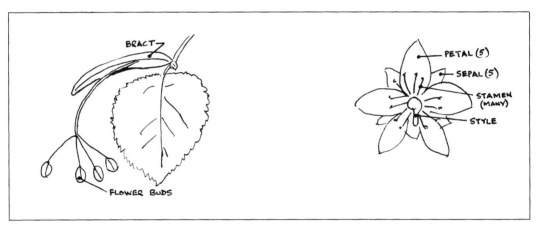

Diagram 2.5.   Lime (Tilia spp.)   Lime flower.

Diagram 2.6.   Dandelion (Taraxacum officinale)   100 to 200 florets   Floret.

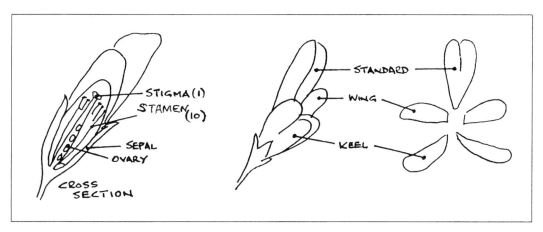

Diagram 2.7.   White clover (Trifolium repens) × section   Flower parts – 5 petals.

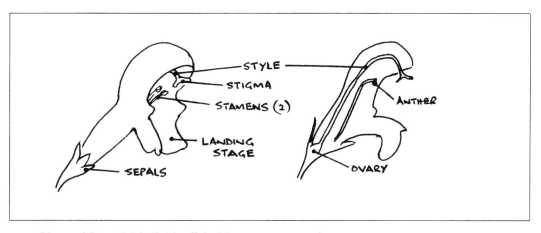

Diagram 2.8.   Salvia (Salvia officinalis)   × section.

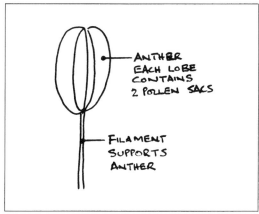

Diagram 2.9.   Stamen

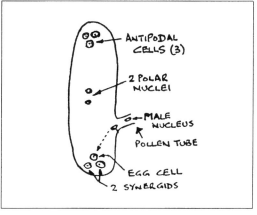

Diagram 2.10.   Embryo sac

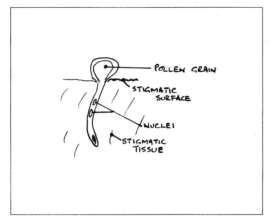

Diagram 2.11.   Pollen grain germinating on stigma.

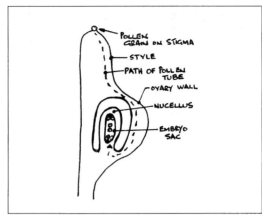

Diagram 2.12.   Fertilisation of female gamete.

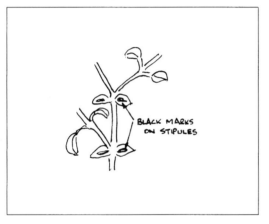

Diagram 2.13.   Field bean (Vicia spp) Extra floral nectaries.

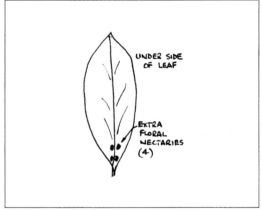

Diagram 2.14.   Cherry laurel (Prunus laurocerasus).

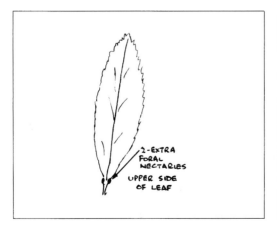

Diagram 2.15.   Cherry (Prunus spp.)

Diagram 2.16.   Bracken (Pteridium aquilinum).

MODULE 3: HONEYBEE DISEASES, PESTS AND POISONING

First, a few introductory words related to disease which do not appear in any of the set reading for the modules of the intermediate or advanced examinations. The words signs and symptoms are very often confused; even in the BBKA examination papers if you look carefully at some of the past ones! Signs of a disease are something you can see, whereas symptoms are something the patient feels or suffers. Pathogens (the agents causing disease) related to bee diseases vary widely in size and in their form, a brief list is shown below:

Virus: the smallest pathogen (6 – 400nm) and, at present, there is no cure for any of the viral infections, eg. Sacbrood, Chronic Bee Paralysis Virus (CBPV), Black Queen Cell Virus (BQCV). A virus attacks the cell and any treatment to kill the virus would kill the cell itself. An electron microscope is required to observe and identify them.

Bacteria: the next largest (0.1 – c.20μm), most can be seen under the light microscope and infections can be treated with antibiotics, eg. EFB.

Fungi: fungal spores are about the size of bacteria, eg.Chalk Brood and Stone Brood. The spores can be killed with acetic acid fumes but the disease, once established in the larvae cannot be treated.

Protozoa: again about the size of bacteria (5 – 12μm) and readily seen under a light microscope, eg. Nosema and Malpighamoeba with a magnification of about ×400.

Mites: all with 8 legs of the spider family (c.120μm – 2mm) readily seen with a hand lens, eg. Acarine (*Acarapis woodi*) in infested trachea and Varoosis (*Varroa jacobsoni*).

Flies: (1 – 1.5mm) always have 6 legs; readily seen by eye, eg. *Braula coeca*, not technically a pathogen); the bee louse (*Braula coeca*) is a wingless fly.

Moths: the wax moths are about the largest pathogens associated with bees.

Now to get the measurements into perspective:

1 metre ÷ 1000 = 1mm (milli-metre) = 10^{-3}m
1mm ÷ 1000 = 1μm (micro-metre or micron) = 10^{-6}m
1μm ÷ 1000 = 1nm (nano-metre) = 10^{-9}m

Epidemic versus endemic.

Epidemic means prevalent among a community at a specific time.
Endemic means regularly and therefore that which can be found all the time.

In an epidemic there is a spatial spread of the disease in a given area or community whereby most individuals suffer and clearly have no resistance to the pathogen causing the disease. In turn the lack of resistance is likely to be due to a new strain or new genetic type, the host and the area. If the disease continues to spread into a much larger area or country the disease then becomes endemic.

Once a disease is endemic there is no discernible spatial pattern and generally a low level of morbidity exists. For a disease to be endemic it depends on the resistance of the host which can be genetic, induced, behavioural or environmental.

Most, if not all, bee diseases are endemic and are not spread directly (except by the beekeeper) but are latent and occur given favourable conditions for the pathogen or conversely unfavourable conditions for the host. Consider for a few moments Chalk Brood, Nosema, EFB and Varroosis. The first two are clearly endemic, there is growing evidence that EFB is also endemic (now you see it now you don't) and Varroosis is in the epidemic stage in UK but will shortly become endemic as it is on the mainland continent of Europe. It is against this background that much of the discussion on diseases which follows in this section will be considered.

The Candidate will be able to give:—

3.1 A detailed account of the field diagnosis of American Foul Brood (AFB) and European Foul Brood (EFB) and a detailed account of the signs of these two diseases.

3.1.1 Field diagnosis of AFB and EFB and the signs of the two diseases.

ADAS leaflet # P306 Revised 1982 'Foul brood of bees: recognition and control' should be obtained (free of charge) which contains some excellent coloured photographs of both brood diseases.

• Both diseases are diseases of the brood and there are no signs associated with the adult bees in an infected colony. In order to diagnose either disease in the field, one has to open up the colony and examine the combs containing brood. To do this properly it is necessary to shake the bees off the comb before examining it, leaving no more than a few bees on the comb. The reason for this is that in the early stages only an odd cell or two will be exhibiting the tell-tale signs. This important aspect of searching for the diseases is frequently overlooked and inadequately expressed in much of the literature. There is a right and a wrong way of shaking bees off combs, the objective is to rid the comb of bees and keep them in the hive (not flying around the apiary); therefore raise the comb slightly and shake it sharply within the brood chamber without jarring the rest of the colony.

• In order to diagnose the diseases in the field it is easier to remember the signs if one has an understanding of the progress of the diseases:

> **AFB (American Foul Brood):** The larva is fed the AFB spores with the larval food. The spores germinate in the ventriculus and the larva dies after the cell is sealed. The germinated spores break through the wall of the ventriculus into the haemolymph and the larva dies of septicaemia * ; then the whole larval form disintegrates, melts down, becomes thick and sticky and finally dries to a hard scale on the lower angle of the cell. During this deathly saga the colour changes from white to black. It is most important to note that prior to the sealing of the cell, the larvae appear to be perfectly healthy. * Septicaemia – is the circulation and multiplication of micro-organisms in the blood.

> **EFB (European Foul Brood):** The larva is again fed the pathogen, this time a bacterium which is not spore forming as was AFB, which multiplies in the ventriculus by using the larval food and the larva dies before the cell is sealed due to starvation. It dies at about day 3 or 4 before the cell is sealed, so it is quite large when it dies. A dead larva is not sealed by the bees and is removed. During the starvation period the larva contorts into unnatural shapes in its cell and changes colour from a pearly white to cream to yellow to light browny green (colours are difficult to describe in words; any deviation from the

pearly shiny white must be regarded with suspicion). When the bees remove the dead larvae, they are removed in one piece. The infected larvae are either there to see or else the signs have been removed.

3.1.2 Signs of AFB (caused by the spore forming bacteria *Paenibacillus larvae* formerly *Bacillus larvae*):

- open brood – no signs,
- sealed brood, many signs as follows:

    1. After the larva dies, the domed cell cappings become moist and darken in colour.
    2. Cappings then sink and become concave (still moist and discoloured).
    3. Holes appear in the cappings (ie. perforated).
    4. Matchstick pushed through sunken capping to test for roping of the contents.
        Length of 'rope' between 1 and 2 cm. This roping is considered to be a positive identification of the disease. Colour of cell deposit is from light brown to nearly black. The roping test can only be done between the time the larva has 'melted' and the remains thickened slightly and before it has dried too much to be sticky.
    5. The remains dry out on the lower angle of the cell and form a hard black scale. By the time the scale is formed, the bees have uncapped the cell completely and tried to remove the scale. In order to see the scale the comb must be held at an angle with the top bar closest to you and the bottom of the frame away from the body (angle about 45° to the vertical). Good light is essential, some books say from the back while others say from the front; we think either is acceptable depending on whether you are in or outdoors. In the early stages of the infection, possibly only one or two cells may have scale and this is why it is so important to clear the frames of all the bees when doing an inspection for foul brood.
    6. Brood combs which have a 'pepperpot' appearance (ie. empty cells among sealed brood) should be treated with suspicion and examined closely for any sign of scale.
- AFB infections have no smell; many books indicate a foul odour. *Paenibacillus larvae* when sporulating releases an antibiotic preventing any secondary infections. If an offensive smell is present it will be due to secondary infections of some other cause or the confusion may arise because when the bacteria are in the rod form all the cells are sealed and no odour can be released. Rely on visual signs not odour for AFB.
- AFB is easily identified visually in the field. However, it can be confirmed if necessary by laboratory tests usually on a piece of scale from the comb.

3.1.3 Signs of EFB (non-spore forming bacteria *Melissococcus pluton*):

- Sealed brood – no signs (the larva dies before sealing).
- Open brood – the signs are as follows:

    1. Larvae are usually in unnatural contorted positions in the cells; twisted spirally or flattened out lengthwise (nb. stomach ache is a good analogy).
    2. The colour changes from a pearly white of a healthy larva to dull cream, to light brown and eventually a greeny hue. The colour change should be associated with the unnatural positions.
    3. The dead larvae have a melted down appearance but still have a larvae like shape.
    4. Again EFB does not itself smell. However very often an offensive smell is present on combs with EFB infected larvae; these are secondary infections often associated with EFB and are another indication that the disease may be present (3 secondary infections

are due to *Paenibacillus alvei* which is very common and has a foul odour, *Bacterium eurydice* which is most common, *Enterococcus faecalis* formerly *Streptococcus faecalis* which is fairly common causing a sour smell and finally *Bacillus laterosporus* which occurs occasionally).

- EFB is very difficult to diagnose positively in the field for the following reasons:

   1. The larvae are removed quickly from the hive once they are dead so the evidence is often removed and not there for the beekeeper to see.
   2. Any diseased larvae can be confused with other brood diseases, such as Sacbrood or Neglected drone brood, unless the beekeeper is very experienced. Most Foul Brood Officers will remove a frame with dead and dying larvae for laboratory analysis.
   3. The best time to look for EFB is when the brood outnumbers the adult bees (see colony population cycle - appendix 7) in the spring about mid April to early May. At this time the chances of spotting the diseased larvae are greater because the house bees are 'fully stretched' under these conditions.

3.1.4 Other points of interest.

3.1.4.1 AFB (*Paenibacilus larvae*).

- The signs are well documented but there are one or two areas where rational explanations are missing. It is well known that the cappings of the cells sink after the larvae die. Why? As the cappings are porous to allow the larvae to breathe, the sinking cannot be due to a change in pressure. We have not been able to find a reasonable explanation for this phenomenon.
- There is a dilemma about smell. Some authorities say AFB has a characteristic fish-glue like smell and others say that there is no smell. Smell occurs during the putrefaction of most animal tissue and as the larvae putrefy it would seem reasonable that a smell is produced. The ingested spores (1.3 x 0.6μm) germinate and start to multiply as rod shaped bacterium (2.5 to 5μm x 0.5 to 0.8μm) and being motile penetrate the gut walls and continue multiplying in the haemolymph until the larvae die of septicaemia. The bacteria stop multiplying and start to sporulate about the same time that putrefaction starts. Secondary organisms are unable to grow due to the antibiotic released and it is the secondary organisms which cause the smell. In the absence of further information on this point we consider that smell is not a good sign for the diagnosis of AFB.
- The most characteristic sign of the disease is that the pupal proboscis protrudes from the scale to the centre of the cell, something which never occurs in other brood diseases.
- It is possible to have both AFB and EFB on the same comb and in the same hive. As some of the secondary infections associated with EFB smell, then confusion can occur.
- Dry scales fluoresce strongly in UV light. As small battery operated UV lights are becoming quite common for security marking, we believe they could be a useful diagnostic tool but we have not tried them out. We have the lamp but not the AFB!
- There are no signs of AFB in open brood; larvae die after the cell is sealed and all signs of the disease are of the sealed brood or much later scale which the bees cannot remove. However, in the very early stages of the infection a suspicious open cell or two may be found where the larvae appears to be 'not right'. Such larvae should be tested for roping. When only a few cells are infected initially the bees open them up and reveal the dead larvae which is usually honey coloured. We saw a demonstration by the SW RBI, Len Davie, showing how to examine an apiary for foul brood. Out of six colonies in the apiary, he found one cell in one colony which was open and a matchstick demonstrated roping of the cell contents. A most excellent demonstration of the expertise we should all be striving to attain.

3.1.4.2 EFB (*Melissococcus pluton* formerly *Streptococcus pluton* and originally *Bacillus pluton*).

- The confusion in the names arose due to an original error in classification; the genus *Bacillus* was spore forming and EFB is a non-spore forming bacterium. Then the guanine and cytosine content of its nucleic acid were determined which excluded it from the genus *Streptococcus* and it was re-named and became the type species of a new genus *Melissococcus.*
- This disease of the brood suddenly appears and just as suddenly disappears during the active season in early summer 'now you see it now you don't'. There is mounting evidence that EFB could well be endemic in UK colonies and research work is being undertaken at the time of writing.
- Again there is confusion about the smell, for example, Bailey states when discussing dead larvae '...turn brown and decompose, often giving off a foul odour or a sour smell, but sometimes having little or no smell'. We believe that smell is an unreliable sign of the disease and visual signs are more reliable.
- To the untrained eye EFB can be confused with Sacbrood and it is always essential to undertake microscopical analysis to determine whether the disease is present. The most reliable way of undertaking a bacteriological examination is to select a larva with a white mid-gut and pull it apart on a slide revealing the the bacteria in white clumps. A healthy or lightly infected larva will have its mid-gut a golden brown colour.
- Larvae that die decompose rapidly and if left in the cells quickly dry to a brown scale which is easily removed by the bees.
- If larvae are infected with *M.pluton* and are capped and manage to pupate, they form either normal adults or undersized adults and leave infective *M.pluton* in their faecal remains in the cell when it is vacated. Thus, undersized adult bees can be a sign of EFB.
- Because the bees remove the dead larvae then a pepper pot brood pattern must always be a possible sign of EFB as well as other bee diseases.

3.2 An account of the life cycle of the causative organisms of AFB and EFB and their development within the larvae.

3.2.1 AFB.

- The infective cycle commences when the larva ingests brood food contaminated with AFB spores introduced by the nurse bees after cell cleaning duties in cells containing scale. Using the figures of 10 spores to infect a day old larva and that it contains 2500 million spores when it dies 11 days after hatching then the spores increase from 10 to 2500×10^6 in 10 days, ie. doubling about every 8 hours.
- It will be clear from section 3.3, that follows, that the life cycle of the causative organism is between 10 and 15 days; ie. from spore to spore through the vegetative stage. Spores remain infective for at least 35 years and have high resistance to heat.
- The multiplication of the rods after germination of the spores, occurs mainly in the haemolymph and after the contents of the larval gut have been voided in the cell. The continual increase leads to septicaemia and the death of the larva.
- Sporulation then occurs and these spores then become the source of re-infection within the colony completing the cycle.

3.2.2 EFB.

- The infectious cycle begins when the larva consumes brood food contaminated with

M. pluton. Once infected, the bacteria establish themselves in the ventriculus and start to multiply. The pathogen is localised in 2 to 3 days between the peritrophic membrane and the food in the ventriculus with continual decrease in food and increase in bacterial mass.

- When the larva dies multiplication ceases. It will be clear that under normal circumstances the life cycle of the organism is very short, however, we have not been able to trace any work done on the time taken for the reproductive cycle.
- If the same criteria are used for EFB as for AFB with an initial infection of 10 bacteria and c. 2,500 million bacteria in the gut at death after 3 days, then the life cycle is between 2 and 3 hours; ie. from bacterium to bacterium with no intermediate vegetative stage.

Note: It seems curious that the EFB life cycle is included in the syllabus when we have been unable to trace any work on the subject relating to the duration of the life cycle.

3.3 A detailed account of the development of AFB and EFB within the colony.

3.3.1 AFB.

- Larvae are infected by contaminated brood food and a minimum number of spores (the threshold level) is required for the larvae to die; young larvae require less than older larvae. For larvae greater than two days old, millions of spores are required whereas only ten spores are required for larvae less than 24 hours old.
- The bactericidal effect of 10-hydroxydecenoic acid from the mandibular glands is found in the brood food (which comes from the hypopharyngeal glands) and prevents the spores from germinating. However, as soon as the larvae ingest the brood food, the spores soon germinate because the larval gut provides the optimum conditions with CO_2 present and the acid food is reduced to a pH of about 6.6.
- Rods (gram positive bacteria) are formed, the vegetative stage, which do not multiply in the lumen to any great extent but penetrate the gut wall and enter the haemolymph. Here they multiply rapidly. It is important to realise that the bacteria penetrate the gut wall after the larvae pupate which is after the cells are sealed.
- The bacteria then proliferate in the tissue when the larvae become quiescent, at the start of metamorphosis, and they die quickly.
- The bacteria then form spores mostly in pro-pupae. Each propupa has about 2500 million spores which is eventually contained in the dried out scale in the bottom angle of the cell.
- The spores in the scale are the source of the spread of the AFB by infecting the mouthparts of the house bees prior to them becoming nurse bees which then completes the cycle of development of the disease within the colony.
- There is no apparent seasonal outbreak of AFB and it can occur at any time.
- If the number of infected larvae are less than 100 the colony is likely to recover but if the number of cells is greater than 100, then the colony is likely to succumb.
- The colony that becomes badly infected gradually becomes weaker and weaker until its demise; the signs are increased pepper pot appearance of the combs and less and less worker bees. The pepper pot empty cells are all lined with scale which cannot be removed and are not re-used for brood rearing.
- The danger now exists with the weak colony being a prime target for robbers.
- Bailey points out that the natural spread of infection of AFB is low mainly because infected larvae are removed by adult bees and because only the youngest larvae are susceptible.

Infected larvae can be detected very soon after infection and a large percentage are removed by the adult bees. This hygienic behaviour pattern coupled with efficient undertaking duties (both genetic traits) is the basis for strains resistant to AFB.

3.3.2 EFB.

- *Melissococcus pluton* is a non spore forming gram positive bacterium (ie. a bacterium that can be stained with iodine solution) which infects the brood food of the young larvae. The bacteria are carried by the nurse bees on their mandibles which generally become infected as a result of cell cleaning duties prior to feeding duties.
- The bacteria are microaerophilic to anaerobic and require CO_2 to multiply together with a temperature about 34°C. This condition is found in the larval food in the gut of the larva where multiplication takes place very rigorously soon filling a large percentage of the volume of the lumen at the expense of the food. The larvae die of starvation.
- Some larvae live and some larvae die; those that die are removed together with the total infection inside the larvae. It is those larvae that survive that are responsible for the spread of the diseases within the colony.
- Due to the under-feeding, sub-normal pupae and adult bees result. Feeble cocoons are spun and larval defaecation contaminates the cells with bacteria which in turn contaminate the mouthparts of the cell cleaners prior to becoming nurse bees.
- Bailey postulates a theory for the sudden appearance and disappearance of the disease. Briefly, he believes that a balance exists in most colonies where it is endemic and the signs are never available to be seen. When a sudden nectar flow leads to a sudden increase in brood production, then severely infected larvae have insufficient glandular brood food. When the change is rapid many young bees are recruited prematurely (?) to foraging duties and the infected larvae die faster than the bees can remove them. When the flow stops suddenly, the reverse happens and the signs disappear. We consider that a similar mechanism occurs when during the normal colony cycle the brood is greater than the adult bees.
- There is every indication that EFB is endemic in the UK and that it is on the increase. There is much to be learnt about it and research is being undertaken at the time of writing.

3.4 A detailed account of the ways in which AFB and EFB are spread from one colony to another.

3.4.1 Spread from colony to colony.

- Both diseases are originally transmitted to the larvae through feeding the spores or bacteria in the larval food by the nurse bees.
- In the case of AFB the larva dies after the cell is sealed. The cell is infected with spores due to larval defaecation and later by the melted down remains and eventually the hard scale. Any infected cell has millions of latent spores. House bees try to clean the cells and their mouth parts become infected, the spores being passed on to the nurse bees during food transfer. The nurse bees then infect the young larvae.
- The mechanism for EFB is similar but in this case the larva dies before the cell is sealed and dies as a result of starvation. If the larva is removed, the infection is removed with it; it is the infected larvae which do not die that spread the disease within the colony. Again the cell is infected by larval defaecation, and passed on to the house bees during cell cleaning and food transfer. Because every cell is not infected it is not as contagious as AFB and this is one reason why EFB can appear and disappear in a colony from time to time. It can be very elusive.

- The spread within the colony is beyond the control of the beekeeper, but the spread between colonies is very much in his hands. It is spread as follows:

  a) By robbing; likely when the infected colony becomes weak and is then robbed by strong healthy colonies either within an apiary or between apiaries.
  b) By drifting; adjacent hives in an apiary which are not orientated in different directions.
  c) By feeding infected honey; bees should always be fed sugar syrup.
  d) By bees gaining access to infected honey, combs, wax and propolis left around the apiary or within foraging distance.
  e) From appliances (eg. hive tools, extractors, etc.).
  f) From second hand infected equipment (combs, hive parts, etc.).
  g) From swarms of unknown origin.
  h) By the exchange of combs between hives.
  i) By the purchase of bees from a doubtful source.

3.4.2 Other points of interset.

The spread of both diseases is sometimes called aetiology (or etiology in American books). The word has wider implications and can embrace the science of the causes of disease.

Examination of the statistics prepared by MAFF over the years show that the treatment by destruction for AFB has been successful and has limited the spread of the disease or, perhaps, contained it below a very low percentage. This is not so with EFB which seems to be increasing with time. 0.1% of the colonies in UK were found to have EFB in 1948 and this had increased to c.0.5% in 1983. More recently the number of diseased colonies either treated or destroyed has doubled from 546 in 1990 to 1165 in 1991, c.0.7% of the colonies in the UK.

The treatment in connection with EFB is interesting:

    1942 - owner destroys the colony
    1952 - standstill orders introduced
    1957 - disease became responsibility of MAFF
    1969 - owner to treat or destroy the colony
    1982 - MAFF to treat or destroy the colony

It would appear that because the disease is increasing the treatment advised by MAFF may be incorrect. Thus we are well aware of the mechanisms for the spread of both diseases but one is kept in check while the other elusively increases.

3.5 A detailed account of the treatment of colonies infected with AFB and EFB including methods of destruction of colonies and the sterilisation of equipment.

3.5.1 Action to be taken if AFB or EFB is diagnosed.
Two avenues exist:

    1. When found by the beekeeper – report findings to MAFF immediately and follow their instructions.
    2. When suspected by the beekeeper and found by MAFF (FBO) – follow their instructions implicitly.

If AFB is diagnosed then the treatment is always to destroy the colony; the beekeeper being served a notice which he must sign. If EFB is diagnosed then the condition may be treated with antibiotics but only at the discretion of the FBO. Individual beekeepers are not allowed to treat their own colonies and it is against the law to do so. The work of destroying a colony falls to the owner but must be supervised by the FBO. The FBO usually administers any antibiotic treatment for the owner which is followed up at a later date by further inspection of the colony and, more than likely, any other colonies in the apiary and or adjacent apiaries. In both diseases a standstill order is put into effect banning the movement of colonies and equipment into or out of the apiary concerned. The standstill order is operative until such time as it is cancelled by the FBO in writing.

3.5.2 Treatment of AFB.

- The earliest treatment for AFB was first proposed by Schirach but was later re-discovered by McEvoy and has been known as the McEvoy Method (c.1907). It was simply shaking the colony off its comb onto clean foundation in a clean hive. The potentially dangerous honey carried by the bees is consumed in comb building.
- Haseman and Childers (1944) began a new era in the USA when they discovered that sodium sulfathiazole provided protection. This is not approved now as a treatment under the US food and drug legislation.
- Gochnauer (1951) found that oxytetracycline hydrochloride (Terramycin) was also effective in the treatment of the disease and is widely used throughout the world today. Generally, there are three methods of administering the drug namely; dusting in powder form, feeding in syrup form and feeding medicated patties. The dosage per colony is variably quoted between 0.5g to 1.0g of actual oxytetracycline hydrochloride in a gallon of syrup or in a 1lb patty made of 0.66lb granulated sugar and 0.33lb vegetable fat. The drug is not fed within 4 weeks of a honey flow.

It is important to note that these treatments are illegal in the United Kingdom.

3.5.3 Colony destruction for AFB.

a) Colony may only be destroyed after dark when all bees of that colony have returned and stopped flying.
b) Before the evening, seal all openings except the entrance which is reduced to c. 2in (50mm) and put zinc gauze over the feed hole.
c) When the bees have stopped flying, block the entrance securely (eg. clod of earth) and then pour pint petrol into the colony through the feed hole. The bees will be dead in a few minutes. Leave for 10 mins.
d) Dig hole $3 \times 3 \times 3ft^3$ ($1m^3$). This can be done earlier and in a position not too far away to minimise carrying equipment to the burning site at the bottom of the hole.
e) Prepare starter paper + 2/3 combs and frames pyramid fashion.
f) Set alight and burn all hive contents including combs, frames and quilts if these are used.
g) Scrape all boxes, floorboard and crown board free of wax and propolis into the fire.
h) When completely burnt out back fill immediately.
i) Scorch all hive parts with a blow lamp to a coffee brown colour paying particular attention to corners and cracks in the woodwork and to the queen excluder.
j) Disinfect any other appliances eg. smoker, feeder, hive tool, etc. in solution of:
    1lb washing soda,
    $^1/_2$lb bleaching powder,
    1 gallon warm water.

Use while warm and rinse in clean water before drying (note that the solution is caustic – take care).

k) Finally obtain a destruction certificate from the FBO to substantiate your insurance claim on BDI.

3.5.4 Treatment of EFB.

In the United Kingdom treatment of EFB is allowed providing it is approved by the Foul Brood Officer or Bee Disease Officer and administered under his / her supervision. Oxytetracycline hydrochloride is again used and its use is widespread around the world.

It is known that commercial beekeepers in the United Kingdom use the drug illegally and that there has been a certain amount of criticism in recent times of the way MAFF personnel have treated commercial enterprise colonies.

3.5.5 Destruction for EFB.

Destruction is undertaken in exactly the same way as for AFB. Generally, colonies in an advanced stage of the disease which are unlikely to recover are destroyed rather than being given treatment.

3.5.6 Sterilisation of equipment.

Sterilisation of equipment is a nonsensical term and it should be disinfecting of equipment. The equipment will never be sterile which in this sense means free from living germs especially bacteria, etc. Once a piece of equipment has been disinfected it will almost immediately become re-infected but hopefully not with the disease pathogens. This was pointed out to us in a lecture on diseases given by Prof. Len Heath in Devon and emphasises the extent to which we fail to think and blindly copy what has been said before.

In our Intermediate Notes we recommended that equipment should be washed in a solution which contained lb bleaching powder as shown above. We have been asked, 'what is bleaching powder?'. To set the record straight:

Bleaching powder is a crude mixture of calcium hypochlorite [$Ca(ClO)_2$] and calcium chloride [$CaCl_2$] made by reacting chlorine with calcium hydroxide:

$$2Ca(OH)_2 + 2Cl_2 \rightarrow Ca(ClO)_2 + CaCl_2 + 2H_2O.$$

It is used as a bleach and a disinfectant. The original recommendation for its use originated in a MAFF leaflet but the most recent leaflets recommend hot soapy water. For examination purposes either would be accepted as correct.

3.6 A detailed account of the statutory requirements relating to foul brood, Varroosis and the importation of honeybees and their implementation in the UK.

It is important that candidates for the examinations obtain and study 'The Bee Diseases Control Order 1982, S.I.107 (AFB, EFB, Varroasis) obtainable from H.M.Stationary Office.

The section on varroa will be out of date and it is important that the up to date legislation is known for examination purposes. For example, at the time of writing there was a Statutory Infested Area (SIA) extending south of a line approximately between the Bristol Channel and the Humber. The latest position of this line is from Cleveland to Gwent via Manchester. Having said that, varroa has been discovered recently in as far north as Perth and Scottish beekeepers are seeking the prosecution of the offending beekeeper. It should be noted that the legislation makes no reference to the SIA.

It should be further noted that an expert group derived from the World Association for the Advancement of Veterinary Parasitology recommended a standardised system for naming (bee) diseases. The suffix used to denote the parasitic infestation should be 'OSIS and this suffix should be attached to the genus of the proper name for the parasite. Therefore, varroasis now becomes varroosis and pronounced in much the same way as before that is 'varro/osis' but not 'varroo/sis'.

Before leaving the subject note a few of the others! malpighamoeba – malpighamoebosis, ascosphaera apis – ascosphaerosis, nosema – nosemosis and acarine which the EEC wanted to call acariosis now becomes acarapiosis. The Examinations Board have only, so far, succumbed to varroosis.

3.6.1 Statutory Instrument 107 was well drafted and is summarised briefly below:

It deals with 3 diseases namely, AFB, EFB and Varroosis.
If disease is suspected the owner must notify it and must not remove the suspected colony until:

　　a) an authorised person has examined the colony,
　　b) a report is received confirming that disease is not present,
　　c) notice has been served removing prohibition.

The authorised person may:

　　a) take samples of bees, combs, etc.,
　　b) mark any hive or appliance.

If the authorised person suspects disease he shall serve a notice prohibiting removal.
Samples to be sent for analysis with all speed.
A report to be sent to the owner withdrawing prohibition if disease free.
If the report confirms disease or the owner agrees with the authorised person that disease is present and signs a copy of the notice, the Minister may:

For AFB:

　　a) give notice to destroy by fire or treat as specified under supervision.
　　b) notice (standstill order) to remain in force until cancelled.

For EFB:

　　a) give notice to destroy by fire or treat as specified under supervision.
　　b) period of 8 weeks to remain in custody after treatment except by special licence.
　　c) notice to remain in force until cancelled.

For Varroosis:

a) Most of the procedures have been changed and the agreed plan for the first discovery of varroosis went by the board for reasons best known to the ministry. Candidates should study and be aware of the latest procedures.
b) Identifying marks shall not be tampered with.
c) The owner to provide information and assistance reasonably required.
d) No treatment is to be given to prevent detection.
e) The owner must comply in all respects with the notices given.

At the time of writing the legal requirements in connection with varroosis are summarised as follows:

• No bees shall be moved from the SIA to north of the line. Bees may be moved from north of the line into the SIA but not out again.
• Discovery of varroosis shall be reported to MAFF. Note that it is not a statutory requirement to provide a sample.
• The owner may treat varroa infested colonies with Bayvarol (licenced for use in the UK).
• The owner may purchase for his own use other medicaments used in the common market countries.
• Queens may be sent from the SIA to north of the line providing a licence for such movement is obtained from MAFF.

3 6.2 The legal aspects of using Bayvarol.

It has been suggested that there is a legal requirement to record, in a special log book, all treatments using Bayvarol. We have been unable to trace the legislation for this and Bayer have also been unable to quote it despite the suggestion coming from them. However, all responsible beekeepers will have the dosages recorded on their hive record cards.

Similarly, it has been stated that Bayvarol cannot be reused. We consider that it can for testing purposes noting that other diseases can be transmitted from one hive to another. There is no statutory requirements preventing the use in this way.

There is confusion, at the time of writing, about the actual use of the strips making a minimum of 4 mandatory and a statutory requirement. We consider that the confusion will continue until such times as Bayer provide meaningful information on the size of colonies being treated and the reduction in surface density of the medicament on the strips as a function of time. Veterinary medicaments are classified and licenced as follows:

'P' category - for sale through a pharmacy.
'POM' – prescription only medicines (purchased with a prescription written by a doctor or vet)
'PML' – available from licenced agricultural merchants or a pharmacy without a prescription. This was the original licensing of Bayvarol.
'GSL' – general sales list and available from any merchant wishing to sell it. Bayvarol now comes under this category, unfortunately rather belatedly.

For more information on Bayvarol see appendix 9, a copy of an article written for Beekeeping in March 1994.

3.6.3 The importation of bees into the United Kingdom.

- Statutory Instrument SI 792/1980 – Bee Diseases, The Importation of Bees Order came into force on 1st July 1980. It included all bees of the genus Apis and in all stages of their life cycle. It prohibits the importation of bees except under licence. This order revoked The Importation of Bees Orders made in 1978 and 1979 together with all their amendments.
- SI 867/1987 – Bee Diseases amended SI 792/1980 by adding after 'all bees', 'bees pests' meaning any organisms or pathogens which are injurious to bees or any cultures of any such organisms or pathogens.
- SI 3249/1993 – Bee Diseases amended further SI 792/1980 and makes provision for part of Council Directive 92/65/EEC relating to bees. The legal drafting is a bit rambling but in essence states that SI 792/1980 shall not apply to importation of bees of the specific Apis melifera (mellifera spelt incorrectly) from member states. Bees may be imported from EEC states only into areas where Varroasis (not Varroosis which is an EEC preference!) has been confirmed. Any importation shall be in conformity with Article 8 of Council Directive 92/65/EEC.

Honeybees and queens, including attendant workers, may only be imported into any part of the United Kingdom under the terms of a licence issued by MAFF from countries that are known to be free from Varroosis. It is mostly queens that are imported from New Zealand and Australia and it incumbent on the importer to send the worker attendant bees to Luddington for disease analysis. To our knowledge we have not come across package bees with a queen being imported over recent years.

Because the attendant workers of imported queens have to be sent to Luddington, the importer, who is usually selling on to the small beekeeper, has to provide additional workers from colonies in this country. In our opinion, the arrangement is open to abuse and is certainly not well policed.

Queens imported from Australia and New Zealand are in transit for a minimum of 4/5 days and arrive in poor condition. They need very careful handling to re-introduce them back into colonies. A very high percentage have Nosema infected attendant worker bees suggesting a high probability of Nosema infected queens which when successfully introduced to colonies are then the subject of a supersedure.

If queens were imported from Italy, the transit time could be reduced to about 20 hours causing less stress and probably less Nosema incidence. Our discussions with importers met with a reluctance to import from Europe as they considered it would have an adverse effect on their business importing from a country with varroa.

There is a body of opinion that all imports should be banned. However, there is an equal body of opinion in favour of the imports being allowed to continue.

3.6.4 The implementation of the regulations.

All regulations in respect of bees, both for importation and the control of notifiable diseases are vested in the Central Science Laboratory (CSL) an agency of MAFF and formerly coming under the auspices of ADAS. The organisation, set up during 1995, provides 10 Regional Bee Inspectors (RBI) to cover the whole of England and Wales. It is too soon to comment on how well this reorganisation will work and how effective it will be. The declared objectives are that the RBIs shall pass their knowledge on to the beekeeping organisations in their regions so that they become self reliant and the need for RBIs will eventually become unecessary. We believe this to be unrealistic and self policing of statutory regulations can never work satisfactorily.

3.7 A description of the life cycle and natural history of *Varroa destructor* including its development within the honeybee colony and its spread to other colonies;

Note: An all round book that we have come across on varroosis is 'Living with Varroa' edited by Andrew Matheson and published by IBRA. We would regard it as essential reading for this part of the syllabus.

3.7.1 The life cycle of *Varroa destructor* Oudemans and its biology.

The mite was discovered first in Indonesia in 1904 on *Apis cerana* and transferred naturally into *Apis mellifera* colonies taken out to the far East to improve honey production. It has spread to Europe, South America, North America and Africa not by its own means but by man moving whole colonies of bees.

It is necessary to understand clearly what we mean by life cycle because the adult fertile varroa female can live for many months (nb. overwintering when there is little or no brood in the colony) on worker bees. This period is called the phoretic stage (from the Greek phoros = bearer) because the mite is living on the bee which is bearing it. No reproduction is taking place during this period. The mite can only reproduce when either worker or drone brood is present in the colony. It is the life cycle during the active beekeeping season that we are concerned with in this section of the syllabus.

An adult fertile female is reddish brown in colour, oval in shape and measures about 1.1mm x 1.6mm with 8 legs. It prefers young worker bees in preference to older workers during the phoretic period according to Hoppe and Ritter. The kairomones from both worker and drone brood attract the female mites with a marked preference for drone kairomone. The female enters the worker brood cell c. 15 hours before sealing and about 45 hours before sealing in the case of drone brood.

The female mite has to force her way down the cell (the bee larva practically fills the cell at this stage) and then becomes immobile immersed in the larval food at the bottom of the cell with only their peritremes (breathing tubes) exposed. When the cell has been sealed and the larval food consumed by the bee larva, the mite is released and then feeds on the larva (by piercing the thin larval exoskeleton to obtain the haemolymph) and later the propupa.

Egg laying commences about 60 hours (we have seen 72 hours quoted) after the cells are sealed. It is probable that the juvenile hormone in the haemolymph of the larva triggers off the egg laying. The female cannot lay eggs when feeding on the adult bee in the phoretic stage (while the female mite is outside a cell on the exoskeleton of the worker bee).

The first egg to be laid is haploid (7 chromosomes) and develops into a male and all the rest are diploid (14 chromosomes) and develop into females.

After the first egg is laid, egg laying continues at intervals of c. 24 hours. The times quoted by different authors varies and 24 may be taken as an average time.

The period from the time the egg is laid to the time new mites are developed is surprisingly variable according to the literature. We examined 6 sources which gave the following figures:

SOURCE	FEMALE	MALE
1	9	6.5
2	7.75	5.75
3	8.5	6.5
4	6.8	6.1
5	7.5	5.5
6	5.3	3.9
Average	6.3 days	5.7 days
Average	151 hours	137 hours

It will be clear that the times are not very precise and different workers have derived different figures; whether this is due to temperature or other factors is unknown but for our purposes we can use the average figures.

A six legged larva develops in the egg and hatches into an 8 legged protonymph which moults into an 8 legged deutonymph which again moults into the imagine form, the fully developed adult. Again the times for each instar are variable depending on which work is being studied and matters little for our purpose except that there is no definitive answer at this stage.
The population produced from each cell is important and has been verified. Knowing that a worker cell is sealed for 12 days or 288 hours and a drone cell is sealed for 14 days or 336 hours we can calculate the emerging mite population as follows:

Total female mite population from worker cell = $\{(288 - 60 - 24) - 151\} \div 24 = 2.2$
Total female mite population from a drone cell = $\{(336 - 60 - 24) - 151\} \div 24 = 4.2$

Experiments have shown that the average number of eggs in a worker cell is 3 to 4 and the maximum number found in drone cells is 7. The calculated figures above therefore appear to be unrealistic. However, recent work in UK by Dr.S.Martin has confirmed that in the UK the number of viable female mites from worker cells is only 1.45.

It will be clear from the above times that the male always reaches maturity before the females ensuring that the females are mated before leaving the cell on their host.

The male never eats and its modified chelicera are for the transfer of sperm to the female of the species. It therefore dies after mating and never leaves the cell.

The mated females live on the young host bee and in turn enter cells themselves to continue reproducing. The daughter mites spend a longer time on the adult than the mites that have produced offspring. We have not been able to ascertain the summer life with any accuracy; Ritter quotes c. 8 weeks (56 days) and that they are in the phoretic state for 4 to 13 days before entering a brood cell. If an average phoretic time of 9 days is used with 12 days reproducing in the worker cell, then the cycle time is 9 + 12 = 21 days. If the summer life is 56 days then each mated female can reproduce twice producing c. 6 mites if worker cells are used.

The population increase is estimated to be by a factor of 10 per year in the colony in the colder climates of Europe whereas much longer phoretic periods have been recorded in warmer climates. This suggests that the rate of infestation is greater in cooler climates.

If the summer breeding period is from March to August, a period of 6 months or 180 days it is at this stage that the arithmetic starts to go awry unless there is a very high natural mortality of varroa mites. There will be a large loss of mites at the end of the season due to the natural mortality of the bees dying away from the hive but this does not account for the large difference from the mites calculated to be present and the oft quoted factor of increase by one order ($\times 10$).

viz. 1 mite increasing to 10 mites by the end of the year.
180 days 21 days = 8.6 vj breeding cycles (say 8)
With 3 mites / cycle, total mites = 3^8 = 6,561 mites
The mortality has to be c.6,550 for a year end figure of 10!

Perhaps this is why Dr.Martin working at the NBU has been counting mite mortality partially funded by the BBKA with the NBU Fund money. His work has produced very different results from work undertaken on the mainland continent of Europe.

It is known now that there could be different species of vj mite and this could account for differing results in the life histories that have been reported and for the differing figures of infestation rates reported. It is well to remember that there is still a lot be learnt about the biology of the *Varroa jacobsoni*.

3.7.2 Development of the infestation of *Varroa jacobsoni* in a colony.

It is instructive to examine the effects of the parasite on the individual worker bee in the colony:

The number of mites per cell (or per bee) has a marked effect on the haemolymph protein content reducing it by 15 to 50%. Brenda Ball quotes 1 to 3 mites cause a 27% reduction and 4 to 6 mites a 50% reduction.

The protein reduction in turn results in a marked reduction in the final weight of the bee (6 to 25 % weight loss) and a reduction in the longevity of about 34% to 68% of the adult life span.

If 5 or more mites are present then there is a high probability that the bee will be killed. If not there will be marked damage to the wings, legs and abdomen.

Infestation must be at an advanced stage and the visible signs such as crawling bees at the entrance and deformation will only represent a very small fraction of the colony damage.

The morphological changes are small when bees are infested with 1 or 2 mites (eg. 1 to 3% reduction in wing length). This demonstrates the importance of early detection in the management of colonies because it is so difficult to detect any damage.

It takes approximately 3 to 5 years before the colony is weakened, that is, when the mite population = 30 to 40% of the adult bee population. At this stage there will be a rapid decline in the adult bee population with severe brood damage, reminiscent of the signs of EFB. The death of the colony will quickly follow.

If the infestation reaches a level of 1 mite/cell and if treatment is not undertaken the colony will die out in 2 to 4 years. At the terminal stage the collapse is very rapid.

It will be clear that due to the general weakening of the bees and the colony coupled with the reduction in longevity, the normal house bee and nurse bee duties will be seriously disrupted leading to poor colony hygiene and a deterioration in the hive environment.

It is not certain what causes the death of a colony that is heavily invested. Whether it succumbs to viral infections or other causes remains to be proven. However, it has been shown that the mite is a vector for ABPV (Acute Bee Paralysis Virus) and many colonies lost in Germany exhibited the signs of this viral infection.

It is clear from the above that the signs of Varroosis are virtually impossible to detect visually until it is too late and early diagnosis is essential for good bee husbandry.

3.7.3 The spread of Varroosis between colonies.

Like any other bee diseases Varroosis is spread between colonies in an apiary by:

Drifting. This can be minimised by good apiary layout but, in our opinion, can never be entirely eliminated. Most drifting in a well laid out apiary is by very young bees on location flights. Also it is well known that drones are accepted into any colony they choose with little or no challenge from the guard bees.

Robbing. This aspect becomes more important when a varroa infested colony is so weakened that it becomes the target for robbers. All weak colonies will eventually be robbed out by stronger colonies.

Migration. When the colony infestation is very high and the colony weakened it gets to the stage where it cannot defend itself and the bees are said to migrate to nearby colonies or the colony of the robbers.

Swarming. A swarm from a varroa infested stock will always carry the mites with it. Swarms cluster and form their own micro-climate outside the environment of the hive and thereby provide a very adequate protection for the phoretic mites. This ensures the survival of the mites over a wide range of climatic zones that the honeybee has inhabited over the millions of years of its evolution.

The transfer of bees from one colony to another by the beekeeper undertaking manipulative bee management methods and techniques.

On a wider scale the spread of varroosis is by:

• Swarming from apiaries and from feral colonies that are not taken or collected and allowed to find their own nest sites. The natural spread by this means is about 3 to 5 km per year. It is to be noted that some of the strains of *Apis mellifera* found in Africa (eg. scutellata), which exhibit hunger swarming traits, will travel much further, even up to 100 km.

• The beekeeper moving colonies for various reasons such as migratory beekeeping, pollination contracts or the sale of bees from one part of the country to another. This unnatural spread is far greater than the natural spread by swarming.

It has been stated many times, and shown to be true, that once varroa is found in a country it is impossible to prevent its spread throughout the whole of that country. It is impossible to prevent it crossing borders between adjacent countries and the spread in Europe is witness to this fact.

We have a prime example of the futility of MAFF policy by attempting to stop the spread of varroosis from south of the line (Severn to Humber) to north of the line by restricting movement of colonies and the massive expense of additional bees officers searching for varroa beyond the line. There would, in our opinion, be better ways of spending the money assisting beekeepers to live with varroosis.

3.8 A detailed account of the signs of Varroosis describing methods of detection and ways of monitoring the presence of the Varroa mite in honeybee colonies.

3.8.1 An outline account of the signs of Varroosis.
Varroosis is the disease caused by *Varroa jacobsoni*, (a mite of the class Arachnida)

Varroosis not only affects the sealed brood where it breeds but it also lives on the adult bee and feeds on its haemolymph at the intersegmental membranes usually on the ventral side. Therefore, it can be classed as both a brood disease and an adult bee disease.

Signs:

It is unlikely that any sign of Varroosis will be apparent until the colony has been infected for about 3 years. The first indications are likely to be a general weakening of the colony.

It is very unlikely that the mites will be seen on the adult bees as they generally inhabit the intersegmental membrane area on the ventral side of the abdomen. The most positive sign is by knock down test using Bayvarol and collecting the knocked down mites on a paper insert below a varroa screen.

As the *V.jacobsoni* breeds in the sealed brood cell (drone preferred) these also cannot be seen except by opening the cells and conducting a systematic search.

At an advanced stage of infestation (say 2 years +), when the infestation has become heavy, underweight workers will be produced due to malnutrition and then deformed worker bees are likely to appear in the colony. Such bees may have stunted bodies and / or deformed bodies, wings and legs. There are some good colour photographs in the MAFF 1992 pamphlet (PB 0925 on the back page) of these deformities. There are likely to be 3 or more mites per cell at this stage and there will also be signs of neglected brood and the spread of secondary infections.

It has been shown in Germany but not in UK that *Varroa jacobsoni* is a vector for Acute Bee Paralysis Virus and it is likely that signs of ABPV may be seen before other signs of *V.jacobsoni* infestation (see section 3.15.1).

When the colony is at an advanced stage of infestation there is every likelihood that it will collapse suddenly and die out most probably at the end of the summer. The mechanism may be that as the queen reduces her laying after the main flow there are less brood cells for the female mite to enter and more than one mite per cell results. With multiple females occupying one worker cell deformed bees are inevitable leading to rapid colony collapse. This emphasises the importance of detecting the mite at an early stage of infestation in order that the colony may be saved in time.

If the beekeeper detects an infestation he is obliged by law to report the situation to MAFF despite the futility of the exercise. Had MAFF decreed that Varroosis found outside the statutory infested area (SIA) had to be reported, then this would have made some sense.

It is incumbent on every beekeeper to make a regular search every year for this scourge and treat it accordingly.

3.8.2 Methods of detecting Varroosis.

There are now a wide number of methods for detecting *Varroa jacobsoni* infested colonies; these are:

Examination of hive debris on the floorboard in early spring. This method has been advocated by the NBU for some years and at the time of writing they will still undertake the examination free of charge. The method has its limitations and is not wholly reliable particularly when the infestation in the colony is light. The debris from all the floorboards in an apiary is collected and bundled together and sent to the NBU with the name and address of the beekeeper and his apiary. After examination the NBU send back a report stating the results. If the sample comes back with a negative result and a light infestation has been missed it will be of little consequence on colony performance during the coming season. The method must be quite attractive to many beekeepers until such times as it is discontinued or until the apiary concerned has been diagnosed positive.

Uncapping brood, particularly drone brood with an uncapping fork during regular colony inspections. Care must be taken when examining the larvae for reddish coloured mites; in the early stages of development the nymphs are virtually colourless and translucent. Special frames of drone foundation can be inserted in the brood chamber for this purpose. Note that this is also a manipulative method of varroa control without chemicals.

Bayvarol test using a varroa screen with paper insert below together with one strip of Bayvarol manufactured by Bayer. Bayvarol is the only medicament approved for use in the UK at the time of writing. Each strip contains 3.5mg of flumethrin and should be left in the colony for 24 to 48 hours. The strip and insert are then removed and the insert examined with a magnifying glass for dead mites. The Bayvarol strip is inserted between the centre frames of the cluster and can be introduced without moving the frames and disturbing the colony. It is the most effective detection method available at the present time. The strip can be re-used to test other colonies in the same apiary noting that other diseases can be transferred from one colony to another on the same strip. When Bayvarol is used for treatment the strips are left in the colony for 5 to 6 weeks, ie. the strips have a working life, according to Bayer, of 6 weeks using 4 strips in an average sized colony. For testing purposes it would be prudent to use the single testing strip in the colonies for say no longer than 21 to 30 days of actual use before it is scrapped thus ensuring a reasonable surface density of flumethrin to knock down any mites that may be present.

Apistan test. These strips which are virtually identical to Bayvarol strips contain another synthetic pyrethroid called fluvalinate and are obtainable in the common market countries. They are cheaper than Bayvarol. It is permissible to use them for testing and treatment provided they are purchased for one's own use; another bit of bureaucratic nonsense, in our opinion.

Tobacco smoke test. We will not describe this test here as so much has been written on tobacco smoke that it may be assumed the method is well known. Compared with the use of a Bayvarol or Apistan strip it must be regarded as a 'stone age' method of testing. We have tried it many times and would not now recommend it. It comatoses a very thick layer of bees on top of the varroa screen at the bottom of the hive which must put the colony under stress. We have tried varying the tobacco quantities and the types of tobacco but the result is the same. There are reports from Germany that the beekeepers there are abandoning the method because of loss of queens; it is not clear how the queens are lost but the most likely mechanism would be that the queen becomes comatosed and then she is balled before she recovers. We now know that tobacco smoke can stun some of the varroa mites as opposed to killing them. They subsequently recover and walk off the paper insert and back into the cluster unless the insert is greased with Vaseline or some other form grease.

Testing a couple of frames taken from a colony during a routine colony inspection, putting them into a nucleus box and smoke testing it. This is a method suggested by DARG but, in our opinion, is not a very practical approach to the problem of detection. For the beekeeper with only one or two stocks, each complete colony could be quickly tested and for the beekeeper with 2 or 3 apiaries time will not normally permit such tinkering during routine inspections.

The use of specially designed floorboards and combined varroa screens and continually counting the number of dead mites appearing on the insert. This really is a monitoring method to know when treatment should be undertaken, whether treatment has been successful, or whether re-infestation has occurred, rather than a detection method. It is a management method and widely used in Germany. The combined floorboards / varroa screens are quite expensive and are not likely to be popular with beekeepers unless they make them themselves. The method relies on the natural mortality of the mites. Using this method German beekeepers use the following data:

> 1 dead mite is equivalent to 120 mites in the colony in summer and 500 mites in autumn or spring. The average mites / day figure is calculated for the whole apiary from say a minimum of 5 hives. The critical infestation point is taken as 10 mites / day giving between 1200 and 5000 mites in the colony. Treatment must be undertaken at this point

otherwise tens of thousands of mites may be expected the following year with colony collapse soon to follow.

Detection with Folbex VA. These fumigation strips containing bromopropylate were specially designed for the treatment of varroa and acarine. They are not generally available now in the UK (said to be carcinogenic) but can still be regarded as an effective detection method. Available from France.

Detection of varroa in swarms is an important aspect of practical beekeeping. Since any mites will be on the bees (no brood), then if they are detected the swarm can be treated accordingly. A simple straightforward method is to shake about half a cupful of bees into a jam jar of petrol. The contents are then coarse filtered to take out the bees and then fine filtered through filter paper to reveal any mites if the swarm is infested.

If a colony is infested and it is to be treated with Bayvarol, the treatment will take 6 weeks and this should be done when the colony has no honey supers above its brood chamber. Working back 6 weeks from April means spring treatment for varroosis should start in about mid February in the south of England. We do not think that this point concerning the early start has been fully appreciated by many beekeepers.

All detection is dependent on being able to recognise a *Varroa destructor* mite and not to confuse it with a *Braula coeca* (bee louse). The physical differences are as follows:

> *Braula coeca*: ellipse shaped c.1 - 2mm with 6 legs, coloured reddish brown. It is a wingless fly. Initially it is white and takes about 12 hours to turn colour after hatching. The head and posterior end of its abdomen are on the ends of the major axis of the ellipse, the legs are on the sides associated with the ends of the minor axis of the ellipse looking down on the dorsal side. Easily seen by eye riding on worker bees and very often the queen is infested. Causes no harm to queen or bees but the larvae spoil capped honey comb with fine tunnels in the cappings.

> *Varroa destructor*: also ellipse shaped c. 1.1 - 1.7mm. with 8 legs, coloured reddish brown the same as the Braula coeca. The legs are on the ventral side and cannot be seen when it is viewed looking down on the dorsal side. It travels 'blunt end first' its legs being on the sides associated with the ends of the major axis. It is an arachnida and is in the spider class in the animal kingdom not the insect class. These mites are difficult to detect as they feed on the haemolymph by piercing the membrane between the addominal segments on the adult bee and breed in the capped brood cells.

Reference should be made to MAFF pamphlet 936 published 1985 (Varroasis of bees -tobacco smoke detection). The leaflet advises testing in October each year and sending the debris to Luddington for analysis. There is no charge for this 'Varroa service'. Additionally, pamphlet P834 revised 1989 (Varroasis - A parasitic disease of honeybees) is also worthy of reference. These two leaflets are the fore runners of the latest leaflet produced by the NBU after varroa was found in UK and as a result of their own detection efforts mainly in Devon at that time. All BBKA members were supplied with it and presumably it is available free of charge to all other beekeepers. It is called: 'Varroasis disease of honeybees – diagnosis and control.' It has no number on the front but the back has 1992 PB 0925. Please see the new leaflet 'Varroosis – a parasitic infestation of honeybees', identified by 1996 PB 2581 on the back cover. This is obtainable from NBU, Sand Hutton, York YO4 1YW (from October, 1996).

The question that has not been addressed fully in the MAFF pamphlets is when should detection of varroosis be undertaken? Until varroosis is detected in an apiary, we believe that detection should be a minimum of twice a year. Once very early at the end of winter / beginning of spring and later at the end of the main honey flow when supers have been removed. If the specially designed floorboards / varroa screens are being used the search can be continuous throughout the season looking for dead mites that have died from natural causes. Our own experience with 3 apiaries within a few miles of each other revealed negative results when sample tested with Bayvarol in the Spring but all were positive when tested the same way in autumn of the same year.

For beekeepers with large numbers of colonies and more than one apiary sample testing (say one hive in three in an apiary) would be satisfactory.

It should be pointed out that, at this stage, there is no preferred method of detection. Our own opinion in this matter is that testing with a Bayvarol strip for 24 hours is the most reliable at present.

3.8.3 Monitoring the presence of the mite in colonies.

Once the mite has been detected in the colonies of an apiary, any monitoring process must involve counting dead mites that have died a natural death or counting the mites killed by knock down tests at regular intervals. If mites have been detected in one colony in an apiary, then it is safe to assume that all colonies in that apiary are infested or will be very shortly even if tests on these other colonies prove negative in the initial stages.

To monitor dead mites it is necessary to have a special floorboard with an integral varroa screen (which are unpopular because of their high cost) or resort to a DIY job with the existing floorboard turned through 180° with a screen above.

The frequency of each monitoring session must be decided and the more often the better for the best results. Whether this is once a week or once a month must rest with the beekeeper and the amount of time that he can devote to the monitoring as part of his management system. Once the number of colonies rises say above five the work of monitoring will quickly become very time consuming and tedious.

It is not much use counting mites as a continual monitoring process unless action is taken if the levels rise above a predetermined threshold. For management purposes it is not clear what this level should be. It should also be noted that if the colony has had supers added then it would be unwise to treat until they are removed which is likely to be at the end of the season. The question must therefore be asked whether there is any purpose in monitoring on a continuous basis throughout the season?

We are of the opinion that any monitoring should be regarded, at present, as experimental in order to determine possible management methods for the future. The equipment required to provide continuous monitoring demands screens that do not corrode and made of a material that cannot be damaged by the bees themselves.

There has been, as far as we are aware, no recommendations for preferred monitoring methods nor any objectives defined for undertaking it on a long term basis. We would have thought that some guidance from the NBU on this point would have been desirable.

It is highly unlikely that bee farmers with commercial enterprises will have sufficient time or effort available to undertake monitoring programmes; the economics of running such businesses would preclude it. Most of the hobbyist beekeepers are unlikely to be interested also. Thus any monitoring is likely to be left to the informed hobbyist beekeeper who has an interest in this new disease. Thus the majority of beekeepers in the UK will require control methods to be applied annually or bi-annually that are simple to use and relatively cheap.

3.9 A detailed account of methods of treatment and control of Varroosis and a knowledge of which are currently available in the U.K.

3.9.1 Methods of control.

Restricting hive or colony movements is not an option for the control of varroosis, normal beekeeping activities must continue, including migratory beekeeping and pollination. Thus control means managing colonies knowing that varroosis is present and that the infestations are endemic and not epidemic. It will always be with us and control will embrace treatment for the infestations.

The control of varroosis must heed the legal requirements, the level of infestation, the methods of control used by neighbouring beekeepers, the time of the year and the capabilities of the beekeeper. We include the latter because while those beekeepers studying for their senior examinations are likely to have the skills required, there will still remain the majority of beekeepers without the necessary expertise.

Control can involve the use of the following methods:

Soft chemicals
Hard chemicals
Biotechnical methods
A combination of any of the previous methods.

Each are examined in the following sub-sections noting, however, that, at the time of writing, only one medicament is licenced for use in the UK even though varroosis was discovered in Devon on 4th April 1992.

3.9.1.1 Soft chemicals.

Formic acid. This is introduced into the colonies and the fumes kill the mites as the acid evaporates. The temperature has to be greater than 12°C for the acid to evaporate at a reasonable rate and the treatment to be effective. 60% formic acid is used and the dosage is 20ml per colony based on 2ml/comb. The colony should be treated 2 or 3 times at intervals of 3 or 4 days presumably depending on temperature. The acid is normally applied on absorbent boards (Kraemer boards in Germany) hung in the colony. Personal protection is necessary when using and preparing the medicament. It is said to cause great excitement and good ventilation is required in the colony. It may kill sealed brood and queen balling (c.5%) has been reported. The efficacy of the treatment has been questioned in relation to the hive material presumably because some of the fumes may be absorbed. It is highly corrosive and will affect ferrous hive fastenings. As far as we are aware, the only reports of use are from Germany.

Lactic acid. Either of the two optical isomers of the acid at a strength of 15% concentration is satisfactory. It is sprayed onto the bees at the rate of 5 to 10ml per comb side which is well covered with bees. Two treatments are said to be required at 1 or 2 day intervals. As it is a contact medicament it is not effective in sealed brood and should therefore be used when the colony is broodless. The temperature should not be below 5° C and it is recommended as a late winter treatment with minimum brood. It is suggested that it is used for swarms and artificial swarms. Efficiency said to be about 90%. For the beekeeper with a large number of colonies it is very labour intensive.

Essential oils. A mixture of natural oils has been made up into pellets using a vermiculite 'carrier' by an Italian manufacturer, Chemicals LAIF. The contents of the pellets are as follows:

74.1% thymol
16.0% eucalyptol
3.7% menthol
3.7% camphor
2.5% vermiculite (carrier)

The pellets (not known how many) are placed on the top of the brood combs and left for 65 days. The efficiency is stated to be 96.4 to 99%, of a similar magnitude to Apistan. They are sold in France under the name of **Apilife VAR** and thus can be purchased for one's own personal use in the UK thus providing an alternative treatment to Bayvarol. As the treatment takes about 2 months, the only feasible time for treatment will be in the autumn after the crop has been removed and the colony prepared for winter.

Dr. Ritter in Germany has also done some work on essential oils and has tested 54 types of oil against the mite and the bees. He found the two best ones were oil of cloves (60% kill rate) and oil of wintergreen (99% kill rate). They were used in aerosol form with 20% oil the highest that could be used before killing the bees.

Oil of wintergreen is, of course, methyl salicylate. This aromatic volatile oil comes from the leaves of the plant wintergreen (*Gaultheria procumbens*) of the family Ericaceae and not from the wintergreen plants in the family *Pyrolaceae*. The leaves contain salicylic acid. This herb has long been used as a medicament for various human ailments. Methyl salicytate is an old medicament used for the treatment of acarine. The information about its use for varroosis is limited but it is well known that it is likely to induce robbing. The high kill rates suggest to us that more attention should be given to this form of treatment (by the NBU?). The chemical 'giants' will not be interested because there will be little profit motive from their point of view.

Powders. It has been suggested that inert powders such as icing sugar, talc, etc. could be used to adhere to the sticky pads on the feet of the mites thus making it incapable of remaining on its host. However, there is little evidence to support the efficacy of powders at the time of writing.

3.9.1.2 Hard chemicals.

Bayvarol. This is the only treatment licenced for use in the UK at the time of writing. All medicines are normally licenced 'P' category (ie. for sale through a pharmacy). The 'P' category is broken down further into 'POM' (ie. only available on prescription from a veterinarian, doctor or dentist) and 'PML' (available from pharmacy and merchants list) which can be sold through licenced agricultural merchants (as was the case of Bayvarol). It is now licenced 'GSL' (general sales list) and can be sold anywhere.

The active medicament is flumethrin ($C_{28}H_{22}CL_2FNO_3$), a synthetic pyrethroid, contained in a polythene strip. The manufacturing process involves coating very tiny beads of polythene with flumethrin and then moulding them into a strip. No plasticisers are used in the moulding process consequently there is no migration of the active material from the inside to the outer surface as the surface flumethrin is used up by contact with the bees. The initial surface (and strip) density of flumethrin is 500μg per gram and each strip contains 3.5mg of flumethrin when new.

The treatment involves a dosage of 4 strips per colony (total 14mg) for a period of 6 weeks. We consider that the best time to treat is in the late summer / autumn when all the supers have been removed from the hives to minimise residues in honey and wax in the supers.

Bayer will not reveal the surface density of the strips after or during use. The surface density drops during use and the only information available is that the efficacy using strips with a density of 250μg/g is much reduced.

Using graphs supplied by Bayer showing the percentage mortality against flumethrin concentrations, the following figures are obtained:

Environmental concentration (%)		Percentage mortality
Mites	10^{-12}	10%
	10^{-11}	40%
	10^{-9}	65%
	10^{-7}	100%
	$>10^{-7}$	100%
Bees	10^{-6}	0%
	10^{-4}	10%
	10^{-3}	90%
	10^{-2}	100%
	$>10^{-2}$	100%

It would be instructive for the reader to draw two graphs (one mites and one bees on the same sheet) using the above data with percentage concentration as the abscissa. It will then be clear that at very low concentrations only a small percentage of mites are killed. Bees start to be killed at much higher concentrations and the bee safety margin is c.10 (ie. between 10^{-7}% and 10^{-6}%; Bayer quote c.100,000 on their graph). If the data is accurate, the environmental concentration for the new strips must be between 10^{-7}% and 10^{-6}% in order to have a maximum mite kill and minimum bee kill. It demonstrates the problem of using medicaments strong enough to kill the mites but not the bees. At low levels of concentration with a low mite kill there are a large number which can breed a resistance to the medicament and demonstrates the necessity of not re-using strips having a low concentration for longer periods. It is a great pity that Bayer are not prepared to provide more meaningful information on the strip densities during and after use. They state that it would be a breach of commercial confidence to do so.

Flumethrin is a nerve poison. It is believed to enter the mite by absorption through the soft pads at the ends of its legs. The toxin acts on the pre-synaptic sodium and potassium channels in the nerve, increasing the number of action potential impulses in the insect nerve leading to a lack of co-ordination, loss of normal bodily functions and death presumably by starvation.

The expiry date on the packages is worthy of comment. The strips are degraded by the action of micro-organisms, ultra violet light and by oxidisation hence the packaging adopted by Bayer. There is an adequate margin of safety on the expiry date and Bayer state that it is highly likely that a much longer shelf life may be expected in 1994 and thereafter. Sensible storage in a cool dark place un-opened would give another year's shelf life from the one stated on the packet.

We have discussed the use of having to wear gloves when using this product as the Bayer film about varroa shows the operator wearing industrial heavy duty gloves. It has been considered by the registration authorities and it is not necessary to wear them due to the low levels of flumethrin on the strips, the low dermal absorption and its overall low toxicity. However, hands should be washed after handling the strips before eating. Additionally, there are people who have pyrethroid allergies and they will of course have to handle the strips with great care.

Bayer have indicated in an article in the magazine 'Beekeeping' that 'there is a requirement for people using the product to record the batch number, expiry date, date of insertion and removal from the hive and any withdrawal period to be observed'. We have followed this up with Bayer who now agree with us that there is no statutory obligation to record such details. However, the diligent beekeeper should have the dates of treatment on the hive record cards for management purposes.

Similarly, in the same article it was stated that 'it is illegal to re-use the strips for treatment and illegal to leave the strips in the hive for more than 6 weeks'. We found this curious when there is no warning on the packet. Bayer contend that the product must be used in accordance with the terms of their Product Licence under the terms of the EC Regulations 2377/90 the so called MRL (maximum residue limit) regulation which imposes a legal requirement on both the 'prescriber' and 'user' to avoid residues in food. In this case there is no prescriber making out a prescription for the medicine (nb. 'POM' – prescription only medicine – category). It is at this point one is led into the Medicines Act 1968 which does not help and then the Food Safety Act 1990 which defines the animals concerned, the substances concerned and the acceptable levels. Hymenoptera is not there and neither is flumethrin! We believe that if there are statutory obligations on the part of the 'user' then they should be included in the instructions on the packet. Finally on this point the strips can be re-used for testing purposes noting of course that other disease pathogens can be transferred from hive to hive in the process. The whole area and the legislation appears to have got into a muddle probably by 'growing like little Topsy' and it is certainly not clear cut to us or apparently to Bayer.

The last point to consider is the question of residues in honey and in wax. We have not been able to determine any specific figures for Bayvarol but we understand that they are very similar to those for Apistan which were measured in France.

We have gone into more detail on Bayvarol than is required for this module examination as it is a new treatment and the only one licenced at present in the UK.

Apistan. Manufactured by Zoecon Corp.,USA. This medicament is probably the most widely used treatment for varroosis at the time of writing. It is virtually identical to Bayvarol as it comes in polythene strips (lanieres) which weigh 8g and contain fluvalinate ($C_{26}H_{22}N_2O_3CF_3$)

another synthetic pyrethroid. The amount of toxin per strip = 800mg (cf.3.5mg of flumethrin in Bayvarol) and only two strips per hive are required for treatment (ie. a total of 1600mg of fluvalinate per hive based on a 10 frame Dadant). The strips are inserted between frames 3 / 4 and 7 / 8. The treatment time is 6 weeks and the strips must be removed before 8 weeks. The instructions advise treatment once per year in the spring for best results. It is not fully understood why spring treatment is best but it does mean an early start for the insertion of the strips if they are to remain in the hive when there are no supers on. We believe that autumn treatment is the best in our climatic conditions.

This medicament can be used in UK if purchased in a common market country for one's own use. However it is not allowed to be sold in this country. The law is said to be an ass! It is considerably cheaper than Bayvarol and it is likely that many beekeepers will be using it in this country before long. The cost of Apistan for treating 5 hives = c.£16 (cf. Bayvarol = £20+). It should be noted that 'bringing it over for a friend' is also technically illegal according to the Veterinary Medicines Directorate who are instrumental in the approval of medicines for use in the animal world of the UK.

Residue measurements, some time ago and made in France, gave the following results using gas chromatography and mass spectrometer techniques:

    1.9mg / kg (1.9 parts per million) for beeswax
    0.003mg / kg (3 parts per 1000 million) for honey

The same comments are applicable to allergies and gloves as apply to Bayvarol. We have no information on the surface densities at the start and finish of the treatment or on the environmental concentrations for mite kill. However, we have heard that it possible to re-use these strips more than once with good results but until we can obtain some reliable data we cannot make any recommendations. If fluvalinate and flumethrin are equally toxic to the mite then a certain amount of re-use seems possible. Care would have to be taken on storage to prevent deterioration.

Perizin (coumophos). Manufactured by Bayer. This is a systemic organophosphate and is the basis of nerve gas used in chemical warfare weapons. It again disrupts the normal working of the nerve synapse in the same way as Bayvarol and Apistan. This treatment is popular in Germany where the registered beekeepers purchase it at a subsidised price in 10ml bottles (100% concentration). The treatment was developed by Dr. Ritter in Germany.

The dosage is 50ml per hive using a 2% solution (1ml coumophos to 49ml water). Each 50ml dose contains 32mg of coumophos. It is dribbled between the combs in the seams of bees. A second treatment 7 days later is recommended. It is a winter treatment (October / November) when the temperature is greater than 5°C.

Residue measurements are as follows:

    0.26mg / kg (26 parts per 100 million) in honey
    12.65mg / kg (12.65 parts per million) in beeswax

Klartan (fluvalinate). This is an agricultural formulation which has been used in France by impregnating cardboard or wooden strips in the solution. Such methods are uncontrolled and should not be used. It has been suggested that it is used in a spray at a strength of about

1.0mg / kg. We have virtually no information about its use in Europe. It is the same toxin as used in Apistan.

Folbex VA. Manufactured by Ciba-Geigy. Each strip contains about 400mg of bromopropylate and is used as a fumigant. Treatment for varroa was recommended as 1 strip 4 times at 4 day intervals undertaken during the evening when the bees have finished flying. It is still manufactured and available in France; not very efficient at 89% and leaves high residues in beeswax = 50 to 100mg / kg (50 to 100 parts per million).

Apitol (cymiazol-hydro-chloride). Manufactured by Ciba-Geigy. It comes in granular form and a solution is made with 2 gms of granules in 100ml of water (ie. 50% solution) to prepare one dose. Two doses are given at an interval of 7 days by dribbling the solution between the frames when the temperature is greater than 10° C. It is widely used throughout Europe.

Amitraz. Marketed as Antivarroa-Schering and manufactured by Schering. The form of application is by aerosol steam. A gas mask is required to effect the treatment. We have virtually no information on this treatment which is regarded as somewhat out dated. It was sprayed at the entrance to the hive.

A more recent development using Amitraz is manufactured in France and sold as **Apivar**. Rigid plastic strips containing Amitraz allow the active ingredient to diffuse through the plastic to the surface (quite unlike Apistan or Bayvarol). Each strip contains 500mg of Amitraz. The method is safe and clean to use and can be used in UK if the medicament is purchased on the continent for one's own use at home thereby providing another treatment if mites become resistant to other treatments.

3.9.1.3 Biotechnical control methods.

There are a variety of methods that have been devised the main ones of interest are listed below:

>   Removal of sealed drone comb.
>   Comb trapping techniques.
>   Varroa tolerant colonies.

Removal of sealed drone comb. This must be the most popular method and used by most beekeepers as it is simple, quick and fits in well with the routine colony inspections. A frame of drone comb is put into the brood nest usually around April time, when the queen is laying well, and removed when the brood is sealed. A further comb is put in and the operation repeated. It relies on the preference of the mite to breed in drone brood.

There are two ways of dealing with the drone comb complete with drone larvae or pupae plus mites. One way is to decap and hang it up for the blue tits to clean out. We do not regard this as a good idea as other bees can be attracted to it and re-infestation is possible unless the comb has been in the freezer to kill both larvae and mites. The other way is to uncap and hose the larvae and mites from the cells with a jet of water.

Instead of a special brood frame containing drone comb a super frame can be put into the middle of the brood nest and the bees will build drone comb on the bottom of the frame. When sealed with brood it can be sliced off and replaced to start the process all over again.

Comb trapping techniques. A special brood frame trap is used for this method whereby the queen is put into the trap on an empty comb. The trap is taken out 9 days later when the frame is full of sealed brood. A new frame with the queen is again placed in the trap and put back in the hive. The frame from the trap can be left in the hive until day 18 or removed. At day 9 a check must be made for queen cells in the rest of the colony. At day 18 the process is repeated and a third frame put in. No need to check for queen cells at this inspection as there will be no larvae to build them on. At day 27 remove the third frame and release the queen. It is advisable to check the brood activity at the next routine inspection (day 36).

We believe this control method to be extremely drastic and must have a stressful effect on the colony ending up in a broodless condition. It could be used on a colony with a very heavy summer infestation with unsealed honey where chemical treatment would be unacceptable.

For the hobbyist beekeeper with a lot of hives and the commercial beekeeper we do not think this method is an option. Similarly, we do not think it is one for a novice beekeeper.

Putting some numbers to the method and using a BS frame which contains c.5,000 worker cells or 3,000 drone cells. Three lots of brood are destroyed, ie. 15,000 worker bees or 9,000 drones. However, this is not the true wastage. If the laying rate of the queen is a modest 1,000 eggs per day the wastage is 27,000 workers and we believe that this must have an adverse effect on honey production. The method has been tried on the continent of Europe where claims are made that honey production is unaffected. This must be accounted for by the different weather and flow conditions compared with those in UK. Overall the method does not seem to have much going for it unless the beekeeper has very strong views about the use of chemicals.

Heat treatment of complete colonies is being used in Russia and Japan but the temperature of 45°C required to kill the mites badly stresses the bees. The method has not found favour in Europe or in USA at the time of writing.

Varroa tolerant colonies. It is now well known that some races of bee are more tolerant than others. For example, *Apis mellifera capensis* due to its grooming habits and *Apis mellifera scutellata* with its slightly shorter brood cycle are both more tolerant than *Apis mellifera mellifera*. It is also known that the strains within races have differing degrees of tolerance. Research is being conducted mainly in Germany (and also Bro.Adam before his retirement) on breeding programmes which will be long term projects before meaningful results are available. The argument put forward by Prof. Pickard that it would be wrong to destroy feral colonies but allow them to evolve naturally must carry some weight; ie. those with any tolerance will survive, those that haven't will perish naturally.

When varroa struck in Tunisia in 1979 80% of the country's colonies were killed by the mite. The remaining 20% are varroa resistant in a curious way. Investigation has shown that bees in these colonies uncap infested cells and the varroa mite then leaves the cell which is then resealed by the workers. Further work with these bees showed that they were unsuited to European conditions because their brood cycle did not coincide with the available forage. It is also well known as a very aggressive bee.

3.9.1.4 Combined methods. It will be necessary to combine the various methods of control that we have available in order to ensure that mites resistant to a particular medicament are not allowed to evolve. This is an area where there are few facts available. We have seen various figures quoted for various medicaments ranging from 3 to 7 years for resistant mites to evolve but with no qualification about the environmental concentrations.

An example of combining the two methods could be to remove the combs from a comb trapping method and put the sealed brood into a special colony which itself is treated separately with a particular medicament.

It seems sensible to vary the methods of control from year to year but no doubt as our expertise increases preferred methods will evolve. At the time of writing there is no preferred approach and we are all very much on a learning curve.

3.9.2 Other points of interest.

Other varroa mites. It is interesting to note that there are two other mites of different species coming from the Eastern bees namely:

Varroa underwoodi in *A. cerana* found in Nepal and South Korea which closely resembles *V. jacobsoni*. Little is known about its distribution and its biology.

Euvarroa sinhai in *A. florea* found in Thailand and in Sri Lanka. Again knowledge is limited but it is known that the biology is similar to the *V. jacobsoni* and it enters drone cells only.

Special comb. This comb, made of plastic, has cell sides that are not parallel. They are wider at the bottom than the top. In order to make the comb, two sheets are sealed together with a central septum between. The number of cells per comb is 30 to 40% less than a normal comb. As the cells are larger at the base more brood food is supplied by the nurse bees and the larva develops more quickly due to the excess in diet. The result is that the cells are sealed for about 24 hours less before emergence and therefore there are less fertile female varroa mites produced. We have not heard of any long term results of this method.

Kairomone research. The pheromones of drone brood are being studied in France with the objective of providing artificial lures to attract the mites and then kill them off. At the time of writing we have no up to date results of this work. See appendix 10 for explanation of kairomones and pheromones.

Maximum breeding cycles. Experiments have been conducted to determine the maximum number of breeding cycles the mite is capable of completing in its lifetime. By repeatedly introducing the same mite into cells ready for sealing it has been found that on average 7 cycles can be completed which is equivalent to c. 30 eggs laid.

National control efforts. Each country faced with varroa seems to adopt different policies to control the spread and re-infestation.

In Czechoslovakia where all beekeepers are registered there is a determined effort to destroy all feral colonies. To this end beekeepers are subsidised to kill them with paraquat which in the process kills some of the apiary colonies which rob the culled feral nests. The beekeepers are then subsidised for the loss of the apiary colonies.

In Germany, again where all beekeepers are registered, treatment is undertaken on an area basis to prevent re-infestation; something which is very unlikely to happen in the UK.

Here in UK we have tried to control the spread by standstill orders from the statutory infected areas to the non-infested area, something every other country has failed to do. There is strong evidence that the other countries were right.

Infestation levels. It has been found that the phoretic period of the mite is shorter in colder climates than in warmer climates. Therefore this makes the varroa population grow faster and infestation levels have been found to be as much as 10 times greater in the cold temperate climates compared with the much warmer tropics and sub-tropics.

3.10 A detailed account of the cause, signs and recommended treatment (if any) of the following brood diseases and conditions:—

Chalk brood, Sacbrood, Chilled brood, Bald brood, Neglected drone brood and Stone brood;

Reference should be made to the following MAFF leaflets:

Honeybee brood diseases and disorders Leaflet 561 (Amended 1980)
Common brood diseases of the honeybee Leaflet P3069 (1987)

The first one is out of print and a copy will have to be borrowed from a library and P3069, the latest issue, omits addled brood, stone brood and neglected drone brood which is a pity.

3.10.1 Chalk brood. Known as *Ascosphaera apis* but was originally known as *Pericystis apis*. Most, if not all, of the recent work on chalk brood has been undertaken at Plymouth University under the guidance of Prof.L.Heath.

Causes.

- The presence of spores on nurse bees, combs and hive parts of an infected hive.
- The spores alone are insufficient to cause the disease.
- It is a stress disease (nb. temperature, CO_2 and protein).
- Temperature drop from the normal brood nest T = 35°C to 30°C is sufficient for spore germination.
- Spores form in spherical aggregates within dark brown-green spore cysts known as the fruiting bodies which are about 60μm in diameter. The spherical aggregates which contain the spores are c. 12μm in diameter and the actual spores are bacterial size 1.9 to 3.2μm.
- Spore cysts are produced by a sexual process and can only be formed if 2 complementary strains are present (+ and − not male and female) which cannot be identified apart until reproduction starts. Both strains are white but where the mycelium touch a black fruiting body will form.
- Spores are sticky and found all around the hive, on the combs and on the bees. Spores are fed to the young larvae by the nurse bees. These spores germinate given the right stress conditions. The larva dies after the cell has been capped. The fungus grows throughout the larva and the remains are hard and chalky filling the complete cell.
- The cells are uncapped and many of the mummies are removed by the house bees.

Signs:

- Larvae die after the cell is capped.
- Occasional cell infected or large areas of brood.
- Cappings removed by the bees.
- Larvae become chalky white, fluffy and swell to fill the hexagonal cells.
- Larvae then shrink and harden.
- When infected with two strains of fungus, the colour becomes dark grey or black.
- Larvae removed by the house bees.
- Dead larvae (mummies) are found outside the stock or in a badly infected stock on the floor board.
- Common in the UK especially in the spring or in newly made nuclei.
- Dry discoloured pollen pellets are sometimes confused with 'mummies' but on closer inspection the layers of pollen of different colours are easily discernible.

Treatment: Nil.

Other points:

Normal brood nest temperatures of 33 to 35° C are likely to be the best prevention to avoid the spread of the disease.

We believe that it is necessary to recognise two of the stresses necessary for spore germination (CO_2 and temperature) in respect of nuclei. When designing a nucleus box (CO_2) is important to ensure that the design reduces it to a minimum and when making up a nucleus (temperature) is important to ensure enough bees to maintain the brood at the correct temperature. Our own design of nucleus box and care in making up a nucleus has resulted in a much reduced incidence of Chalk Brood fatality.

Some strains of bee seem to be more resistant than others and a colony susceptible to Chalk Brood will perform very badly compared with colonies of other strains of bee on the same site. As an example see an apiary analysis on page 51 in 'Nudge nudge, hint hint' published by Northern Bee Books.

3.10.2 Sacbrood.

Causes:

- The disease is caused by Sacbrood virus (size c. 30nm) when added to the brood food of young larvae. 2 day old larvae are the most susceptible and the larvae die shortly after the cell is sealed.
- The virus multiplies in the body tissues and appear normal until the cell is sealed when they are unable to shed their last larval skin because the endocuticle remains undissolved. This is when they die.
- Each dead larvae contains about 1mg of Sacbrood virus enough to kill all the larvae in about 1000 colonies.
- Cells containing dead larvae are uncapped and the larvae removed by the house bees. In those larvae remaining, the virus loses its infectivity quickly in the dried remains. It is the adult bees that carry the infection where the virus multiplies without causing distress.

- The youngest workers are the most susceptible when removing dead larvae. The virus collects in the hypopharyngeal glands and is transmitted in the brood food.
- Infected bees cease to eat pollen and quickly cease to feed larvae. This appears to be a survival mechanism at work.
- When they become foragers they fail to forage for pollen. Again the survival mechanism at work; ie. the collected and stored pollen would become infected.
- The lives of infected workers are shortened due to protein deficiencies.

Signs.

- The infection interferes with the moulting process and the final larval moult does not occur (ie. 5th moult after the cell is sealed) with a result the larva does not pupate and dies stretched out in its cell.
- Cells containing dead larvae are uncapped by the bees.
- As the moulting fluid collects between the body and the unshed skin, the colour changes from pearly white to pale yellow and then has a sac-like appearance.
- After death, a few days later, the colour changes to dark brown; the head changing colour first.
- Finally, the larva dries down to a flattened shape with a slightly upturned head (Chinese slipper effect).
- In the yellow colour stage it can be confused with EFB and in the Chinese slipper stage it can be confused with AFB.
- Disease is very common in UK (30% of colonies are likely to have it).
- It is likely to be noticed more often in the spring and early summer when the ratio of brood to adult bees is high.

Treatment.

There is no known treatment for Sacbrood. Requeening is said to be effective in severe cases.

Other points.

Sacbrood infection is widespread throughout the world as well as in UK.

When it appears in a colony it remains generally as a light infection, appears in May and disappears in late summer.

Drones appear to be unaffected by the virus but large quantities are found in their brains whereas the hypopharyngeal glands in the worker is the main source of infection.

3.10.3 Chilled Brood.

Chilled Brood is brood in all stages which is killed due to exposure to low temperatures. All stages means from the hatched larva to the sealed pupa and for this reason it is very easy to diagnose as no other diseases kill brood of all stages in one fell swoop. It will be clear that it is not a disease but a condition as no pathogen is involved. Bailey states that unsealed larvae can survive several days at room temperature of c. 65°F, so the temperature drop must be quite severe or prolonged to kill them in a colony. We have never seen chilled brood in a colony but have produced it artificially in the refrigerator.

Causes.

- When a colony is approaching starvation (there is no carbohydrate to convert into heat energy).
- Due to spray poisoning (many bees lost).
- Stated to be due to mishandling by the beekeeper (opening a colony for too long in low temperatures).

Signs

- Brood of all stages dead.
- Dead brood at the periphery of the brood nest.
- Some of the capped cells may be perforated.
- Larvae turn grey and then to black in colour and remain shiny though they are discoloured. This is a very important sign and is discrete to chilled brood only. A very positive sign.
- In the later stages a black scale is formed which is easily removed by the bees.

Treatment. Nil. Prevention is better than cure; it is usually the fault of the beekeeper when this condition occurs.

3.10.4 Bald Brood.

Causes.

There are two causes of bald brood:

a) Due to the Greater Wax Moth (*Galleria mellonella*) larva chewing its way through brood cappings in a straight line.
b) Due to a genetic trait in some strains of bee where often small patches of brood are uncapped.

Signs.

A *Galleria mellonella* larva hatches among the brood and chews its way through brood cappings in a straight line. The bees remove the silk tunnels and leave the bee larvae bare which are not recapped.

Often the capping is not quite cleared at the angles of the hexagonal giving a slightly raised appearance at the edges of the cells.

If it is due to the wax moth, the bare cells are in a straight line where the wax moth larva has eaten its way forwards.

Treatment.

There is no treatment for Bald brood. The brood emerges normally in the case of the genetic fault but is sometimes crippled with deformed wings and legs due to faecal pellets from the wax moth larva.

3.10.5 Neglected Drone Brood.

This is not technically a disease, it is a condition of the colony (it is not initiated by a pathogen).

Cause.
It is caused by a drone laying queen or by a colony with no queen and laying workers.

Signs.

- The colony is usually small and will have dwindled, the drones produced in worker cells being in evidence (stunted and malformed).
- Typical raised and domed cappings on worker cells are evident.
- Because the colony dwindles, the bees eventually neglect drone brood in worker cells which then die of starvation before sealing of the cell occurs. They then start to decompose, lose their normal shape and become discoloured (white to yellow to brown).
- The decomposing larvae become a brown watery mass (which does not 'rope') and eventually dries to scale which can be removed by the bees. The colony is usually so dispirited by this time that many are not removed.
- It should be noted that neglected drone brood can be confused with EFB during the discoloured larvae stage and with AFB at the scaling stage.

Treatment.

There is no treatment for this condition. The colony has reached a point of no return when neglected drone brood is in evidence and laying workers are present. The colony should be destroyed.

3.10.6 Stone brood.

Cause.

The disease is very rare and caused by two fungi namely, *Aspergillus flavus* and *Aspergillus fumigatus*. Both fungi are common and occur in the soil and in cereal products (eg. mouldy hay). Probably the spores do not normally germinate in the bee or its environment, thus making it rare in the UK.

Signs.

- The disease is very rare in the UK.
- Most larvae generally die after they have been capped prior to pupation.
- Larvae with Stone Brood may be either capped or uncapped.
- Larvae infected with *A. flavus* (the most common but both are rare) have a yellow / green appearance while those infected with *A. fumigatus* have a grey / green appearance.
- The dead larvae are similar to chalk brood except in colour.

Treatment: Leaflet #561 indicates that only 3 cases have been recorded in UK between 1950 and 1980 and the recommended treatment is by burning. This appears to be sound advice when Bailey points out that the virulence of *A. flavus* is raised as a result of its passage in insect hosts. Thus if it became established in a colony more virulent strains may become selected.

Other points.
It should be noted that both fungi can affect animals and humans. It is important not to sniff or smell the combs with stone brood as respiratory infections are likely to result which are difficult to cure as they are resistant to antibiotic treatment.

Aspergillus fumigatus is used to prepare the antibiotic Fumidil 'B' for the treatment of Nosema.

3.10. 7 Other brood conditions.

Addled Brood.

Originally addled brood was attributed to the death of advanced pupae or bees ready to emerge often with small stunted abdomens. The cells may have had dark, moist, perforated and sunken cappings similar to AFB. The cause was said to be a genetic fault of the queen and the treatment was to requeen.

No pathogen has been identified and attributed to addled brood. At one time the NBU called every brood abnormality, that could not be identified, as addled brood; it is not clear what they do at present as the statistics show only two categories, the 'diseases found' and 'no disease found'. It would be more informative if the 'no disease found' column could state whether the brood was abnormal.

Hereditary faults do occur and often the failure of the propupa to shed its last larval skin, for whatever reason, can cause the same signs as Sacbrood. Thus Sacbrood, which is now very common, years ago was often wrongly diagnosed as addled brood. Other hereditary faults occur with signs very similar to EFB but a known pathogen cannot be identified. These hereditary faults, according to Bailey, are probably less common than was once believed.

It is doubtful if there is any such thing as addled brood and it seems that some form of directive could usefully be given by the NBU. In our opinion the term should be dropped.

Starved brood. This is caused when a colony does not have an adequate supply of nectar or honey

Signs:

- The first indications will be outside the hive at the entrance where the larval and pupal skins will be seen that have been sucked dry, the contents of which have been eaten by the starving adult bees.
- Egg laying will have ceased before the larval skins are seen.
- The blood sugar content will slowly reduce in all bees in the colony and their movements will become slower and slower until they stop completely.
- They finally do not have sufficient strength to remain on the comb and fall to the bottom of the hive. Some (quite a lot) will be found dead or dying head first in the cells. This is the classic sign of starvation in a colony.
- The queen and a few workers are always the last to die invariably on the comb in the brood nest. All brood will have been eaten and will have disappeared at this stage.

Treatment: If there is even the slightest movement of any of the bees it is often possible to save the colony. The queen should be found and provided she is alive, lightly spray her and the bees with a 50:50 sugar syrup solution (the strength is important as 50:50 can be metabolised immediately). Then spray the rest of the bees. Within about 10 minutes the colony will be coming to life and going back on the combs. Spray all the bees and then feed with a rapid feeder. Never let it happen again, it is the sign of a bad beekeeper!

Finally, it should be noted that varroosis is a brood disease and has been dealt with adequately elsewhere. A candidate for the examination should be capable of answering questions on all 9 brood abnormalities of the honeybee.

3.11 A detailed account of the cause, signs and treatment (if any) of adult bee diseases currently found in the UK; these diseases to include Nosema, Dysentery, Acarine, Amoeba and Chronic Bee Paralysis Virus (both syndromes);

There are two other adult bee diseases, namely Acute Bee Paralysis virus (ABPV) and Varroosis. The last, varroosis can be classed as both an adult bee disease and a brood disease; it has been adequately addressed in previous sections and will not be considered here. ABPV has only been found on the continent of Europe associated with Varroosis, *Varroa jacobsoni* being the vector. Curiously no ABPV has been found in Varroa infested colonies in the UK at the time of writing.

Reference should be made to the following publications:

ADAS Leaflet 'Common diseases of the adult honeybee' Number P3015 (revised 1991).
ADAS Leaflet 'Nosema and Amoeba' Number 473 (reprinted 1979,1982, 1984).
ADAS Leaflet 'Acarine' Number 330 (reprinted 1979, revised 1982).

The last two are out of print but are worth looking at if old copies can be obtained.

3.11.1 *Nosema apis* (Zander)

Nosema apis is a spore forming protozoa.

The Nosema spore (6 to 8μm) can only be observed using a compound microscope. It was discovered by Prof. Enoch Zander at Erlangen in the early part of the century. The protozoa multiply in the ventriculus (30 to 50 million spores when infection fully developed) and impair the digestion of pollen thereby shortening the life of the bee. It does not affect the honeybee larvae.

Signs.

- Infected bees themselves show no outward signs of the disease.
- Colonies fail to build up normally in the spring.
- In badly infected colonies in the early part of the year, a) exhibit signs of dysentery (soiled combs and soiled entrance) and b) generally have dead bees outside hive entrance (after cleansing flights).
- Diagnosis of nosema can only be confirmed by microscopic examination.

Treatment.

- Fumidil 'B' inhibits the spores reproducing in the ventriculus. It does not kill the spores.
- Autumn treatment: Fumidil 'B' followed by spring treatment the following year.
- Spring treatment: Bailey frame change plus Fumidil 'B' (see appendix 10).
- Fumidil 'B' administered in syrup 166mg to one gallon per colony.
- Good beekeeping practices prevents spread of infection in both the hive and the apiary eg. no squashing of bees during manipulations and prevention of robbing, drifting, minimising stress, etc.
- Disinfection of infected comb and hive parts with 80% acetic acid (100ml/brood box for one week). Note that acetic acid should be placed on top of the frames because the fumes are heavier than air and sink to the bottom between the frames. It is also very corrosive and metal ends should be removed from frames and any remaining metal work should be greased before treatment.

Other points.

- Due to the high incidence of nosema in UK. it is essential to monitor twice a year by taking samples in spring and autumn and treating as required. It is understood that using Fumidil 'B' regularly as a prophylactic for nosema is unlikely, but not impossible, to produce forms of *Nosema apis* resistant to the antibiotic Fumidil 'B' (Prof. L.Heath). It should be noted that it is generally bad practice to blanket treat on an annual basis. It is important to ensure that any Fumidil 'B' used for this treatment is not time expired and has been stored in a cool dark place.
- *Nosema apis* (Zander) is a spore forming protozoa with two nuclei and a coiled polar filament. The spore attacks the proliferating epithelial cells of the ventriculus by extruding the hollow polar filament and allowing the germ from the spore to pass into the epithelial cell where multiplication takes then place. With a well set up light microscope with good optics it is possible to distinguish the two nuclei. When infection is fully developed after about 10 days between 30 and 50 million spores may be found in the ventriculus. Spores take about 5 days to form at 30° C.
- As the epithelial cells provide the enzymes for digesting the proteins contained in the pollen grains, it will be clear that the adult bee has a protein deficient diet when infected. The result of this is to shorten its life by 50% (Maurizio 1946) and to inhibit the development and hence severely reduce the secretions from the hypopharyngeal glands.
- Lotmar (1939) found in infected bees that there was a reduction in the nitrogen content of the fat bodies of winter bees which contained about 6mg compared with 14 to 23mg in healthy bees. Shortage of amino acids in the haemolymph have also been recorded. These are all factors leading to the shortening of the life of the bee.
- The rectal contents of infected bees gain weight more rapidly and dysenteric tendencies are aggravated by the infection rather than being a prime cause. Thus, particularly after wintering if staining of combs and frames are observed this may be a sign that nosema may be present.
- Queens can be infected by nosema (we have excised the ventriculus of queens from infected colonies) and it is stated that they die within a few weeks of becoming infected (Fyg 1948 and L'Arrivee 1965). We find this difficult to understand as a result of requeening and treating infected colonies. The old queens have been found to be infected yet they have been alive and laying when taken from the colonies.
- In general, there are no signs attributable to nosema except that the colony is likely to fail to build up in the spring, hence the old name of 'spring dwindling'.
- The disease is endemic in the UK and is widespread throughout the world.

- There are three common viruses associated with Nosema, namely, Black Queen Cell Virus, Filamentous Virus and Bee Virus Y.

3.11.2 Dysentery.

Dysentery means to soil the combs or hive parts with excrement. It does not mean the passing of blood, inflammation of the bowel or presence of infection. Dysentery is not a disease but a condition.

Causes.

Dysentery is caused by excess water in the intestine which manifests itself mainly in the winter and can be due to any of the following:

- unripe honey and or late feeding,
- granulated stores,
- alcohol due to fermenting stores,
- brown sugar, raw sugar and acid inverted sugars although the reason is not known,
- possibly wintering for long periods solely on heather honey.

Signs.

- Fouling of combs, hive parts and around the hive entrance.
- When the rectum weight of the bee = $\frac{1}{3}$ weight bee, comb soiling starts.
- When the rectum weight of the bee = $\frac{1}{2}$ weight bee, then dysentery is certain.
- In severe cases, in bad weather, it can kill a colony, but it is more likely that the bees and the colony are so weakened that the colony succumbs due to viral infections.

Treatment.

- Warm thick syrup is said to be helpful.

3.11.3 Acarine.

Cause.

Acarine is caused by '*Acarapis woodi*' (Rennie), a mite in the class Arachnida.

- These mites, (c. 150μm $\times$ 65μm require a microscope to see them) were discovered by Dr. Rennie at Aberdeen University as a research project funded by the philanthropist Mr. Wood. It is usual for a new biological discovery to be partially named after the scientist who did the research work. In this case both the scientist and the philanthropist are named. This work on Acarine (called at that time 'the Isle of Wight Disease') was commissioned in 1921 after many colonies had been wiped out in UK.
- The EEC terminology for Acarine is Acariosis and there are proposals at the time of writing that it should become a notifiable disease in the EEC.

Signs.

- Despite the large number of references to the signs of Acarine in beekeeping literature,

Dr. Bailey's work has proved that there are no visible external signs of this disease. The disease has no effect on the flying ability of the bee but it does shorten its life slightly (time not quantified).

- The following signs are those of Chronic Bee Paralysis Virus:

    1. Crawling with fluttering wings.
    2. Clinging to plants and stems near the hive.
    3. Bloated abdomens.
    4. Crawlers may be in large numbers.
    5. Dislocated or partially spread wings (K-wings).
    6. Huddled together on the top bars or on top of the cluster in the hive.

- Diagnosis of Acarine can only be confirmed by dissection and microscopic examination of the first thoracic trachea. When the disease is present the trachea will be discoloured and not the normal creamy colour of healthy adult bees. The trachea can be infested either on one or both sides.
- It should be noted that there is no correlation between the *Acarapis woodi* and CBPV and *Acarapis woodi* has not been proved as a vector for the spread of CBPV. This is very curious because when crawling bees, etc. are found in a colony and the bees are examined, in a large percentage of the cases Acarine will be present.

Treatment.

- Folbex (Chlorobenzilate) or Folbex VA (Bromopropylate). Both are equally effective. The VA stands for Varroa and Acarine. Used in warm weather when the supers have been removed, the bees are flying well and there is no risk of contaminating honey for human consumption. See any text book for method of application. Two strips are usually necessary applied c. one week apart. It is to be noted that Folbex is not now produced and Folbex VA has been withdrawn in early 1990, thereby leaving UK with no approved medicament! It is available on the continent by post from 'Swarm SA, 2 Cote de la Jouchere, 79380 Bougival, France.
- Other treatments are used and these include Frow Mixture*, fumes of burning sulphur, methylsalicylate, etc. which are not generally used these days by the modern beekeeper.

    * Frow Mixture = 2 parts nitrobenzene, 1 part safrol and 2 parts petrol.

Other points

The mite that is under consideration in this part of the syllabus is *Acarapis woodi*. However, we consider that the existence of other Acarapis mites should be known to the candidate taking the examination. *Acarapis woodi* infests the first thoracic trachea but the other mites live externally on the honeybee, are stated to be common but have received little attention in the general literature. The three external mites quoted in the classical literature are as follows:

Acarapis externus. This was first found in Switzerland by Morgenthaler in 1934. It is found behind the head capsule on the ventral side of the neck.
Acarapis dorsalis. This was first found in UK by Morison in 1931. It is found in the V groove between the mesoscutum and the mesoscutellum. Eggs, eggshells, larvae and larval skins can be found lying in a contiguous row with their long axes parallel to the groove in the posterior region.

Acarapis vagans. This was first found by Schneider in 1941. It is found near the wing roots of the hind wings.

There is little work on the life cycles of these external mites which have not been studied in depth. The most recent paper on all four Acarapis mites is contained in a paper prepared by M. Delfinado-Baker and E.W.Baker published in the International Journal of Acarology, volume 8, number 4 and is a result of work undertaken by the USA government when heavy colony losses were being experienced in the United States. It reviews all past literature and sets out to identify and define each one. *Acarapis vagans* could not be identified and it is now regarded to be a nomen dubium. Thus there are only three mites presently recognised, namely, *Acarapis woodi, externus and dorsalis.*

• Delfinado-baker and Baker emphasise the difficulty in being able to distinguish one mite from another, all three being very similar with minute differences on the ventral side and legs of the mites. Their research found no Acarapis woodi outside the prothoracic trachea.

• We must emphasise again that there are no signs of Acarine disease. In particular, the crawling and more importantly the sign known as K wings are stated by Bailey to be the signs of CBPV. No signs have been documented, to our knowledge, about the infestation due to *A. dorsalis* which were found in predominance by Delfinado-Baker and Baker at the wing bases. However, Schneider and Brugger in 1949 showed that damage by Acarapis mites (which ones ?) at the wing bases made it possible to pull off hind wings with a force of 2 grams against a normal of about 20 grams possibly indicating the cause of the sign of K wings being due to physical lesions caused by the mites. There is no evidence in the literature that *Acarapis woodi* migrate to the wing bases so the culprits are most likely to be *A. dorsalis* but we ask is this a sign of CBPV or *Acarapis dorsalis*? Further research is clearly required. Note that examination of apparently sick (crawling plus K wings) and healthy bees from heavily infested colonies revealed both had tracheal staining but only the sick ones had CBPV.

This short discussion about the signs of Acarine disease amply demonstrates our meagre knowledge about bee diseases generally. For examination purposes at the present time, there are no signs attributable to infestation by *Acarapis woodi* in the prothoracic trachea. However, there is one symptom of the disease and that is the life of the bee is shortened slightly which can lead to spring dwindling.

3.11.4 Amoeba.

This disease is caused by the cyst *Malpighamoeba mellificae* (Prell) and also by the name *Vahlkampfia mellificae* (Steinhaus 1949) and infests the lumen of the malpighian tubules.

Cause.

Amoeba, *Malpighamoeba mellificae,* is a protozoan amoeba-like parasite which ultimately encysts in the malpighian tubules.

• The cyst which is found in the malpighian tubules is c. 10 – 12μm in diameter and can only be detected using a compound microscope. The cysts germinate, develop and multiply in the ventriculus. The amoeba then make their way into the tubules and eventually form cysts which pass through the small intestine and rectum and are voided in the faeces. The infection seems to have no effect on the colony.

Signs.

- There are no external signs.

Treatment.

- No medicaments are available for treatment and putting the colony onto clean comb, as for Nosema, and then sterilising the comb and hive parts is the only treatment available.

Other points.

Cysts are ingested by the bee which excyst, in the pyloric region of the ventriculus, into a flagellated amoeba. Being motile, this then migrates into the malpighian tubules becoming a trophic amoeba (Schulz-Langer 1958). The trophic amoeba finally encysts and the cysts are voided into the intestine and hence to the rectum to be evacuated. The life cycle is about 22 to 24 days. When fully infected there are c. 500,000 cysts / bee. Because of the smaller number of pathogens and the longer life cycle it is very much less infectious than Nosema. The cysts are spherical with a well defined wall and are between 10μm and 12μm in diameter.

It is often associated with Nosema but does occur independently. The only case reported in queens is one by G. Ingold of Devon and was recorded by Bailey.

The disease has no signs and no apparent effect on the bee. Liu (1985) reported that when the disease is present the epithelium of the malpighian tubules atrophies.

3.11.5 CBPV.

Chronic Bee Paralysis Virus is a viral infection which occurs in two syndromes (The definition of syndrome = concurrent symptoms in a disease). Thus the symptoms (in this case it should be signs) exist at the same time. The virus is ellipsoid in shape with a size of 20×30 to 60nm which can only be observed with an electron microscope thus making it outside the beekeeper's diagnostic skills.

It should be noted that there are no cures for any viral infection, they are immune from any antibiotic treatment. Viruses only multiply in living cells of their hosts and any medicament which kills the virus would kill the cell and the host. CBPV is responsible for the death of most colonies that succumb to the adult bee diseases. Nosema, Acarine, etc. do not kill the colony, they only weaken it and thereby allow the viral infection to take over. It is for this reason that Dr. Bailey considers that it was not Acarine (the I.O.W. disease) that killed so many colonies at the early part of the century but viral infections; in all probability CBPV which of course had not been identified at that time. An electron microscope is required to see the viruses and to identify them. This type of microscope had not been invented at that time. It is now clear, from work mainly undertaken at Rothamsted, that there is an association between many of the viruses and diseases caused by other pathogens.

Cause.

Chronic Bee Paralysis Virus. This virus disease has two distinct syndromes, type 1 and type 2; the signs are quite different.

Signs syndrome 1.

a) abnormal trembling of wings and body,
b) bees fail to fly and often crawl on the ground and up plant stems,
c) sometimes the crawling bees are in masses of 1000's,
d) huddle together on top of the cluster or on top bars (do not move when smoked),
e) often have bloated elongated abdomens (due to bloated honey sac),
f) partially spread or dislocated wings.

Signs syndrome 2.

a) affected bees can fly but they are almost hairless (look like robbers),
b) bees appear dark or black and being hairless appear smaller,
c) relatively broad abdomen,
d) suffer nibbling attacks by older bees in the colony; this may be the cause of hairlessness,
e) they are hindered at the entrance by the guards,
f) a few days after infection trembling sets in then flightlessness and then they soon die.

Both syndromes can exist in the same colony but it is usual for either one or the other to predominate. Hereditary factors are believed to have some bearing on the susceptibility to the disease.

It will be clear that most of the signs of syndrome 1 are those stated in much of the literature to be those of Acarine but in fact are CBPV.

In the authors' experience most colonies terminally weakened with Nosema or Acarine seem to exhibit signs of both syndromes particularly clustering on top bars and continual trembling.

3.11.6 Other viral diseases.

ABPV.

Acute Bee Paralysis Virus is another viral infection discovered by Bailey in 1963 as a laboratory phenomenon and was unknown in UK at that time to cause mortality. Bees with the virus appeared to be perfectly healthy.

Work in recent years has found that ABPV has been identified as the cause of bee and brood mortality in colonies in Europe infested with *Varroa jacobsoni* (Ball and Allen 1988). Therefore, it now becomes of some importance in UK with the advent of Varroosis because the mite is a vector for the virus. The virus is contained in tissues not immediately essential for life. The vj mite activates the virus or the release of it from tissues when they pierce the integument of the bees which then soon become systemically infected and die. Adult bees can transmit the virus to larvae and pupae before they die and these immature forms then develop signs very similar to EFB and AFB as a result of the infection. Severely infected larvae die in the cells before the cell is sealed.

It will be clear that the signs are not particularly well documented or precise at the present time in the classical and up to date literature on the subject. Because of the larval infections and mortality, we now have the dilemma of ABPV being both an adult bee disease and a brood disease.

Work at Rothamsted is continuing on ABPV and the vector Varroa jacobsoni at the time of writing.

Deformed wing virus.

Deformed wing virus, as far as we are aware, has not been scientifically identified in diseased brood, dead adults and newly emerged deformed honeybees associated with colonies infested with varroosis. We mention this because there have been on various occasions contrary statements in the bee press.

Black queen cell virus.

- This virus is associated with queen cells which develop dark brown to black cell walls. The cells contain dead pro-pupa or pupa (full of the virus), pale yellow in colour with tough sac like skin (similar to Sacbrood).
- Often noticeable in queenless and broodless colonies being used for cell building with grafted larvae.
- This viral infection is intimately associated with Nosema together with two other viral infections namely: Filamentous virus and Bee virus Y. All three of these viruses multiply only in individual bees that have Nosema.
- Recently shown to be associated with colonies heavily infested with *Varroa jacobsoni*.

Viral diseases.

Many of the viral infections of the honeybee are associated only with its adult form such as Chronic Bee Paralysis Virus (CBPV), Acute Bee Paralysis Virus (ABPV), Black Queen Cell Virus, Bee Virus X, Bee Virus Y, Slow Bee Paralysis Virus (SBPV), Filamentous Virus, etc. They could be classed as adult bee diseases. Conversely there are few viral infections associated with brood diseases such as Sacbrood Virus.

- Viral diseases shown to be associated with varroa infestation are BQCV, BVX, BVY, ABPV (Germany only), CBPV (Germany mainly, low in UK), SBPV (recently in UK).

3.12 An outline account of the life cycle of the causative organisms of adult honeybee diseases.

3.12.1 Acarine. The female mites collect in the prothoracic trachea within 24 hours of the bees emergence; only very young bees are attractive to the mite. Why this is so is unknown but it is likely to be a mechanism associated with a pheromone. The story about the hairs surrounding the trachea being soft in a newly emerged bee has been proved incorrect by removing the hairs of older bees which do not become infected.

The ratio of female mites to male mites found within the trachea range from 1:3 (Morgenthaler, 1931) to 3:1 (Otis et al., 1988). Henderson and Morse state that mating occurs in the trachea but are not explicit whether this is a sister brother relatioship as in the case of *Varroa destructor* in the sealed brood cell. It would appear that only mated female mites enter the trachea but the fate of the males is less clear; we presume that they die after mating.

The female of the species is the largest measuring 143 - 174μm long × 77 – 81μm wide whereas the male is 125 – 136μm × 60 – 77μm. The best morphological description of the mites is contained in the paper by Delfinado-Baker and Baker mentioned previously.

After entering the trachea the female mite will lay 5 to 7 eggs during a period of 3 to 4 days, say at intervals of between 10 and 19 hours. The eggs hatch to six legged larvae after a further period of 3 to 4 days, followed by a nymphal stage and then finally developing into adults. The times from hatching to adult are 11 to 12 days for the male and 14 to 15 days for an adult female. The shorter period for the male ensures that sexually mature males are available before the females mature.

It is not uncommon to see eggs, larvae and adults in the trachea of infested bees. We have not been able to establish when the female dies or indeed whether a further batch of eggs are produced. The mite must have the capability of overwintering with the overwintering bee and whether the overwintering takes place in the trachea or elsewhere is not known.

It will be apparent that we have a meagre knowledge of the biology of the mite yet the disease has been identified since the early part of the century.

3.12.2 Nosema and amoeba. The little that is known about the life cycles has been discussed in sections 3.11.1 and 3.11.4 respectively.

3.12.3 CBPV, ABPV and SBPV. All viruses multiply in the cells while the cell is alive. As the viral content of the cell increases, so a point is reached when the cell dies and the virus ceases to multiply. We have not been able to establish the rate of increase for these viruses.

The number of viruses required to infect a bee is many millions by mouth in the food ingested but about 100 or less if injected into the haemolymph.

3.13 A detailed account of the treatments for adult bee diseases.

3.13.1 Acarine. There are basically two methods of treatment namely, manipulative and chemotherapy. The manipulative treatment requires the removal of sealed brood which is hatched in an incubator and then given an uninfested queen. It is claimed that the complete eradication of the disease can be achieved by this method but because it is so laborious it has been rarely used except for research purposes.

The chemotherapy methods have used many substances by the following methods:

- Smouldering strips (fumigation techniques)
- Impregnated strips (which volatilize spontaneously)
- Aerosol sprays (directly on to the bees on both sides of each comb)
- Systemic methods (fed in sugar syrup)

At the time of writing there is no approved methods of treatment for the disease in UK. The older methods include the following:

Burning sulphur. This method is not used or recommended these days. Corrugated paper soaked and dried in a solution of saltpetre and then again in a solution of flowers of sulphur in carbon bisulphide used in the smoker are said to have been effective in Switzerland.

Methyl salicylate. This method is not often used these days except by older beekeepers who have used it in the past. Methyl salicylate has been used as a winter treatment when the bees are virtually confined to the hive. It is a synthetic product produced by the action of salicylic acid on methyl alcohol but oil of gaulthenia or oil of wintergreen contains 99% methyl salicylate and the other 1% of ketones are said (?) to make the treatment more efficacious. A 1oz (28ml) bottle and wick is all that is required; we have never used it. The oil of wintergreen is put into the stock in late autumn (on the floor board at the rear of the colony) and removed in the spring.

Frow mixture. Frow Mixture = 2 parts nitrobenzene, 1 part safrol and 2 parts petrol, all by volume. Your chemist will make up this for you but he will tell you that nitrobenzene ($C_6H_5.NO_2$ = 123.11) is unavailable. Advise him that it can be obtained from Timstar Laboratory Suppliers Ltd., Unit S1, Herald Park Industrial Estate, Herald Drive, Crewe, Cheshire CW1 1EA, telephone 01270 250459. 500ml costs £4.04 plus VAT. The dosage per colony is very small, 7ml three times (total 21ml) once per week for three weeks. We use an old tobacco tin which contains a piece of polyurethane foam. 7ml of the mixture are poured onto the foam and then the tin is inverted over the feed hole of the crown board. The treatment is stated to induce robbing and to damage open brood. Therefore it should be carried out in the autumn with reduced entrance blocks.

Folbex and Folbex VA. Folbex VA is available by post from Swarm SA, 2 Cote de la Jouchere, 79380 Bougival, France. The strips are also useful for treating Varroosis. The method is simple and should only be used when there are no supers on the colony. The crown board is raised and an empty eke is placed on top of the brood chamber and covered with the crown board. The strip is hung on a short piece of wire attached to a small piece of plywood which covers the feed hole. In the evening when all the bees have stopped flying the hive entrance is closed; the strip is then lit (and the flame blown out so that it smoulders) and inserted into the eke through the feed hole which is then sealed with the small plywood cover. The colony will give a sharp buzz as the fumes start to generate. The fanning of the bees ensures a good distribution of the fumes around the colony. The strip burns out in a about a minute but the colony is left closed up for one hour before the entrance is opened. A second treatment should be given after two weeks.

Other methods are:

Menthol crystals. These were found to be effective by Vecchi and Giordani (1968) and has been revived in the USA when many colonies were lost during the period 1986 to 1989. In hot weather the crystals are put at the bottom of the hive on the floorboard away from the entrance and in cold weather on the top bars, the warmest part of the hive. The effective temperature is stated to be greater than 21°C (70°F). the dosage is 25 gms for a period of 1 to 2 months.

Turpineol. 10 to 50ml on a pad over the feed hole. The pads may be contained in tobacco tins which are inverted over the feed hole thus preventing evaporation outside the colony.

Formic acid. 70% strength soaked in cardboard sheets (30 × 20 × 0.15 cms). Dosage two sheets per hive given one sheet at a time at 7 day interval on the floor board away from the entrance.

Other treatments. It is likely that treatments for Varroosis will be effective against *Acarapis woodi* and perhaps make the *Braula coeca* an endangered species. We know of experiments being conducted in Devon for the treatment of Acarine using Perizin (coumophos) but results are not yet available.

It is clear that the NBU appear to be failing the UK beekeeping industry by not providing a lead on the treatment of this endemic disease.

3.13.2 Nosema. Treatment is fully covered in section 3.11.1. It should be recognised that the disease can be aggravated by putting the colony under stress. The following stressful operations will give rise to Nosema:

- Moving bees from one site to another. In many cases the bees arrive in a stressful state and defaecate on the combs infecting them with spores. The worst time is late winter or early spring when the bees have been confined for a long period.
- Small mating nuclei which are populated by old bees with little or no brood.
- We have noted also that in most years our queen rearing cell builder invariably ends the season with Nosema thus indicating that long periods of queenlessness stresses the colony in some way and aggravates the onset of the disease.
- Poor seasons and sparse forage which can be manifested also by over population of colonies in a given area.

3.13.3 Amoeba. There is no known treatment for this disease although there have been several attempts to find a medicament but none have been successful.

3.13.4 CBPV and ABPV. There is no treatment for either. Killing a virus would lead to the death of the cell in which it is multiplying leading to the death of the bee.

3.13.5 Varroosis. See sections 3.9 where treatment is discussed.

3.14 A detailed account of the laboratory methods of diagnosis of Acarine, Nosema and Amoeba disease in worker honeybees.

Reference should be made to:

ADAS Leaflet 'Examination of bees for Acarine' Number 362 (reprinted 1980) which is excellent but unfortunately out of print.
ADAS Leaflet 'Nosema and amoeba' Number 473 (1984). Out of print.
ADAS Leaflet 'Acarine' Number 330 (1979). Again, out of print.
Beekeeping Senior Study Notes – Part 1 section 3.2, 3.3 and appendices 3 and 4.

The NBU have another leaflet, ADAS P3015 - revised 1991 'Common diseases of the adult honey bee', which contains details on the examination of samples but will only make it available to those who avail themselves of their diagnostic services which are generally considered to be too expensive for the average beekeeper. It contains minor errors but has some excellent photographs. We believe it should be made available the same as other leaflets from ADAS.

The sample. As each bee has to be dissected it is important that the sample is as fresh as possible (within 2 / 3 days of being taken from the colony) in order to make the dissection as easy as possible. The best way of killing them is by freezing in the freezer compartment of a refrigerator where the temperature is less than -12° C. If they are hard and brittle, they can be prepared for dissection quickly by 'cooking' them for a few seconds in the microwave oven until pliable again.

The size of the sample is important and 30 is a good compromise figure to ensure that the best representation of the colony population is obtained.

Acarine. Briefly the procedure is as follows:

- The bee is laid on its back and pinned with an 'Acarine needle' to the block between the 2nd and 3rd pair of legs.
- Remove the head and 1st pair of legs with the forceps by gripping them between the forceps and pulling and twisting; they should come away cleanly revealing the collar.
- Remove the collar by peeling it off from one end to the other to reveal the first thoracic trachea on both sides of the bee right up to the spiracle. This is the most difficult part of the dissection but practice will make perfect. The collar covers that part of the trachea adjacent to the spiracle.
- A binocular dissecting microscope is required with a magnification of between ×10 and ×20 depending on preference.
- Healthy trachea are a clean creamy colour. Any variation from this, from slight discolouration to light grey to black is a sign of infestation. The infestation can be on one side or on both.
- If in doubt the trachea can be removed with a dissecting needle onto a microscope slide and examined under a compound microscope with magnification from × 40 to × 600. Eggs, nymphs or adult forms will be easily detected. When the first infested trachea is found, determine the percentage colony infestation using the 99% possibility curve for the size of the sample being analysed (Appendix 1, pp 64/66 Notes for the Microscopy Certificate).

Nosema and Amoeba.

- The abdomens of the decapitated Acarine sample plus the heads and legs removed are crushed up with a few drops of water to make a watery paste.
- A very small drop of the liquid is put onto a microscope slide and covered with a cover slip which should be firmly pressed down with the back end of the forceps. No liquid should ooze out of the edges of the cover slip if the right amount was put on the slide.
- Examine with a compound microscope of magnification between × 400 to × 1000. Nosema spores are rice grained in shape with a double nucleus and amoeba spores are spherical with a grainy texture inside which can be determined by racking with the fine focusing control. The dimensions of the pathogens are as follows:

  Nosema – c. 5 to 8μm long and 2 to 3μm wide
  Amoeba – c. 6 to 10μm diameter

- Calculate the size of the image of each pathogen that you would expect to see based on the magnification that you are using.
- If no pathogen is found move to 4 or 5 other fields of view and examine very carefully before pronouncing that the specimen is clear. Because Nosema is endemic it is often possible to find an odd spore after a careful search.

Now comes the $50,000 question. If, after a lot of searching, only one spore is seen, has the colony got Nosema? In our opinion we don't think so. We rate it as infected if we can find a minimum of one spore in two consecutive fields of view and then we treat the colony. There is no laid down standard for this but the above would indicate a good working knowledge of the diagnostic process.

A more precise method developed by the US Department of Agriculture in the Insect Pathology Laboratory in Maryland and described in the American Bee Journal by George E. Cantwell use a haemocytometer, a special cavity slide for counting blood cells. It depends on the engraved mesh of squares on the cavity slide which holds a known volume of the prepared smear or solution. The number of spores are counted in five lots of squares, averaged and the infection calculated into low, medium and high. The method depends on preparing the smear with a known amount of water (1ml water / bee).

A simplification of the method uses an ordinary slide and cover slip but putting a known amount of smear on the slide with a calibrated loop (0.01ml) and again counting the spores and calculating the number in a fixed amount of fluid to determine the infection.

We believe that it is high time the NBU provided guidance on this matter postulating and giving lead to a national standard.

For the written examination there is no better way of understanding the subject than by actually having some hands on experience; it cannot reasonably be learnt from a text book.

3.15 A detailed description of the fumigation of comb using acetic acid (ethanoic acid), including safety precautions to be taken.

3.15.1 Acetic acid.

Acetic acid is a colourless liquid and when pure and concentrated is termed 'glacial acetic acid' because it solidifies and forms large crystals at low temperatures.

It is available in two grades AR and LR. The former grade, AR, is the analytical grade and markets for £4.23 + VAT per 500ml. The laboratory grade, LR, also goes under the name of ethanoic acid and markets for £2.28 + VAT at the time of writing from Timstar in Cheshire.

The chemical formula for both is $CH_3.COOH$. The only difference in the two grades is the purity and the LR is perfectly adequate for fumigation purposes.

If 100% concentrated acid was to be used for fumigation purposes it would be difficult to use because of the crystallisation effects. For general fumigation use it is diluted to 80% which prevents this problem.

As the acid evaporates at normal room temperatures, the fumes are heavier than air; an important point when considering the best way of fumigating combs.

3.15.2 What it kills.

The disease pathogens that are known to be killed by acetic acid fumes are as follows:

Melissococcus pluton, (EFB), providing the spores are not buried in wax and debris.
Nosema apis spores (Nosema).
Malpighamoeba mellificae cysts (Amoeba).
Ascosphaera apis spores (Chalk brood).
Galleria mellonella and *Achroia grisella* eggs, larvae and adult forms of both wax moths.

The pupal forms of the wax moths appear to be protected by the cocoon that they spin which provides a very effective coat of armour.

3.15.3 Method for fumigating combs.

- The frames should be cleaned up first by scraping the woodwork to remove wax and propolis and if metal ends are used these should be removed (they can be disinfected by boiling in water).
- The brood box should also be scraped clean of wax and propolis and the metal runners polished with wire wool. The metal runners should then be given a good coating of Vaseline or motor car grease to prevent any fumes reaching the metal work.
- The frames are carefully replaced in the brood box which is then placed on a flat board outside any buildings or sheds. Acetic acid fumes corrode concrete.
- An empty eke is placed over the brood box and covered by a suitable board (eg a sealed crown board).
- The acetic acid is poured onto an old piece of rag in a shallow dish standing on the tops of the frames. The rag extends over the edge of the dish acting as a wick. The fumes are heavier than air and fall between the frames.
- The amount of 80% acetic acid required for 11 frames in a BS brood box is 100ml.
- All joints should be sealed with tape to make the set up as air tight as possible. A spare roof on top completes the set up.
- Finally, chalk the date on the outside when fumigation started.
- At normal summer temperatures fumigation will be complete in about 7 days. Note that the warmer it is the faster the acid evaporates and the more leaks the faster the fumes will leak out and be ineffective. The air tightness is the most important factor. No matter how careful one is all the acid will have evaporated after 7 days and the dish and rag will be dry.

The frames may be stored for winter using PDB or put back into use after airing for 24 hours.

3.15.4 Safety requirements.

The fumes are highly corrosive and great care must be taken with eyes and lungs. Irreparable damage can be done to the lungs if the fumes are inhaled; there is no mistaking the smell of vinegar.

Great care should also be taken to avoid contact with the skin. It is best to use both gloves and goggles when using this acid.

As it always seems to be dispensed in small quantities (often in bottles such as lemonade) it is MOST IMPORTANT that it correctly labelled and the old labels removed. In this respect, particular attention should be paid to the cap or stopper which often is metallic and which will corrode to nothing in a fairly short time.

We are advised that it is an offence to carry dangerous acids in a motor vehicle because of the damage it could cause in the event of an accident. The mind boggles as to how each beekeeper should get a supply to his home or apiary!

3.15.5 Other points.

A much better solution for fumigating with acetic acid is to have a specially constructed fumigation box rather than use brood boxes where, with the best will in the world, one ends up with corroded runners. The fumes enter the slot on the underside unless the two ends are sealed with a blob of grease.

We have one about 6 feet long and is called the 'coffin'. It holds a lot of frames and is our long term storage space for drawn comb. When a box of combs is put in with another 100ml of acid any existing combs have a second or sometimes a third treatment.

Particular attention was paid to the sealing when it was constructed using silicon rubber on all the joints. Even so we get an occasional whiff of acetic acid on a very warm day.

All comb taken out of service should be fumigated as described before storage. This is a prime management requirement for maintaining a healthy apiary.

3.16 A description of the effects of Acute Bee Paralysis Virus and an elementary account of other viruses affecting honeybees including their association with other bee diseases where applicable.

3.16.1 Acute Bee Paralysis Virus (ABPV).

There is little information available on this virus (ABPV) and the most up to date, at the time of writing, is contained in 'Honeybee Pathology 2nd edition' by L.Bailey and B.V.Ball. Nowhere have we been able to find a clear and concise description of the signs of ABPV. It is not clear from the syllabus whether the effects of ABPV are those required on the bee or on the colony or on both.

ABPV was discovered by Bailey in 1963 while he was investigating CBPV. It occurs commonly in bees in the UK but has not been associated with any of the other known bee diseases in the UK. This contrasts sharply with mainland Europe where most colonies that are heavily infested with Varroosis succumb due to ABPV where it is a major cause of adult bee and brood mortality. Similar findings have been reported in infested colonies in Florida USA. Bailey was only able to infect bees in this country by injection in the laboratory.

It has been found that once the bees have been injected with ABPV, the virus multiplies more rapidly in bees at 35°C compared with bees kept at 30°C. However, it kills bees more quickly at the lower temperatures which is just the opposite to CBPV.

The present state of our knowledge indicates that ABPV is only associated with Varroosis. The mite *Varroa jacobsoni* appears to activate the virus or cause it to be released from tissues when the mite pierces the body wall of an apparently uninfected host. The virus multiplies and soon kills the bees if the infection levels are sufficiently high.

The signs of ABPV in Varroosis infested colonies, in mainland Europe, can be confused with EFB and AFB especially the infected larvae and pupae in heavily infested colonies. Infected bees where the virus has been activated by *Varroa destructor* can in turn infect larvae by adding the virus to the larval food from gland secretions.

Finally, at the time of writing, Varroosis is now about 3 years old in Devon where it was first discovered and there is evidence that it starting to take its toll. We lost one colony this year with suspicious looking larvae. We could find no evidence of either AFB or EFB when we examined these dead larvae and on reflection it would have been instructive to send them to Rothamsted for viral analysis. It seems illogical that colonies infested with Varroosis in UK apparently differ from those on the mainland continent. Our knowledge is of a very meagre kind!

3.16.2 Viruses associated with other diseases.

Deformed wing virus.

This virus has not so far been associated with colonies that are infested with *Varroa jacobsoni*.

The mite transmits the virus in the same way as ABPV. Pupae infected at the white eye stage generally survive to emergence but soon die with deformed or poorly developed wings.

During 1995 we have observed an increasing number of colonies exhibiting these signs.

Black Queen Cell Virus (BQCV).

This virus is one of three associated with Nosema infected colonies (the other two are Filamentous Virus and Bee Virus Y). The walls of queen cells, when infected, become dark brown to black in colour. They contain dead pupae which are initially pale yellow in appearance with a tough sac-like skin (similar to Sacbrood)

Filamentous Virus.

Associated with Nosema. It multiplies in the fat bodies and ovarian tissue of adult worker bees. In severely infected bees the haemolymph becomes a milky white with particles. No other signs are known. Similarly no symptoms have been reported. It has a cyclic peak in about May in the UK and a trough in September.

Bee Virus Y.

Associated with Nosema. Occurs in adult bees in early summer. Experimental work with this virus has shown that experimentally when infected food is fed it multiplies at 30°C but not at 35°C. It does not multiply in bees injected with the virus. There are no signs of the infection.

Bee Virus X.

Associated with *Malpighamoeba mellificae* in dead bees in late winter, more frequently than can be expected by chance according to Bailey. It is known to shorten the life of the bee perhaps more than *M. mellificae*. Likely to be the cause of the demise of colonies heavily infested with Amoeba in the winter.

3.16.3 Other viruses found in the UK.

The following viruses have been found in the UK but are not associated with any other diseases of the honeybee. Little work has been undertaken on them because of their relative unimportance.

Cloudy Wing Virus.

The virus is common in the UK with about 15% of all colonies being infected. The only signs are bees with a loss of transparency of their wings when heavily infested. The virus is suggested to be airborne entering the tracheal system. Infected individuals soon die.

Slow Paralysis Virus.

By injection it causes death after about 12 days. In recent investigations in the UK, SPV has unexpectedly increased in prevalence and has caused both adult bee and brood mortality in Varroa mite infested colonies.

3.16.4 Other points.

The viral diseases are responsible for the demise of most bee colonies and not the other diseases with which they are associated. The exceptions are the two foul broods. The other diseases debilitate the colony putting the bees under stress and allowing the viral infections to take over, eg. Nosema, Acarine, etc.

3.17 The scientific names of the causative organisms associated with diseases of honeybees.

We have used the correct names of all the disease pathogens in this module relating to diseases. They are in italics if the names are the scientific names. We suggest that candidates for examination should make their own list and learn the spelling of all the scientific names appropriate to this module sections 3.1 to 3.27. Marks are likely to be deducted when the examination scripts are marked if the names are incorrectly spelt.

3.18 An outline account of the life cycle of *Braula coeca* and a description of the differences between adult *Braula coeca* and *Varroa destructor*.

Reference should be made to section 3.8.2 which outlines the physical differences between *Braula coeca* and *Varroa destructor* and section 3.71. describes the life cycle of *Varroa destructor*.

It should be noted that only an outline account is required because a lot of the detailed biology of the louse is unknown.

3.18.1 Braulidae (Bee lice).

Braula coeca (Nitzch) in the family Braulidae is called a bee louse but in effect it is a wingless fly and not a true louse. The family is contained in the order Diptera (true flies). The two true lice orders are namely, Anoplura (sucking lice) and Mallophaga (biting lice). The relationship between Braulidae and other Diptera is still enigmatic and discussion continues about the placement of Braulidae in the animal kingdom. All adult Braulidae lack halteres and wings.

There are 5 known species which are as follows:

   B. coeca (Nitzch) found mainly in Europe
   B. orientalis (Orosi) found mainly in USSR
   B. pretoriensis (Orosi) found mainly in S.Africa
   B. angulata (Orosi) found mainly in Asia
   B. kohli (Schmitz) one male specimen found in Zaire

All are reported to be inquiline (an animal living in the home of another animal) and none are reported to be harmful to the colony.

3.18.2 Biology of *Braula coeca*.

For a full description of the adult please refer to section 3.8.2 where it is compared with a *Varroa jacobsoni*. It is specific only to honeybees.

- Eggs are laid on the inner side of honey cappings and sometimes on the wall of cells filled with honey.
- Eggs hatch to larvae which feed on wax and pollen (found in their intestines) forming ever lengthening tunnels in the wax cappings which widen as the larvae grow.
- The larvae pupate at the wide end of the tunnels and finally emerge as adults.
- At emergence the adult *B.coeca* is white and changes to its characteristic reddish / brown colour in 12 hours as its exoskeleton hardens.
- Development is entirely under the cappings of honey cells and it is not associated with brood cells in any way.
- There is surprisingly little information about the times of the life cycle and the only figure we can trace is 16 to 23 days from egg laying to emergence of the adult. We have found no information on hatching times, larval and pupa times.
- Adults mainly inhabit the petiole of worker bees, queens and occasionally drones. They move to the mouthparts of the bee when it starts to feed.
- When the bee is feeding the *B.coeca* resides on the open mandibles and labium reaching into the cavity at the base of the extended glossa near the opening of the duct of the salivary glands. It is not clear whether it feeds on the salivary gland secretions but it is thought to be highly likely.
- The queen appears to be more attractive than the other castes and the maximum number on a queen has been reported as 30 at one time. The maximum daily collection from a queen is reported as 371! Some authorities consider that infestation at these levels would have some effect on reducing the laying ability of a queen.
- Breeding takes place between May and September and the louse has the ability to overwinter with the bee.
- There is no information on mating, where this takes place, the number of males to females

or the number of breeding cycles per female. The life of the adult is also not clear nor are the overwintering habits.

3.18.3 Effect on the colony.

• Possible adverse effect on the queen but this has not been proven.
• No ill effects on the colony have ever been reported.
• Damage to cappings for sections and cut comb honey. It is always advisable to put prepared comb for sale into the freezer (-15° C) for a couple of days to kill any eggs and larvae.

3.18.4 Treatment.

It is seldom necessary to specifically treat a colony for Braula infestation. It is likely that all treatment for Varroosis will be lethal to the *Braula coeca* and it could possibly become an endangered species.

3.19 An outline account of the signs of poisoning by natural substances, pesticides, herbicides and other chemicals to which honeybees may be exposed.

The natural substances collected by the honeybee where poisoning can occur are as follows:

pollen, nectar, water and other man made sugars that are inadvertently toxic and collected by the bee.

The pesticides and herbicides (including fungicides) are a long complex list of chemicals and trade names which have been approved for use by farmers and growers which need not be repeated here or learnt for examination purposes. It is useful to know that the basic technology all started with compounds of arsenic but is now very complex with the sprays based on:

chlorinated hydrocarbons, phosphates, carbamates and pyrethroids.

Death of an insect is, in general, caused by failure of the alimentary system and eventual starvation or by poisons affecting the nervous system leading to complete lack of co-ordination of the normal bodily functions and again leading to death by starvation.

Pesticides and herbicides poisoning.

• Only laboratory test and analysis can provide a satisfactory answer.
• A few or many bees die quickly which can happen suddenly depending on the poison and how much has been taken in to the colony or how many foragers have been affected.
• The number of foragers at the entrance is often less than normal.
• Poisoned bees from inside the hive are ejected.
• The first signs are large numbers of dead bees outside the entrance which usually occurs when the weather is good and the bees are foraging.
• The quantities can be very large (measured in litres of bees).
• Dead bees usually have their proboscis extended.

- The poisoned bees will not be admitted to the hive and are likely to be crawling, trembling, falling over and spinning round on their sides. Can be confused with CBPV.
- The colony is likely to become aggressive and throwing out infected bees inside (fighting).
- If it is only the foragers that have been poisoned the colony will start to recover in c.2 weeks as new brood hatches out and house bees become guards and foragers by natural progression.
- If the house bees have been poisoned, the colony will be very depleted of bees, brood will be uncapped and dead larvae and pupae will be in evidence dead in the cells due to starvation. Finally, there will be only a few bees left with the queen (not usually affected due to her royal jelly diet) and they may abscond.
- Honey is not usually affected. Generally poisoned bees are not admitted into the hive and therefore not unloaded by the house bees. Thus there is no transfer of food to other workers providing an automatic protective mechanism.

Natural poisoning.

- The signs are very similar but generally not as intense.
- Often bees can be found under the offending plant or tree providing toxic nectar or pollen.

In both cases many bees are lost in the field and poisoned bees do not act normally (nb. aggression and foraging behaviour).

3.20 A list of crops most likely to be sprayed with chemicals harmful to honeybees and the sprays most likely to be hazardous to honeybees.

3.20.1 A list of crops likely to be sprayed thereby causing damage to honeybee colonies.

Crops are sprayed with pesticides in order to eliminate pests on them and thereby produce a greater or a higher quality end product. They are sprayed with pesticides, a generic term which includes insecticides, acaricides, herbicides and fungicides. Pesticides may be chemical substances, plants or micro organisms (bacteria, fungi, viruses or mycoplasmas) that destroy the pests but in this part of the syllabus attention is directed mainly at chemical substances. These chemical substances come in a variety of forms such as powders and dust, granules, liquids, etc. and can be applied in a variety of ways.

It may be assumed that all crops are likely to be sprayed and include the following categories:

All fruit trees and orchards. These cause little damage to bees mainly because the growers understand the problems and they require bees to be brought to their orchards for pollination purposes.

All soft fruits (eg. currents, gooseberries, etc.). Our own experience with a permanent apiary on a 'pick your own' farm with a lot of soft fruit gives little trouble. Here again the apiary is for pollination purposes and the growers realise the value of the bee for pollination.

All farm crops such as brassicas (eg. rape), field bean, borage, etc. These are the crops that cause most problems mainly because the bee is not essential for pollination purposes. Crops of vegetables for food and seed such as onions, cabbage, Brussel sprouts, swede, turnip, peas, etc. All the legumes such as clover grown for pasture and seed.

All cereals, particularly in damp climates, are sprayed for fungal infections and bees, though not working the crop, can be poisoned flying through it while it is being sprayed.

All weeds that the honeybee may be working eg. poppy, ragwort, dandelion, charlock, treacle mustard, etc. These weeds can be on farms and all cultivated land and gardens together with local authority spraying of the roadside verges.

The major pests that are likely to be the subject of spraying can include aphids, flea beetles, cabbage root fly, cabbage stem weevil, butterfly (small white), peach potato aphid, cabbage aphid, pea aphid, pea moth, pea midge, thrips, cabbage stem flea beetle, pollen beetle, cabbage seed weevil, pod midge, etc. Some of these are associated with crops that the bee doesn't work, eg. peas and cereals and in this respect it should be noted that the bees flight path could be through a field of these crops that are being sprayed. The honeybee does not have to be working a crop to suffer damage.

It will be clear from the above that there are no bee forage plants which can be assumed to be 100% safe. In the past much damage has been done to honeybee colonies particularly in brassica growing areas when the acreage of oil seed rape was increasing in the UK. However, the Control of Pesticides Regulations 1986 brought stricter measures on the control and use of pesticides. Curiously much spraying is undertaken in the orchards of fruit growing areas but it is these orchards which cause the least damage to bee colonies possibly because the growers more fully recognise the value of bees for pollination purposes.

The two major points in the regulations which have benefitted beekeepers and provided much more protection to their colonies of bee are as follows:

a) Spray contractors have to provide the beekeeper's spray warning scheme with 48 hours notice prior to spraying.
b) All spray contractors are now required to have obtained a certificate of competency.

3.20.2 Sprays most likely to be hazardous to bees.

We are not at all sure whether candidates for this examination are expected to be able to reel off lists of chemicals hazardous to bees. The syllabus says that it does but fails to state how many and how hazardous they have to be. We consider the learning of a list parrot fashion to be an outdated form of education.

Reference to the book 'Pest Control Safe for Bees' published by IBRA (mainly for the tropics and sub-tropics) derived its list of chemicals from information and data gathered in temperate climates and is therefore applicable in our situation in the UK. It lists 4 categories namely:

67 substances most toxic to bees (toxicity high 10 hours after application)
 9 substances very toxic to bees (toxicity low 8 hours after application)
49 substances less toxic to bees (toxicity low 3 hours after application)
50 substances least toxic to bees (toxicity low on application)

Generally, dusts are more hazardous than liquid sprays and fine sprays are less toxic than coarse sprays.

The toxicity has been defined as the lethal dose (LD_{50} factor) which is the amount in μg/bee to cause a 50% kill as follows:

Highly toxic – LD_{50} = 0.001 to 1.99μg/bee. Classified – dangerous.
Moderately toxic – LD_{50} = 2.0 to 10.99μg/bee. Classified – harmful.
Relatively non-toxic – LD_{50} = above 11μg/bee. Classified – presenting minimal hazard when used as directed.

We suggest that a list of pesticides is consulted and one or two are memorised for the examination such as Fastac (alphamethrin) which is regarded as safe for bees. The literature which can be consulted is as follows:

'The pesticides manual: a world compendium' edited by C.R.Worthing.
'Honeybee poisoning by chemicals: signs, contributory factors, current problems and prevention' which was published in Bee World 60(3):109 – 127.

3.21 An outline description of methods of application of pesticides, herbicides and fungicides.

• Some growers and farmers undertake the spraying of their own crops, others retain the services of professional spraying organisations. Spraying is a skilled job. Troubles associated with bee fatalities only occur when inexperienced and untrained staff are left unsupervised or the operators take short cuts and/or do not follow the makers instructions. There is now legislation requiring the owner of the crop to provide the beekeeper with a minimum of 48 hours notice if he has colonies nearby and which are likely to be affected (Control of Pesticides Regulations 1986).
• Bees and brood can be killed by toxic chemicals in three ways:

1. By direct contact (through the integument).
2. By eating (into the alimentary tract).
3. By breathing (fumigation into the trachea via spiracles).

• Contact with the poison can occur in three ways:

1. By direct contact on flowers, that the bees are working, which has accidentally been sprayed with the treated crop (eg. weeds in the hedgerows). Note that the treated crop may not necessarily be in bloom.
2. By being caught in the spray on the crop the bees are working.
3. By flying over a crop which is being sprayed.

There are basically three methods of spraying as follows:

By fixed wing aircraft. This is the worst method for controlling the sprays which can drift over quite large distances depending on wind speed and weather conditions. One of us, while sitting the Senior Part 1, was asked by the Examiner whether the number of a plane spraying the field adjacent to the apiary had been noted. We assume a 'brownie point' was lost on that one! From 1st January 1989 the Control of Pesticides Regulations have imposed stiffer controls on all methods of application and aerial spraying is included with limitations on wind speed, distance from livestock and buildings, etc.

By helicopter. More controlled than the fixed wing aircraft method but the down draught is still a problem. Not practised in this country as the operating costs of helicopters is likely to preclude it on economic grounds.

By tractor. The most common and the safest of all three.

Generally the aircraft methods are for use during daylight hours but by using the tractor, spraying can be undertaken at night, after sundown, when bees have ceased to fly. We have found that where our out apiaries are sited one on a 'pick your own' fruit and vegetable farm and the other on an estate running sheep and growing cereals and brassicas, the owners, farmers and managers tend to bend over backwards to ensure that our bees come to no harm. It takes time to develop such a relationship but it is worth more than any legislation on the subject.

Fruit growers spray the most and cause the least damage to bees. The worst crops for spray damage to bees are crucifers (eg. rape) and field beans. Note that field beans are often sprayed while they are in the early stages of flowering to combat aphid infestation; honeybees are not working the crop at this stage but it is likely to kill off all the bumblebees and therefore ruin a possible honey crop by the honeybees. The authors have found some farmers unaware of the damage they have done in this respect. The time that spraying is actually carried out is very important; this is related to the times that honeybees are expected to be flying:

- Before 8 am and after 8 pm are the best times.
- During the day is the worst time irrespective of the weather conditions.

3.22 A detailed description of the action to take, and practical measures possible, when prior notification of application of toxic chemicals to crops is given.

There are 5 main aspects whereby the beekeeper can minimise damage to his colonies, these are:

1. Collaboration with farmers within the flying distance of the hives.
2. Participating in the spray liaison scheme if this is operative.
3. Partially closing up the colonies concerned.
4. Completely closing up the colonies concerned.
5. Moving the colonies more than 3 miles while spraying is undertaken.

Collaboration with farmers. We believe that it is incumbent on all beekeepers to make contact with farmers on whose land their bees are likely to forage. They should provide their name, address and telephone number to facilitate the 48 hour warning of spraying which is a statutory requirement on all farmers and sprayers. A pot of honey does not go amiss at such a liaison meeting. In our experience such liaison is appreciated and subsequently the farmers have asked us whether it would be in order for them to spray! All now spray in the late evening or at night as a result and we have never had to close a hive or move one.

Spray liaison scheme. Our own county, Devon, must be rated as one of the failures to make the scheme work and we have little experience with an efficient county scheme. However, having said that we have heard good reports of other counties. Details of the working of these schemes varies from county to county but in essence it requires the liaison officers to maintain a register of hives, beekeepers and sites so that there is a central point of contact for all spraying operations. It is a BBKA scheme and, of course, there are still those outside the scheme who are not members. In Devon, we have now persuaded our RBI to be the Spray Liaison Officer because in his official work he makes contact with beekeepers who are not members of the association.

Partially closing up the colonies. Large quantities of grass/straw are placed in front of the hives covering up and obstructing the entrances. At best it delays the bees going out to forage. We do not consider it a very satisfactory method.

Completely closing the colonies. This is also fraught with danger particularly if the colony is a large one. The basic requirements are as follows:

- Additional comb space must be provided to contain temperature rises.
- A good supply of water must be provided in the hive for cooling purposes (suitable container and sponges to prevent drowning when the water is taken).
- Good ventilation to remove excess heat.
- Entrance to be completely blacked out not allowing light to enter.
- Large quantities of insulation (straw, etc.) over the hives to prevent internal temperature rise due to the sun.
- The absolute maximum that the colonies should be closed in summer is 24 hours.
- All precautions are aimed at keeping the temperature rise to a minimum. Unless this can be contained, there is a very real danger of melted combs and honey and the colony drowning in the sticky mess.

Moving the colonies. We believe that the amount of work involved is less than trying to close the colony up and a much safer approach to the problem. The prudent beekeeper will always have an alternative site arranged for just such an occasion.

See also BBKA Advisory Pamphlet # 27 'Protecting Honeybees from Pesticides'.

3.23 An outline description of a spray liaison scheme operated by a beekeeping association.

3.23.1 General considerations.

It was probably the increase in acreage of oil seed rape grown in the UK that prompted the formation of spray warning schemes as they are often called. The situation has changed radically since c.1976 when MAFF advised farmers to get to know their local beekeepers and to warn them in advance of any likely spraying operations. This advice was given in 'Approved Substances for Farmers and Growers' which we understand is published annually. By 1983 the advice had changed to get to know your local beekeepers and ask them to nominate a local spray liaison officer. The responsibility changed, over a 10 year period from MAFF to the beekeepers.

Our own personal opinion in this matter is that the onus should be on MAFF, and not on the beekeeper, to set up a scheme within their own organisation which is structured on a regional basis and has the resources that are non-existent in the BBKA associations. For example mapping facilities are required together with continuing daily intelligence updates with immediate action on the updates using an efficient communication system. MAFF have the information and logistics. The BBKA associations do not have them. Additionally, there are about the same number of beekeepers outside the BBKA as those within and details of both these are maintained on a MAFF database of all beekeepers. However, it is quite clear that the BBKA has taken responsibility for spray warning schemes and the success of these is very varied through the country. We understand that Essex has a well tried and efficient scheme but the one we know about in Devon is a dismal failure.

The only publication on the subject that we have been able to find is 'Spray Liaison' by Malcolm Russell published by the Essex BKA. We are not aware of any BBKA leaflets or directives on how such schemes should be set up and structured.

Most, if not all, spraying is undertaken by spray contractors who are specialist in the application of agro-chemicals. Occasionally farmers or their staff have a certificate of competency and undertake the work themselves.

3.23.2 The objectives of a spray liaison scheme.

The objectives of the scheme may be summarised as follows:

- Communication is required between the farmer or his spray contractor and the beekeeper concerned whose hives are within flying distance of the crop to be sprayed.
- There must be a central point of contact known to both the farmers, spray contractors and beekeepers.
- The central point of contact must be the County Spray Liaison Officer (CSLO) on the beekeepers side.
- The CSLO must have direct contact with an opposite number in the National Farmers Union (NFU) representing the farmers and spray contractors.
- Both these points of contact require data bases of the beekeepers apiaries which should include addresses and telephone numbers of the beekeepers, map references of their apiaries and the number of hives at each site. They should both have suitable maps showing a breakdown of the county into branch managed areas.
- Each branch of the association should appoint a Branch Spray Liaison Officer (BSLO) who has all the details of beekeepers in his own area.
- When a farmer or spray contractor is going to spray he advises the spray liaison officer in the NFU who passes the details to the CSLO.
- The CSLO passes the information to the BSLO and then to the beekeeper concerned.
- The information goes up one route and comes down the other. Where communication can be effected direct then this is desirable; it shortens the lines of communication. The long route provides for all eventualities.

3.23.3 The practical aspects of the scheme.

While setting up such a scheme it is desirable that it should not preclude the beekeeper making direct contact with farmers in the immediate flying area of his bees. He should provide farmers concerned with his name and address and telephone number and persuade him to use sprays that cause minimal damage to bees. A pot of honey for the farmer on these sorties is received with thanks and creates a favourable impression. The beekeeper should ensure that his name and telephone number are available at the apiary in a prominent position in case the farmer or spray contractor wants to make urgent contact (all seem to have mobile telephones these days).

The scheme will only work if the BSLOs are committed to their task. If they are not, it will fail. It will fall on their shoulders the task of collecting from their members all the base data on the apiaries (map references, addresses, etc.). Many beekeepers are not prepared to divulge where they keep their bees and it follows these members cannot be included in the scheme.

Provision must be made for those concerned being sick or going on holiday. Most of the spray liaising is required to be done during March to September and therefore falls during the traditional holiday season. Finally, the BSLO should have a fairly sound knowledge of pests likely to be encountered on various crops and the agro-chemicals likely to be used by the spray contractors. He should also be able to advise his fellow beekeeper members on what action to take with their hives and bees to minimise any spray damage.

3.24 An account of the action to be taken when spray damage is suspected.

3.24.1 Action to be taken when spray poisoning is suspected:

1. Comply with the agreed procedure of your local spray warning scheme.
2. Record as much detail as possible about the incident because if litigation is involved it will be some considerable time in the future.
3. Photographs of the colonies and the sprayed crop are often overlooked and are extremely useful at a later date.
4. A large sample is required for reasons outlined above; BBKA Advisory Pamphlet # 27 advises 3 samples each of c. 300 bees to be sent to Luddington with the Spray Incident Report which should include the following details:

- Time and date discovered.
- # of hives affected plus observations on each.
- Estimate of dead bees from each hive.
- Condition of bees and colour of the pollen sample from dead bees.
- Behaviour of colonies (eg. temper, bees being ejected, etc.).
- Sketch map of area and OS grid references showing apiary and crop (don't forget to mark North).
- Weather conditions (wind speed and direction, temperature, rain/fine/sunny/etc.).
- Discuss with crop owner and seek confirmation of spraying and the spray used.
- Visit site with owner, if possible, and determine crop acreage and weeds treated.
- Determine method and time of application together with the flowering state of the crop (nb. photograph of crop).
- Names, addresses and telephone numbers of all concerned including any witnesses.

5. It is important to advise your Branch Sec. and/or your Spray Liaison Scheme representative in order that they may alert other beekeepers in the same area.

6. Don't forget to label the samples and mark the hives!

7. We believe that it is prudent to keep an additional sample in the deep freeze for the Public Analyst in the event of litigation. We understand that samples sent to Luddington will only be used by them in litigation protecting wild life by prosecuting the sprayer or farmer. Any compensation to the beekeeper at law may well depend on this sample kept in reserve and will be the subject of your own proceedings not those of Luddington.

8. Feed any poisoned stock which is alive with 50:50 strength syrup immediately, it will dilute any residual toxins in the honey sacs of foraging bees.

3.24.2 The expert services available to the beekeeper at national and county level.

At national level the following organisations can be contacted in the event of information being required on spray poisoning and diseases:

National Beekeeping Adviser, Luddington, Warwickshire; for analysis of samples for all diseases and poisoning incidents. It should be noted that charges are levied for most of their services and these charges should be ascertained before entering into a contract with MAFF for any services required.

IBRA which is now located in Cardiff; an extensive library and many publications for sale are available.

BBKA can provide many useful publications and also provides initial advice on legal matters. Contact should first be made with the General Secretary at Stoneleigh.

At county level, advice and assistance is available from various organisations depending on which county you reside in:

County Beekeeping Association (contact the Secretary).

District or Branch Association (usually the first person to contact would be your own Secretary).

Local MAFF Officers (to obtain assistance for suspected foul brood infection). It should be noted that most counties only maintain this assistance on a part time basis from April to October. There is no charge levied for suspected foul brood inspections by these officers.

County Bee Instructors (CBI) or Lecturers (CBL) will give advice if they are available. Many of the posts are now abandoned and where they do exist many are part time only.

Agricultural Colleges can often give assistance. Most of the CBIs are based at such a college.

The secretaries of most district and branch associations are in a position to provide addresses and telephone numbers as they receive (or should receive) all the up to date information.

3.25 A description of the damage caused to colonies and equipment by mice, woodpeckers and other pests and ways of preventing this.

3.25.1 Mice.

These include the common or domestic mouse (*Mus musculus*), the wood mouse (*Apodemus sylvaticus*) and the field mouse (*Mus sylvaticus*). They will enter hives in the autumn seeking somewhere dry and warm to build a nest for hibernation purposes. This activity is prompted by the shorter days and a drop in temperature. The moral is to have a mouse guard on the hive in plenty of time to ensure that the mouse does not enter.

- Mice feed on pollen, honey and bees. They cause damage to comb, frames and hive equipment. In winter they will disturb the winter cluster and this disturbance can kill the colony if the temperatures are very low. The bees can sting mice to death and they have been known to be embalmed in propolis because the bees cannot eject them from the hive. Any droppings and urine are generally cleared out by the bees.
- Mice have oval skulls and can squeeze through a $\frac{3}{8}$ in wide slot but they cannot pass through a $\frac{3}{8}$ in diameter hole. Mice are therefore not a problem to keep out of the hive and if they do enter, it is the fault of the beekeeper not taking the necessary precautions in time.
- Mice are easily precluded from entry by the use of mouse guards which are simply a series holes of $\frac{3}{8}$ in diameter to replace the normal entrance to the hive. Our own mouse guards are part of the entrance block which has a reduced entrance (c. 4 in × $\frac{3}{8}$ in) one way and nine $\frac{3}{8}$ in diameter holes the other way when it is rotated through 90°. The nine holes are spaced equidistant apart along the length of the entrance block and represent an area of c. 1 square inch, dimensioned to give the optimum ventilation in winter without causing a draught through the hive. We prefer these to any other type. They cost nothing as an entrance block is required in any event. If the entrance block is stored diagonally on top of the crown board it is always ready for use when required.
- Three other methods are a) the grill of holes in aluminium sheet which has to be pinned or fixed in some other way over the entrance, b) using a $\frac{5}{16}$ in slot and c) nails at $\frac{5}{16}$ in spacing in the ordinary entrance block. We do not recommend any of them. The first knocks valuable pollen loads off the legs of returning workers in the spring. The second eventually becomes worn and increases in size mainly due to bees chewing at the woodwork. The last one is difficult to make accurately and requires nonferrous nails. It is much easier to drill the nine holes in the entrance block with the right sized drill and then slightly countersink them on each side to remove the sharp edges. These holes also get chewed by the bees but they do not enlarge the hole right through the whole thickness of the block.

3.25.2 Woodpeckers.

The main culprit is the green woodpecker *(Picus viridis)* in very cold and frosty weather when they find it difficult to forage for their normal food in the hard ground. They usually peck through at the hand hold on National and Commercial hives and in a matter of an hour can make a hole of sufficient size to enter. If they are not spotted in time the colony will surely perish for it will occur in periods of hard frost or snow on the ground. Combs, frames and hive parts will be damaged.

There are a variety of ways of combatting the damage inflicted to the hives and colonies

- The whole apiary can be caged in rather like a soft fruit cage in a garden but with a coarse mesh to stop the woodpeckers flying into the apiary. This is expensive but it has the advantage of keeping out other birds and other animal pests.
- Surrounding each hive with chicken netting so that the woodpecker's beak cannot reach the woodwork of the hive. This is the preferred method.
- Covering the hive in plastic (old blue bags are popular and cheap) thereby denying the woodpecker a toe hold necessary for the pecking operation. It has the disadvantage of interrupting the ventilation of the hive and not allowing the woodwork to breathe.

3.25.3 Other mammal pests.

These include shrews, rats, moles, squirrels, hedgehogs, etc. All these can disturb an over-wintering colony and in this respect can cause damage to it, but many of them are hibernating themselves. We have noticed pronounced scratch marks at the entrance to some of our hives at one apiary and believe it to be due to badgers although we have not caught them in the act. There is little trouble from these animals and if the grass is well trimmed for winter around the hives the worst that seems to happen is one may seek refuge below the hive for winter. All our hives are raised on concrete blocks and refuge is sought usually between the blocks

3.25.4 Birds as pests.

Birds other than the green woodpecker are swifts, tits, swallows, shrikes, etc. taking bees on the wing (including queens on mating flights). We have watched sparrows in the early morning sitting on top of the hive waiting for bees to come out, catching them and taking them back to their nest for the fledglings. Pheasants also have a taste for bees; we wondered why one colony at one apiary was very often irritable until one morning we saw a pheasant tapping at the entrance and eating the bees as they came out to investigate.

In general beekeepers are lucky in the UK for they have little trouble with pests upsetting the normal functioning of the hive. Compared with bears in Canada and termites, hornets and ants in the tropics, we have an easy ride. Having said that, we have just experienced a very hot summer with drought like conditions which has been good for all wild life. Wasps predominated and in September three hives succumbed to these pests. We have not found a satisfactory way of combatting them when a few strong nests are close to the apiary other than destroying the nests.

3.25.5 Other harmless pests.

3.25.5.1 Mites.

The pollen mite (*Carpoglyphus lactis*) is a minute mite that burrows into pollen filled cells scattering it over the combs. Generally found in brood frames that have been taken out of service and not treated with acetic acid. The mite is quite harmless to bees and is seldom found in strong colonies. It is the only way we know of cleaning out pollen clogged combs.

The sugar mite (*Glycophagus domesticus*) is small and colourless often to be found in floorboard scrapings and debris. It causes no harm to the bees.

3.25.5.2 Fungi.

Pollen mould (*Bettsia alvei*) is very common and unmistakable by its whiteness. Formerly called *Pericystus alvei* and also *Ascosphaera alvei*, it is genetically related to Chalk Brood. However, it does not affect either brood or bees and is quite harmless. The fungus grows on pollen at low temperatures and high humidities being common in the spring. The bees clear it up when the colony environment is stronger and warmer. It will develop in stored comb and the surface mould will invade the whole pollen mass which becomes hard and dry.

3.26 A detailed account of wax moth damage and the life cycle of both the Lesser and Greater wax moth *(Achroia grisella and Galleria mellonella).*

3.26.1 Greater wax moth *(Galleria mellonella).*

- The adults have a wing span of 1 to $1\frac{1}{2}$in and enter the hives at night to lay eggs. The eggs hatch to larvae and when fully grown they are about $\frac{7}{8}$ in long and quite distinctive with a dark head. The larvae pupate, usually in a boat shaped groove chewed into the woodwork of a frame. The chrysalis eventually hatching to the adult form. The damage is caused during the development of the larval form. The larva has the ability to digest wax but it also needs protein which is obtained from pollen and larval debris of the honeybee.
- The life cycle is approximately egg – 7 days, larva – 15 days, pupa – 28 to 32 days. The times are very variable and depend on temperature (egg to adult on average is 50 to 54 days).
- Adults live 3 to 30 days but most die at about 7 days.
- Eggs hatch in 3 to 5 days at temperatures of 29 to 35°C and take 30 days to hatch at 18°C.
- In warm weather there is the possibility of all the comb in a full brood chamber being turned to dust in about 14 days and much of the woodwork damaged if it is not in use by the bees. A strong colony will not tolerate the moth and keeps itself in a healthy state and no damage is caused. Weak colonies can be damaged with the bees in occupation.
- These moths are generally only troublesome in UK when the comb is not in use, however, they can be very real pests in tropical climates.
- It is possible to introduce bacteriological control by impregnating the wax foundation with spores of *Bacillus thuringiensis* which kills the wax moth larvae. This form of control has been used in USA but is not practised widely in UK at the present time (It is sold under the trade name CERTAN).
- Eggs are killed when $T\geqslant 46°$ C for c. 1 hour and when $T\leqslant 0°C$ for c. 5 hours.
- The larvae are gregarious and often collect in layers at the bottom of a hive. If there is a food shortage they become cannibal and the larger larvae eat the smaller ones.

3.26.2 Lesser wax moth *(Achroia grisella).*

- This silver coloured moth is much smaller than the Greater Wax Moth, has a wing span of about $\frac{3}{4}$ in to 1 in and the larvae do not cause damage to the woodwork. The larvae still consume and digest the wax comb and while doing so they produce a large web of silk tunnels.
- It is not so much of a pest as the greater wax moth but can completely ruin comb if an infestation occurs and no protective measures are taken.
- The life cycle of this moth is unknown to us. We have searched most of the classical literature from 'Beekeeping New and Old' by Herrod-Hempsall to 'Honeybee Pests, Predators and Diseases' by Morse and Nowogradzki without success. It is therefore doubtful whether the life cycle should be included in this syllabus if the information is not readily available!

3.26.3 Death's head hawk moth *(Acherontia atropos).*

This is a magnificent looking moth with a skull and cross bones marking on its thorax on the dorsal side. It is attracted to bee hives and is now quite rare in UK; it originates from N. Africa and Spain. It is worth having a look at one in a natural history museum. A few have been found in Devon and the south coast of UK.

3.27 A detailed account of methods of treating or storing comb with particular reference to preventing wax moth damage.

3.27.1 Types of comb to be stored: are super and brood comb.

- **Super combs.** These can be stored either wet (with honey) or dry after being cleaned up by bees and removed from the hive again. This comb consists only of wax and honey (if stored wet).
- **Brood combs.** This type of comb is very different containing wax, pollen, larval skins and faeces, propolis, etc. making them much more attractive to attack by other insects and mammals.

3.27.2 The main causes of damaged comb are by:

- Mammals such as mice, rats, squirrels, etc. which are easily excluded with travelling screens or queen excluders at the top and bottom of the stacks of boxes of frames.
- Insects, the main cause of damage being the wax moths. There are two:

    1. The lesser wax moth (*Achroia grisella*) and
    2. The greater wax moth *(Galleria mellonella)* which is regarded as the major pest. However both can cause very extensive damage in a short time if precautions are not taken.

3.27.3 Methods of protection against wax moth damage.

There are four methods namely paradichlorobenzene (PDB), acetic acid (80%), heating and cooling. Each of these either kill (k) or have no effect (ne) on the various stages of development ie. egg, larva, chrysalis and adult. Reference to published literature reveals the following in the table below:

STAGE	PDB	ACETIC	FREEZING	HEATING
Egg	ne	k	k	k
Larva	k	ne	k	k
Chrysalis	?	?	k	k
Adult	k	k	k	k

T (FREEZING) = 0°C to –17°C for a few hours to a few days depending on temperature and bulk of frames.
T (HEATING) = 49°C (120°F) . Note the melting point of wax = 63°C (145°F)
? = no reference could be found in the standard literature.

It will be clear from the above table that the best method is freezing before storage at normal temperatures. No airing of the combs is necessary. A good method for supers where the risk of disease is very low compared with brood frames.

Heating would also be possible but wax is very malleable at 49°C (120°F) and the temperature control would have to be precise.

Gamma radiation is known to kill all stages in the life cycle but is expensive and not really a practical method for the hobbyist beekeeper. For the average beekeeper fumigation is the more usual method and it will be clear that both acetic acid and PDB is necessary and is the accepted method of dealing with brood frames.

Brood frames. These should first be fumigated with 80% acetic acid as described in section 3.15.

After fumigation (not less than 7 days) with acetic acid they should be stacked as follows:

- Mouse excluder with newspaper over.
- Sprinkle one dessertspoonful of PDB crystals onto newspaper and place brood box over.
- Cover with newspaper, PDB another brood box, etc. finishing with a screen and crown board.

Supers. It is unnecessary to fumigate with acetic acid and they can be stacked straight away with PDB and newspaper. At the end of the season it is important to get all frames cleaned up (by removing the excess wax and propolis by scraping clean), fumigated and stacked for winter as soon as possible. While the weather is warm the wax moth can do considerable damage.

Note that if supers are stored wet it is necessary to make them beeproof if they are stored outside otherwise they must be in a beeproof shed or room. When the frames are wet, they are not attractive to wax moth so they can be stored without PDB. They do become very damp (honey hygroscopic) and tend to grow mould during the winter. We prefer storing supers dry.

3.27.4 Other relevant points:

- PDB crystals should never come into contact with the wax comb. They will dissolve in it and it is impossible to remove it from the wax.
- Disinfection with acetic acid is the approved method of cleaning comb infected with Nosema spores, so the storage treatment ensures that there is no risk of the spread of infection the next season when the comb is reused. Other pathogens are killed with acetic acid such as Chalk Brood fungus spores so it is good beekeeping practice to make this storage the norm.
- Rather than have the trouble of stacking and sealing boxes for acetic acid treatment it is probably better to have a permanent installation to hold as many frames as required. It can be custom built and made completely air tight thereby using less acetic acid. The box automatically can become a frame storage box in the winter.
- After any fumigation, combs should be well aired before re-use in the hive.

MODULE 4: INTERMEDIATE HONEYBEE BIOLOGY

All candidates sitting the examination for this module should be able to reproduce the sketches with labelling which appear at the end of the notes on this module. The Candidate shall be able to give simple accounts (note not detailed accounts) of:

4.1 The structure and function of the alimentary system.

The alimentary canal (transmitting food through an animal body from mouth to anus) consists of :

> Pharynx (mouth),
> Oesophagus (tube),
> Honey sac or honey stomach or crop,
> Proventriculus (valve),
> Ventriculus (mid gut),
> Pyloric valve,
> Small intestine (+Malpighian tubules),
> Rectum,
> Anus.

Note that the salivary glands are not strictly part of the alimentary canal but are often included in literature on the bee and its anatomy. A simple account would not include their use and may be ignored for this module. Each of the above are examined below; reference should be made to diagram 4.18 of the alimentary tract.

4.1.1 The structure and function of the alimentary system.

4.1.1.1 Pharynx: the true mouth cavity with:

1) Inlets from the hypopharyngeal glands and the proboscis,
2) Entrance to the oesophagus,
3) Inlet / outlet via the mandibles.

4.1.1.2 Oesophagus: a tube through the thorax connecting pharynx to the honey sac. Its only function is to provide a passage for food in both directions.

4.1.1.3 Honey sac: transparent bag at the anterior end of the abdomen and capable of considerable dilation. Maximum load c. 100mg with an average load 20 to 30mg. Its function is to carry and temporarily store nectar, honey and water.

4.1.1.4 Proventriculus: is a one way valve which:-

1) Prevents (when necessary) nectar and honey flowing into the ventriculus.
2) Separates the pollen from the nectar/honey. The pollen is collected in four pouches behind the four lips of the valve; the filtration being done by very fine hairs (capable of filtering to 1μm). When a pouch is full, a bolus of pollen is passed into the ventriculus.

4.1.1.5 Ventriculus: is the true stomach of the bee where digestion of foods take place. Note the shape which is like 'gas mask tubing' which is ideally designed for peristalsis which moves the food and waste matter through the final parts of the alimentary canal. The ventriculus is lined with an epithelium which produces proliferating cells continually; these sloughed off cells contain enzymes. The enzymes enter the pollen grains through the germ pores and digest the proteins in the grain. The resulting nutrients are then absorbed through the walls of the ventriculus and into the haemolymph (blood) in the abdominal cavity. A similar digestion process occurs with honey and nectar, the enzymes breaking down the polysaccharides into monosaccharides which can then be absorbed into the haemolymph through the walls of the ventriculus. The epithelium is covered with a jelly like substance, the inner surface of which forms the peritrophic membrane. This encloses the food and is said to prevent abrasion of the ventricular wall. Waste matter produced in the ventriculus contains pollen husks, fat globules and uric acid and nitrogenous waste from the Malpighian tubules which enter the alimentary canal at the posterior end of the ventriculus.

4.1.1.6 Pyloric valve: this is a thickening of the walls at the anterior end of the small intestine just behind the entry point of the Malpighian tubules. The valve is lined with backward facing hairs said to assist in directing the contents in the backward direction.

4.1.1.7 Small intestine: is constructed in a fluted formation of 6 flutes. This type of formation provides a large surface area and slows down the passage of food. This suggests that absorption of digested food could take place in this region but as far as we are aware has not been proven.

4.1.1.8 Rectum: this is similar to the honey sac in so far as it can be dilated to such an extent that it can fill the whole abdomen. Six rectal pads are found on the outer surface of the rectum. They are quite distinctive but the function is so far unknown. It has been suggested that they extract water from the contents and return it to the haemolymph; the microscopic structure does not support this. Other suggestions are for the absorption of digested fats and maintaining the concentration of salt in the blood. The function of the rectum is to store waste products prior to the bee taking a cleansing flight.

4.1.1.9 Anus: the final outlet from the alimentary canal.

4.1.1.10 Malpighian tubules: there are about 100 of these tubules, closed at the distal end which join the alimentary canal adjacent to the pyloric valve. They spread throughout the abdominal cavity and absorb, through their walls, nitrogenous waste from the blood. These are the main excretory organs and collect the waste matter from the nutrients used in the blood and tissues.

Note that two adult bee diseases are associated with the alimentary canal, these are:

Nosema apis (Zander) – in the ventriculus restricting the digestion of proteins from the pollen grains.
Malpighamoeba mellificae (Prell) – in the Malpighian tubules.

4.1.2 The digestion of pollen and honey.

Pollen and honey are the only two foods consumed by the bee for its well being and to sustain its life. Nectars and other sources of sugars are collected to produce honey. Other sources include those that are naturally occurring such as honeydew and man made sugars from artificial sources. In order that they can be digested it is necessary in some cases for enzymes to be added as shown below:

	FOOD	+ ENZYME ADDED	= IN THE BLOOD
POLLEN:	protein	+ protease	= amino acids
	fat	+ lipase	= fatty acids and glycerol
	minerals	+ nil	= minerals
	vitamins	+ nil	= vitamins
HONEY:	sucrose	+ invertase	= fructose + glucose
	glucose	+ nil	= glucose
	fructose	+ nil	= fructose
	polysaccharides	+ glycosidases	= monosaccharides
	minerals	+ nil	= minerals
	vitamins	+ nil	= vitamins

It has not been shown in the classical literature what the mineral and vitamin requirements are during the life of the bee or in its larval form.

4.2 The excretory, circulatory, respiratory and nervous systems including the sense organs.

Reference should be made to the diagrams at the end of this module.

4.2.1 Excretory system including function of the Malpighian tubules.

The excretory system consists of:

1) The Malpighian tubules
2) The small intestine
3) The rectum and anus
4) The tracheae.

The tracheae discharge both CO_2 and water vapour from the spiracles and therefore are technically part of the excretory system although many text books do not treat them as such.

The Malpighian tubules.

- Approximately 100 Malpighian tubules (named after the Italian biologist / entomologist, Malpighi) enter the posterior end of the ventriculus adjacent to the pyloric valve. They spread throughout the whole of the abdomen, are surrounded by blood and are closed at their distal ends. They are the principal organs of excretion.
- The walls of the tubules are composed of a single layer of cells and through their walls

nitrogenous waste and salts are absorbed from the blood. This waste passes down into the ventriculus and then into the small intestine.

- It is in these tubules that the cysts of the protozoan parasite *Malpighamoeba mellificae* are found. Curiously these cysts seem to have no ill effect on the bee, although it is difficult to comprehend how the tubules work effectively in severe infections when the tubules are 'solid' with cysts.

The small intestine.

- Entry is from the ventriculus via the pyloric valve which is itself formed by a thickening of the walls of the small intestine at this point. The small intestine is constructed in a fluted configuration, the 6 flutes running longitudinally providing a large surface area. The inside of the pyloric valve is small in diameter (cf. the ventriculus and small intestine) and contains fine backward facing hairs which prevent digested food from returning into the ventriculus.
- The constriction of the pyloric valve coupled with the large surface area of the small intestine is compatible with slowing down the passage of food and absorption of it in the small intestine. It is thought that excess waste water is absorbed through the walls of the small intestine and passed with other waste products into the rectum at the posterior end.

The rectum.

- The rectum is a flexible transparent bag with 6 rectal pads which are quite distinctive and correspond to the fluting on the small intestine. The function of the rectal pads is unknown.
- The rectum stores the faeces until the bee can exit the hive and fly. The bee normally defaecates on the wing. In winter when the bee cannot fly outside the hive, the rectum is capable of distending to fill a very large part of the abdomen. Any fouling of comb or top bars during winter means dysentery and if Nosema is present, it is spread around the colony by food transfer as the bees try to clean up the fouled combs. Excess water, causing dysentery, cannot be retained in the rectum and is the basic cause of comb fouling in winter.
- Faeces are evacuated via the anus and are made up of:

    a) indigestible starch (dextrine),
    b) pollen fat (globules),
    c) pollen husks,
    d) exhausted epithelial cells from ventriculus,
    e) nitrogenous waste (eg. uric acid) and salts,
    f) water.

Tracheae.

- The tracheae form the main 'highways' of the respiratory system and provide an inlet passage for O_2 and an outlet passage for CO_2. See section 4.2.3

4.2.2 The circulatory system (heart, dorsal and ventral diaphragms).

The circulatory system (see system diagram 4.16) consists of:

- heart,
- dorsal diaphragm,
- ventral diaphragm,

- blood (haemolymph),
- aorta,
- antennal vesicle.

Heart: elongated organ of 5 segments laying just under and extending along virtually the whole length of the roof of the abdomen. It has 5 pairs of openings or one way valves (ostia) allowing the blood to enter the heart when it is dilated. Conversely the ostia are closed when the heart is contracted. It is closed at the posterior end and the anterior end leads directly into the aorta.

- Heart is suspended from the dorsal side of the exoskeleton and is also attached to points on the dorsal diaphragm by branching threads at the ends of the muscles in the dorsal diaphragm.
- Heart beats forwards from behind in successive waves of contractions produced by the muscles. It is not proved that the muscular action of the heart is controlled by the nervous system. No nerve connections have been found to the appropriate muscles.
- Function of the heart is to circulate the blood around the whole body of the bee.

Dorsal/ventral diaphragms: are thin transparent membranes which are attached at points on tergites and sternites. From the attachment points (dorsal A3–A7, ventral T2–A7) muscles fibres radiate.

- The diaphragms are responsible for setting up a circulation inside the abdomen and drawing blood into the abdomen from the thorax.
- By contractions of the diaphragm muscles, waves are set up in the thin sheets which, in turn, create currents of blood between them and the abdominal walls of the exoskeleton.
- The blood flow is forwards in the dorsal sinus and backwards in the ventral sinus.

Aorta: is continuous with the heart and passes into the thorax at the petiole. At this point it is convoluted and then passes between the indirect flight muscles in the thorax as a simple tube and then on to the head where it is open ended just behind the brain.

- The convoluted tube acts as a heat exchanger extracting heat from the thorax muscles cooling them as blood flows inside the aorta in the forward direction.

Antennal vesicle: without this vesicle there would be no way of supplying blood to the antennae. This pulsating vesicle has two tubular outlets which pumps blood to the ends of the antennae. The tubes run down the antennae parallel to the antennal nerve. The return flow is outside the vesicle tubes.

Blood: the whole of the body, heart, etc. is filled with blood together with legs and wing roots which are contiguous with the body shell. Blood is colourless plasma and contains haemocytes (white blood corpuscles) which act as phagocytes by ingesting and destroying bacteria. The flow of blood is generated by the heart and diaphragms, the pumping action creating a pressure gradient, high at the head and low in the abdomen, which results in a return flow. The function of the blood is as follows:

- to carry nutritive substances from the alimentary tract to cells and tissues where they are consumed.

- to transport the waste products of metabolism from tissues to the Malpighian tubules,
- O_2 diffuses through the blood at the end of the tracheoles, these tracheoles transport the gas to the tissues for respiration,
- similarly CO_2 diffuses through the blood in the reverse direction to be eliminated via the spiracles,
- distributes heat around the body. Note that the bee is poikilothermic and takes up the temperature of its surroundings.
- to fill the complete body cavity, maintaining it under pressure and thereby maintaining the body shape (turgor effect).

4.2.3 The respiratory system (interchange of O_2 and CO_2).

The respiratory system (see diagram 4.17) consists of:

1) spiracles (vents at the sides of the thorax and abdomen),
2) tracheae (walled tubules),
3) tracheal sacs (expandable bags),
4) tracheoles (fine tubules where O_2 is absorbed and CO_2 removed).

Spiracles: 10 pairs, 3 on thorax, 7 on abdomen (6 visible, the last near sting is invisible)

- 1st – on T2 of thorax, it is the largest and cannot be closed, (nb. Acarine). It provides entry for the major air intake during flight.
- 2nd – on T3 of thorax, it is the smallest and concealed.
- 3rd – on A1 of thorax, it is also large and the major outlet for CO_2 during flight.
- 4th to 9th – on A2 to A7 of the abdomen.
- 10th – cannot be seen externally as it is contained in the sting chamber.
- All the spiracles have valves except segment T3. The valve on T2 cannot be closed although it does have muscles apparently for this purpose. The valves on A1 to A8 are identical, the spiracle being the entry into a chamber (atrium) with the valve at the inlet to the trachea.
- Larvae have the same number of spiracles but only use one side from the time they hatch until sealing because they are lying in a pool of brood food and spiracles on the lower side are below the surface of the liquid food.

Tracheae.

- Tracheae connect the spiracles to the tracheal sacs. They are maintained in the dilated state by spiral thickenings (taenidiae) in the cuticle wall. 1st spiracle and trachea on segment T2 is branched to both the thorax and the head. All other trachea lead to the tracheal sacs.

Tracheal sacs.

- Tracheal sacs are thin walled flexible air sacs which are expanded by air and contracted by blood pressure as a result of muscular action causing a 'bellows type' movement of the abdomen, nb. breathing (inlet of O_2, outlet of CO_2).
- There are 2 large sacs in the abdomen as well as smaller ones in both the abdomen, thorax, head and even the legs. The purpose of these sacs is to act as a reservoir when air is being used rapidly, the trachea and tracheoles, being small in diameter, would create too greater resistance to flow for the amount of air being used.

Tracheoles.

- These are the branching tubules from the tracheal sacs which spread out to all parts of the bee's anatomy. The cavities of the exoskeleton are literally full of them. They are surrounded by blood and the open ends also contain some blood.
- This network of tracheoles is in close proximity to all the tissues (eg. muscles). Oxygen from the air in the tracheoles diffuses into the blood and carbon dioxide, the result of the oxidisation process of metabolism, is removed via the same route.
- The major use of O_2 is while the bee is in flight, in order to supply the large indirect muscles in the thorax. These muscles when dissected are a bright pink colour due to their cytochrome content, a substance which facilitates the gas exchange.

Other points.

- CO_2 is used as an anaesthetic for queen bees during artificial insemination.
- Insects can withstand much higher concentrations of this gas than homo sapiens. The normal concentration in the brood nest 1% and if this rises to 2% Chalk Brood spores will germinate, a necessary condition for their reproduction.

4.2.4 The nervous system.

The brain of the honeybee is very small and undeveloped compared with the brain of a human. It is a mechanism for nervous co-ordination responding to external stimuli received by sense organs. All actions of the honeybee are automatic responses to external conditions or to internal chemical conditions. The honeybee is not credited with having the powers of reasoning and intelligence. The honeybee has a limited and short lived power of memory. It is well to remember that the honeybee has evolved, during a period of about 30 million years, from a worm like ancestor. This primitive ancestor had 19 segments each with a 'knot' of nervous tissue (ganglion). Each ganglion had radiating nerve fibres to muscles and other segmental organs. Most insects have evolved from this ancient ancestor whereby the first 6 segments have become the head (H1 to H6), the next 3 the thorax (T1 to T3) and the last 10 the abdomen (A1 to A10). In the case of the honeybee evolution has include A1 in the thorax thus making 4 segments and the abdomen having one less, that is A2 to A10 inclusive. The primitive ganglia have also, in some cases combined. Reference should be made to the sketch of the nervous system in diagram 4.19 at the end of this module.

The nervous system of the honeybee, though simple in concept, is remarkable in scope. It is capable of reacting to the following external stimuli: light, touch, smell, taste, sound (vibration), temperature, humidity, electrostatic charge and magnetic force. A full discussion and understanding is not required for this module, a simple account only is required.

4.2.4.1 The structure of the system.

In tabular form the drawing shows how the adult nervous system is formed from that of the larva:

GANGLIA	DERIVED FROM	CONTROLLING
Brain	H1 to H3 incl.	Simple + compound eyes, antennae, labrum, frons and cibarium.
Sub-oesophageal	H4 to H6 incl	Mandibles, proboscis
1st Thoracic (Tg1)	T1	Fore legs
2nd Thoracic (Tg2)	T2, T3, A1 and A2	Wings (front and rear), middle and rear legs
1st Abdominal (Ag1)	A3	Muscles and tissue in A3
2nd Abdominal (Ag2)	A4	Muscles and tissue in A4
3rd Abdominal (Ag3)	A5	Muscles and tissue in A5
4th Abdominal (Ag4)	A6	Muscles and tissue in A6
5th Abdominal (Ag5)	A7 to A10	Muscles and tissue in A7 to A10 including the sting and reproductive organs in queens and drones

All the ganglia from the brain through to Ag5 are connected together by longitudinal commissures. The whole system is located close to the ventral parts of the exoskeleton of the thorax and abdomen. In the abdomen both the ganglia and the longitudinal commissures are in the lower part of the ventral sinus under the ventral diaphragm and from there pass through the petiole into the thorax.

All the ganglia while being connected to the brain via the longitudinal commissures still retain a remarkable degree of independent control. This is readily demonstrated by the sting. If ganglion Ag5 is still attached to the sting but detached from the rest of the bee (as happens normally in the course of stinging) the sting continues to operate and control the muscles operating the stylets. Similarly, if a bee is beheaded then the legs and other appendages still continue to function for a while.

4.2.5 The sense organs.

Ocelli (simple eyes).

The ocelli are three simple eyes on top of the head between the large compound eyes. They each consist of a simple lens above a layer of simple retinal cells connected to nerve fibres. The geometry of the optics is such that no image can fall on the retina and it is believed that they function only as detectors of light intensity and in some way related to the compound eyes.

Compound eyes.

The compound eyes are complicated sense organs located at the side of the head. They each have thousands of individual retinal cells called ommatidia. Each eye of a queen has c.4000 ommatidia, that of a worker c. 5000 and the eye of a drone c.8000. Each ommatidium has its own lens and nerve fibres which produce a mosaic of small dots as an image similar to a black and white newspaper picture. The greater the number of dots (ommatidia) the better the image. It follows that the drone has the best vision of the three castes. The construction allows the bee to see ultra violet light and it can also distinguish polarised light from unpolarised. The colour spectrum is different from that of man which extends from red (c. 7 kÅ) to violet (c. 4

kÅ) whereas the bee's spectrum extends from bee-yellow (c. 6.5 kÅ) to ultra violet (c. 3 kÅ). All the nerve endings of the ommatidia connect directly into the brain. The bee's ability to detect UV and polarised light enables it to navigate with a remarkable degree of accuracy.

Antennae.

Each antenna consists of a scape and a flagellum which is segmented along its whole length. The number of segments of the flagellum is 11 for the queen and worker and 12 for the drone. The first segment on the flagellum is called the pedicel which contains the Organ of Johnston. The whole of the flagellum is covered with sensilla of different types but the density is greater towards the distal end of the flagellum. The Organ of Johnston is believed to measure vibration and can therefore act as an air speed indicator. Observation of the bee at work shows much touching and connecting of their antennae one with another. The sensilla on the flagella are organs for smell, taste, touch, etc. but so far no antennal language has been discovered as a means of communication. It is understood that the sensilla associated with smell are instrumental to the drone for mating purposes and can detect amounts as small as a molecule of the pheromones concerned. See diagram 4.11.

Sensillum.

There are a wide variety of sensilla such as simple hairs (bristle), pegs (short thick hair or peg), pit hairs, pit pegs, plates, etc. They are responsible for detecting all the sensations through touch, temperature, taste, etc. The vast number of sensilla occur on all parts of the bee's body from the mouth through the legs to the sting chamber including the whole of the exoskeleton. Each sensillum has a nerve fibre connecting to the integrated nervous system via networks of nerve meshes called synapses where chemical changes produce changes in electrical potential. Most poisoning incidents affect the nervous system of the bee upsetting the balance of the potassium and sodium channels causing, eventually, complete disorientation of the bodily functions, starvation and then death.

4.3 The exocrine glands and their secretions including the hypopharyngeal, mandibular, Nasonov, sting and wax glands.

The exocrine glands (those secreting externally) are:

- hypopharyngeal
- mandibular
- Nasonov
- sting
- wax
- thoracic and post-cerebral (salivary glands).

(Note that not all books regard the sting as an exocrine gland but the sting has glands which secrete externally. The secretions are the alarm pheromone, iso pentyl acetate, as well as the venom).

Hypopharyngeal: located above the pharynx and under the frons. There are 2 glands one on each side of the head. An axial duct from each gland opens via a small pore on to the hypopharyngeal plate and the secretion accumulates in the pre-oral cavity (food channel in the base of the proboscis inside the pharynx or mouth).

a) The secretion from the glands is called brood food or royal jelly. They are basically the same but there are chemical differences depending on whether it is being fed to worker or queen larvae in order to produce the two female castes. It should be noted that the adult queen lives solely on a diet of royal jelly which is very high in protein. The feeder bee folds back its proboscis, opens its mandibles and raises its labrum to allow the entry of the queen bee's proboscis.

b) The glands are large in the worker, rudimentary in the queen and non existent in the drone. Glands are thread like with round cells (acini) which are active in workers 5–15 days old (nurse bees) after which the acini shrink and become inactive (they become atrophied). It should be noted that older foraging bees can, if the needs of the colony so require it, consume pollen and re-activate their hypopharyngeal glands for brood feeding. Workers deposit the brood food in the cells, directing it into place with their mandibles.

c) In older bees the hypopharyngeal glands are believed to be the source of invertase although extracts from the glands have not been separated for analysis. Dade makes the point that analysis of the secretion of the postcerebral glands show surprisingly differing results, some workers indicating the presence of invertase others denying it. For practical purposes modern thinking is 'invertase from the hypopharyngeal glands'.

d) Brood food (bee milk in some books) and royal jelly contains mainly:
  – proteins,
  – several vitamins of the B group,
  – vitamins C & D but not E,
  – (E)-10–hydroxy-2–decenoic acid (10–HDA), which acts as a preservative preventing bacterial infection of the food while it is lying in the cell, but note this comes from the mandibular glands.

Mandibular: sited in the head under the genae and immediately above the mandibles. Ducts open into grooves in the mandibles, the outlets being controlled by muscles.

a) The glands are very large in the queen, smaller in the worker and rudimentary in the drone.

b) Secretions contain:

Worker	– 10–HDA (preservative),
	– 2–heptanone (alarm pheromone),
	– other unidentified substances (maybe for working wax).
Queens	– (E)-9–oxo-2–decenoic acid (popularly known as 9–ODA),
	– (E)-9–hydroxy-2–decenoic acid (popularly known as 9–HDA),
	– 13 other identified pheromones,
	– a number of other unidentified pheromones.

c) The secretion from the queen glands is popularly known as queen substance; it is very important in controlling colony behaviour. It has two known functions inside the hive, namely:
  – inhibiting queen cell production
  – inhibiting worker ovary development

It is distributed around the colony by food transfer and is very attractive to worker bees. Outside the hive queen substance is a drone attractant during queen mating flights and also holds swarms together as a cohesive unit.

Nasonov: (see diagram 4.1) scent gland located at the anterior end of tergite A7 in a transverse groove adjacent to the posterior end of tergite A6. It is exposed in use by flexing the two abdominal tergites to allow the secretion to evaporate; the process being assisted by fanning.

a) The gland secretes into the scent canal (transverse groove) the secretion containing:
  – E citral and geranic acid, the 2 most important components,
  – Z citral, geraniol, nerol, nerolic acid and E,E farnesol.
b) Maximum production is found in foragers; it is low in winter and high in the spring.
c) The pheromone is highly attractive to bees and is in much evidence when bees are shaken, swarms being hived, etc. It is only found in workers and is used generally at or near the hive entrance. Colloquially known as 'the come in and join us' pheromone.
d) Associated with the collection of water (foragers release Nasonov pheromone) but not with nectar or pollen. Also used on rich sources of sugar syrup as this also is odourless.

The sting. (see diagrams 4.2 and 4.14)The actual sting consists basically of 3 parts: stylet and 2 lancets (barbed). There are other associated parts namely, bulb and umbrella valves, the rami, oblong plate (fixed), quadrate plate (moveable), triangular plate (moveable), muscles connected to the oblong and quadrate plates, acid sac, acid gland and alkaline gland.

a) The lancets slide on tracks on the stylet and the 3 parts form a tube (the venom canal).
b) The stylet and lancets are connected to a bulb via vents and umbrella valves which deliver the venom from the bulb down through the venom canal.
c) Each lancet is connected to a corresponding ramus which in turn is connected to a pivoting triangular plate. Movement of the triangular plate is rotational, activated by a moving quadrilateral plate and also a fixed oblong plate. One corner of the triangular plate is pivoted to the fixed oblong plate.
d) As one lancet is pushed forward, a simultaneous action withdraws the other and vice versa.
e) Movement of the ramus and lancet also operates the umbrella valve in the bulb, thereby ejecting venom from the bulb into the venom canal.
f) The bulb (venom reservoir) is connected to the venom gland via the acid sac. Another gland, the alkaline gland appears to supply the bulb but actually secretes into the sting chamber.
g) The use of the alkaline gland is not exactly known. Suggested uses are lubricant for the stylet and in the case of the queen for gumming eggs to the base of the cell. Neither uses are proven. The acid gland produces the venom which contains:

Phospholipase A *   enzyme
Hyaluronidase *   enzyme
Acid phosphatase   enzyme
Allergen C *
Mellitin *
Mellitin F
Mast cell degranulator peptides
Secapin, tertiapin, etc.
(* = main allergens).

Note that the above are the main constituents of bee venom, but other substances are present in small quantities.
h) Use of the sting – only known to be used for self defence and defence of the colony.

It should be noted that different strains of bee have a greater or lesser degree of colony defensive behaviour.

i) When a bee leaves its sting in the victim and tears itself away, the associated ganglion and muscles are still attached to the sting and the lancets continue to operate, the sting penetrating deeper and deeper. It should be scraped out with a knife or finger nail as quickly as possible. The enzymes in the venom cause the release of histamine from mast cells which causes swelling. Other allergens effect the nervous system.

j) The queen only uses her slightly curved sting against rival queens. Most books state that her sting is barbless; there are however 2 or 3 small barbs at the tip of the sting.

Wax glands and wax production (see diagram 4.3): the glands are located inside the exoskeleton on sternites A4–A7 inclusive. There are 2 glands on each sternite, making 4 pairs in all. The glands secrete a liquid which passes through the mirrors and oxidises as a flake of wax in the wax pockets. The glands, mirrors and pockets being known colloquially as the 'waistcoat pockets'.

a) Wax is secreted at relatively high temperatures (33°C-36°C) after consumption of large amounts of honey. Various estimates are quoted for the amount of honey to metabolise 1lb of wax. 5–8lb. being a realistic estimate.

b) Wax glands are best developed in worker bees 12–18 days old.

c) When building comb, bees hang in festoons near the building place, after gorging themselves with honey, waiting for the wax to form.

d) The wax glands inside the exoskeleton are covered with fat bodies and other cells. The major components of beeswax are:

– hydrocarbons	16%
– monohydric alchohols	31%
– hydroxy acids	13%
– fatty acids	31%
– diols	3%
– other substances	6%

e) The chemistry of how the wax is produced and how it diffuses through the mirrors is extremely complex and it is not necessary to know the detail; however it is necessary to know that a diffusion process is involved.

f) Wax is normally white but can be tinged with yellow hues caused by pigments that originate in pollen (eg. when a colony is working dandelion, new comb is noticeably coloured yellow).

g) For completeness a few of the physical properties of wax are:

– SG = 0.95 (Honey like odour & faint taste),
– when pure, melts at 147.9°F (64.4°C), solidifies at 146.3°F (63.5°C).

Salivary glands (thoracic and post-cerebral): there are two pairs of glands, one behind the brain (post-cerebral) and the other in the thorax. From these glands a duct from each emerges. The two ducts join, in the head, into a common duct leading to the salivary syringe at the top of the proboscis. Secretions from both glands run down the glossal tube and mingle with food which is then sucked up the food canal of the proboscis.

a) The secretions are used to dilute honey and to dissolve sugar crystals at times when water is scarce. The secretions are slightly alkaline and their use is not fully understood.

b) Analysis of the secretions have given very diverse results.

c) The thoracic glands in the adult worker bee are derived from the silk glands of the larva and not from the thoracic glands (more correctly pro-thoracic glands) of the larva which are used for secreting hormones during its development stage.

4.4 The storage of metabolites in the fat body.

Reference should be made to 'Anatomy and Physiology of the Honeybee' by Snodgrass figure 83 (1956 edition) for diagrams of the fat bodies.

The fat bodies are the storage cells of the developing larva and the adult bee. The cytoplasm of the cell contains small globules of yellowish oily liquid (fat), albuminoid granules (protein) and glycogen (sugar).

- In the larva, the fat body, consisting of small polygonal cells, increases in size and number with each stage of development. Finally before the cell is sealed the fat bodies occupy most of the space within the larval body cavity (65% of the body weight). In the pupal stage the fat cells release their contents into the blood where it becomes the building material for the newly developing imaginal tissues (metamorphosis). The white colour of the larva is due to the density and whiteness of the fat tissue pressed against the transparent skin of the larva.

- The fat bodies of the adult bee consists of thin layers of cells in loose strings spread against the body wall of the abdomen especially in the dorsal and ventral sinuses. In a young insect these cells resemble the haemocytes. The content and number of the cells varying with the age of the developing bee and with the season of the year ie. summer or winter bee. In the summer the fat bodies, swollen with large globules of fat will act as reserves of protein and glycogen to be used in the production of brood food and wax. In the winter the fat bodies contain large amounts of albuminoids acting as reserves of food for winter.

- Sugars are broken down to be stored as glycogen in the fat bodies. Glycogen can be broken down for energy (Kreb's cycle) by the body cells.

- It is a well known fact the bees need to consume large amounts of pollen (protein) before the hypopharyngeal glands will produce brood food and in order to survive the winter ie. associated with the longevity of the winter bee.

- Oenocytes, or oil cells, are found embedded in the fat body.

- Urates, excretory cells are found distributed among the cells of the fat body in developing larvae.

- The wax glands of the adult honey bee are richly supplied with oenocytes and fat bodies.

- In summary the fat body varies as follows:

Winter bee – long life – low fat content – high protein content

Summer bee – short life – high fat content – low protein content

The longevity of queenless bees is due to the absence of brood rearing and the high level of protein in the hypopharyngeal glands and fat bodies.

The variation of bees as a percentage of colony population with well developed hypopharyngeal glands and winter fat bodies is shown in diagram 4.4.

4.5 Metamorphosis in the honeybee including the duration of the stages of development of the larva and the pupa.

4.5.1 Definitions:

- Metamorphosis – change in form by magic or by natural development or change (usually rapid) between immature form and adult state.
- Caste (zoological definition) – form of social insect having a particular function.

It should be noted that some books and authors recognises two female castes and the drone (male caste). We believe the question of two or three castes is a matter of opinion, there being arguments in favour of both. As three have been recognised for over 100 years, the change seems unnecessary and we have not changed our original notes.

4.5.2 The three castes:

- worker – from a fertilised egg (female)   32 chromosomes
- queen – from a fertilised egg (female)   32 chromosomes
- drone – from an unfertilised egg (male)   16 chromosomes

4.5.3 Stages in the life cycle:

	WORKER	QUEEN	DRONE
OPEN CELL:			
Egg	3d	3d	3d
Larva (4 moults)	5d	5d	7d
SEALED CELL:			
Larva/pro-pupa (1 moult)	3d	2d	4d
Pupa (1 moult)	10d	6d	10d
From egg to emergence	21d	16d	24d
AFTER EMERGENCE:			
Summer bee	6w	c.3y	c.4m
Winter bee	c.6m	ditto	n/a

Note that the above times can vary by a few hours before emergence due to variations in temperature of the brood nest. [c.= approximately, d = day, w = weeks, m = months and y = years].

4.5.4 Description of the stages in the life cycles.

Worker (before emergence):

1st day of egg	– vertical, stuck to the bottom of the cell and parallel to the cell walls
2nd day	– at an angle of c. 45°
3rd day	– horizontal, egg laying on the bottom of cell. Egg hatches after 3 days.
4th-8th day	– larva grows, moulting every 24 hours, until it fills the whole cell diameter. The cell is sealed on 8th day after the larva's last meal.

8th-21st day	– the connection between the ventriculus and the hind gut opens and the Malpighian tubules open into hind gut; excreta enters hind gut and is voided into cell. Larva changes position and stretches out the full length of the cell (head outwards) and spins a cocoon. Metamorphosis occurs and the larva changes to a pupa after 5th moult 3 days after sealing. The pupa is still white but of adult form. It completes development, slowly changing colour and emerges from its cell by nibbling the capping on day 21. The 6th moult occurs just before emergence.

Queen and drone:

Similar but with the different timings shown above.

After eggs hatch, the larvae are immediately capable of eating food:

Workers and drones – are progressively fed with brood food for first 2–3 days, then a mixture of brood food, pollen and honey. No food is consumed during the pupal stage. Queens – are fed by mass provisioning with royal jelly throughout the larval stage. Queens are generally over fed and excess can usually be seen in the cell after emergence.

4.6 Caste differentiation in female honeybees particularly with respect to feeding.

4.6.1 Caste determination: both the queen and the worker are derived from a fertilised egg. Therefore, differentiation between queen and worker cannot be due to any genetic differences and must be due something else (e.g. feeding).

4.6.2 The queen is fed on royal jelly (a glandular secretion from the hypopharyngeal and mandibular glands of the worker bee) throughout the whole period from hatching of the egg to the propupa stage of development. A plentiful supply of royal jelly is available at all times for the larva. The larva continues to feed on the same diet after the cell is sealed.

4.6.3 The worker is fed on brood food (sometimes referred to as 'bee milk') for the first 2–3 days after the egg hatches, then honey and pollen are added to the brood food up to the sealing of the cell. Note that no food is left in the cell as in the case of the queen.

4.6.4 Analysis of larval food has given variable results:

- In 1888 Planta postulated that differing foods determined the female caste (queen or worker),
- In 1943 Haydak postulated that it was not the type of food that determined caste but the amount consumed. Experiments to test this theory have not been fully conclusive.
- In 1956 Weaver carried out feeding experiments to confirm Von Rheim's work in 1933 that there was a 'fugitive' substance in the larval food.
- In 1961 Jay disputed the interpretation of Weaver's results.

It is clear that, at present, the exact mechanism determining caste of the female is not fully understood and more work is required to answer the problem fully. The problem is not an easy one to understand and the subject is taken further in Module 5 (Volume 2). However for examination purposes for module 4, summarising present thinking about caste determination is as follows:

- It is triggered by the sugar content of the larval diet under 3 days old,
- The sugars induce increased food intake and growth of the corpora allata (CA) an internal gland which produces a special hormone,
- The hormone in some way is responsible for the differentiation in the anatomical and morphological characteristics. The precise mechanism is unknown at present.

4.6.5 Cell differences. The only other differences are in the cell (ie. worker and queen cells); the size and orientation have been shown to have no effect on caste determination.

4.7 Laying workers and drone laying queens and the conditions leading to their development.

4.7.1 Detection of a drone laying queen & the causes for this failure.

4.7.1.1 The visual signs:

- Unmistakable worker cells with drone cappings (raised).
- Presence of a queen (actually seen).
- Drones produced are small and abnormal (stunted).

4.7.1.2 During the season:

- Queen produces small areas of drone brood in the middle of large patches of worker brood.
- As the season progresses, worker brood becomes less and drone brood increases.
- Because some worker brood remains, it is clear that a queen must be laying.
- Eventually there will be nothing but drone cappings. At this stage the colony will be reasonably large.
- Drones are smaller and the abdomen stunted.

4.7.1.3 In the spring:

- Very difficult to detect at the first examination of the colony ie. a small colony with one or two frames of drone brood only (no worker).
- Is it a drone laying queen or laying workers?
- If a queen (drone layer), the laying pattern will be orderly i.e. compact patches of brood with very few empty cells.

4.7.1.4 Possible causes for a queen becoming a drone layer:

- Shortage of sperm – inadequate mating or due to age.
- Physical inability of queen to fertilise eggs correctly.
- Genetic fault.

4.7.1.5 Treatment:

- Requeen or
- unite after removing old drone laying queen.

4.7.2 Detection of laying workers and description of why they occur.

4.7.2.1 Detection of laying workers:

- Drones in worker cells (typical raised domes).
- Drones produced in this way are small and abnormal (stunted).
- Laying pattern is scattered and haphazard (cf. drone laying queen which is compact and orderly).
- Colony endeavours to build charged queen cells (note: this can happen with drone laying queen but is unusual).
- Workers generally lay more than one egg/cell and they are more often than not on the sides of the cells because a worker's abdomen is much shorter than a queen. We have seen as many as 7 eggs in one cell but 2 or 3 are more normal for this condition.

4.7.2.2 Pheromones. In the absence of the queen and normal worker brood there is an absence of pheromones from the queen herself and from worker brood. These pheromones, particularly that produced by the queen, inhibit development of a workers' ovaries. The workers start laying after about 21 days of being in the queenless state when their vestigial ovaries are sufficiently developed.

4.7.2.3 Causes for a colony having laying workers:

- Queenlessness.
- Inability to produce emergency queen cells (no fertilised eggs).

4.7.2.4 Treatment: it is generally agreed that little can be done except to shake the colony out near a strong stock and let them take 'pot luck' after the hive and all its parts have been removed.

The following points are pertinent:

- Difficult (impossible?) to requeen;
- a colony usually kills an introduced queen.
- Bees are mostly old and not much use to another colony.
- If they are united to a queenright colony it has been found that there is the likelihood of them killing the queen of the colony to which they are united.
- Experiments conducted in France in 1989 on the introduction of queens to colonies of laying workers by dipping the queen in royal jelly and water (70% and 30% respectively) are claimed to be a successful treatment. We regard this to be of academic interest only and has no practical value in beekeeping management.

4.8 The external structure of queen, worker and drone and the differences between them.

4.8.1 Description of the structure and segmentation of the exoskeleton.

The exoskeleton consists of (see diagram 4.5):

- epicuticle – thin outside greasy waterproof layer,
- cuticle – consisting of two parts:
    (1) exo cuticle – hard sclerotin,
    (2) endo cuticle – soft chitin,
- epidermis – cellular, which secretes to form the cuticle.
- basement membrane – on the lower side of the epidermis; it is to this basement membrane that many muscles are attached. The sensilla of most of the sense organs are formed in the epidermis.

Some of the terms used when describing the exoskeleton and the anatomy of the bee are as follows:

Ventral	under side
Dorsal	upper or back side
Anterior	head end
Posterior	tail end
Lateral	side
Proximal	near to point of attachment
Distal	away from point of attachment

The exoskeleton is divided into three parts namely:

Head, thorax and abdomen (see diagrams 4.6 to 4.8).

4.8.1.1 Head – is derived from the 6 basic segments (see Dade fig.1 & pl.2)

Appendages – 2 antennae, mouthparts and eyes (5). There has been extensive specialisation of each of the basic segments to form these parts.

4.8.1.2 Thorax – consists of 4 basic segments:
    prothorax (T1)
    mesothorax (T2)
    metathorax (T3)
    propodeum (A1)

In many insects there is a constriction between the thorax and the abdomen; in the order hymenoptera this constriction (petiole) has developed between the first and second abdominal segments of the worm-like ancestors of the insects.

Each true thoracic segment consists of 4 plates:
Tergite	on the dorsal surface
Sternite	on the ventral surface
2 pleurites on	on the lateral surfaces or the sides.

Appendages – 6 legs (2 on each thoracic segment) and 4 wings connected between tergite and pleurites of T2 & T3

4.8.1.3 Abdomen – is derived from 9 basic segments consisting of 2 plates only; a tergite and a sternite.

Note that there are 10 basic abdominal segments. A1 is on the thorax and A2 to A10 are on the abdomen. On the actual abdomen only 6 can be seen (A2 to A7); A8 to A10 are part of the internal structure and cannot be seen externally.

4.8.1.4 Exoskeleton. A large part of the exoskeleton is covered in hair; a vital part of the anatomy enabling the bee to collect pollen. Flexible joints consisting of a membrane with a thin layer of cuticle connect the rigid plates of the exoskeleton. Note the differences in size and shape of the exoskeletons of the queen worker and drone (there are good diagrams in Dade which is invaluable for this part of the module).

4.8.1.5 Other parts on the exoskeleton which are visible externally are:

- Nasonov gland – located on the dorsal side in the inter segmental joint between A6 and A7 (worker only).
- 10 pairs of spiracles (9 prs. visible; 10th pr. on A8 associated with the sting)
    1st pr. largest on T2, the valve cannot be closed.
    2nd pr. smallest on T3
    3rd pr. largest outlet on A1
    4th to 9th visible on A2 to A7
- 4 prs. of wax glands are situated under sternites A4 to A7 inclusive (worker only). These cannot be seen normally, however the wax scales being produced by worker bees are often in evidence during nectar flows.

4.8.2 Detailed description of external structure of queen, drone and worker.

4.8.2.1 Structure common to all three: head, thorax and abdomen:

- Head   2 compound eyes, 3 simple eyes (ocelli),
              2 antennae (scape + flagellum),
              2 mandibles,
              1 proboscis.
- Thorax – 4 segments (T1 to T3 plus A1),
              2 prs. wings (between tergites and pleurites of T2 & T3),
              3 prs. legs (on segments T1, T2 and T3).

- Abdomen   6 visible segments (A2 to A7),
              3 invisible segments A8 to A10 (which are internal and part of the sting chamber).

4.8.2.2 Physical size: Worker about $\frac{5}{8}$in (16mm) long.
                          Queen about 1in (25mm) long but larger than a worker in diameter; nb. queen excluder.
                          Drone about $\frac{3}{4}$in (19mm) long (much fatter than q. or w.).

4.8.2.3 Head:	Worker – triangular in shape with long proboscis.
	Queen – similar to w. but rounder with short proboscis.
	Drone – almost circular (n.b. large compound eyes). Antenna has extra joint (flagellum 12 segments) and mandibles are very small. The proboscis is short.
4.8.2.4 Thorax:	Worker/queen – similar in size; dorsal side in q. appears hairless cf. a worker.
	Drone – larger/stronger, larger wings (stronger flier).
4.8.2.5 Abdomen:	Queen – very distinctive (long/tapering).
	Drone – also distinctive (fat and furry).
	Worker – specialised (wax and Nasonov glands).
	All castes have 10 prs. spiracles on segments T2 to A8, the last being invisible and inside the abdomen.
4.8.2.6 Legs:	All have the same formation – coxa, trochanter, femur, tibia, 5 tarsal joints and a foot (pretarsus).
	Note: the fore legs of all 3 castes have an antenna cleaner and only workers have pollen collecting equipment on the rear legs. The hairs on the basitarsi of the fore legs are used as a brush for cleaning the eyes and head in all castes (see diagram 4.10).
4.8.2.7 Wings:	Forward pr. large with fold to engage with the hamuli on the smaller rear wing. Drone wings much larger. In all 3 castes the wings are folded at rest and lay flat on dorsal side of the abdomen.
4.8.2.8 Hair:	The whole of the exoskeleton is covered in plumose hairs which have an important function in the worker for trapping pollen

4.9 The structure and function of mouthparts, legs, antennae, sting and wings of the adult honeybee.

It is important to refer to a diagrams 4.6 and 4.9.

4.9.1 Mouthparts – consist of:

1 clypeus	– below the antennae.
1 labrum	– hinged to the clypeus and below it. Soft pad (the epipharynx) on the under side of the labrum is shaped to fit the proboscis. When in use it makes an airtight seal around the proboscis at the laciniae to allow it to function as a sucking pump.
2 mandibles	– working in horizontal plane are hinged to the genae. Concave and ridged on inner side. Both have grooves which connect to a duct in the mandibular glands. Note the differences in q., d. and w. mandibles.
	Function: shovelling food into the mouth, handling, biting, cutting and kneading wax, building comb, collecting and applying propolis, feeding brood food and pollen to larvae, dragging debris out of hive, grooming, fighting and for supporting the proboscis when extended.

1 proboscis	– (complicated structure: see diagram in Dade Plate 3 and diagrams 4.9 and 4.13) It consists of 2 basic parts – the central portion (glossa, etc.), – outer portion (maxillae, labial palps).

- Central portion – postmentum, prementum, paraglossa, glossa and flabellum. The last 3 are surrounded by 2 labial palps.
- Outer portion – 2 maxillae, each consisting of stipe, lacinia and galea.
- The maxillae are connected laterally to the postmentum by two lora and by two cardines to the fossa (in a fore and aft direction).
- The labial palps and the galeae are formed into a hollow section with the glossa in the middle. Honey, nectar and water are sucked up this section via the inter-space (food canal) outside the glossa.
- Saliva (mixed secretions from the postcerebral and thoracic glands) flows into a pouch (the salivarium) near the junction of the glossa and the prementum. It runs down inside the glossa ('C' shaped section) and mixes with nectar or syrup taken up the food canal.
- The proboscis when at rest is folded underneath and is hinged at the junction of the prementum and paraglossa.
- The proboscis when in use is extended forward and raised to mouth level, sealed by the epipharynx of the labrum and grasped by the mandibles to steady it. Honey, nectar or water are then sucked up.
- If the quantity of liquid is small, the end of the glossa (hair covered) picks up small droplets due to surface tension and the glossa is then retracted into the food canal where it can then be sucked up as before.
- Note the difference in length of the antennae in the three castes and the variations that occur between different species of apis mellifera.

4.9.2 Antennae.

The bee has two antennae (diagram 4.11) each consisting of:

- the scape (nearest to the head),
- the flagellum (segmented, 11 segs. in q. and w., 12 in d.). Note 1st segment is called the pedicel.

The antennae are the sense organs used for a variety of sensing purposes. The flagellum of the antenna is covered in sensilla (sensors connected to nerves through the exoskeleton) of different types and used for different purposes as follows:-

- touch	sensilla trichodia	hairs
- smell	s. basiconica	pegs
- CO_2, RH, T	s. coeloconica	pits
- stress/strain	s. campaniformia	bells
- smell	s. placodea	plates

Sensilla appear in great numbers on the 8 distal segments. The s. placodea associated with the 3 castes are as follows:–

- Queen – 2 to 3000
- Worker – 5 to 6000
- Drone – c. 30,000

A drone can detect the presence of a queen in flight at a distance of c. 50 metres using the s. placodea to detect the pheromone 'queen substance'. Experiments amputating the segments on the flagellum show that the senses are virtually lost when 8 segments are removed.

The 'Organ of Johnston' is situated in the pedicel and is believed to detect vibrations and is used by the bee as a wind speed indicator.

The antennae are used continually during food transfer and appear to be play an important part in this function. However, no antennal language has yet been discovered.

4.9.3 Wings.

The wings (diagram 4.12) are used for:

- Flying and hovering (forwards, backwards, up and down).
- Fanning for   – ventilation (cooling),
                – ripening honey,
                – distributing pheromones (e.g. Nasonov).

- 2 pairs wings (fore and rear; fore wing on segment T2 and rear on T3. Fore wing is the larger of the two.
- When the wings are furled, and at rest, they are separate one from the other. As they are unfurled, ready for flight, they are joined by hamuli (hooks) on fore edge of the rear wing connecting on to the fold on the rear edge of the fore wing. There are about 20 hamuli on each of the rear wings. The exact number can vary slightly.
- The wing roots attach to tergite and pleurite on segments T2 & T3 – pleurite provides a fulcrum for movement of the wings.
- In flight , the wings are operated by large indirect muscles in the thorax; these muscles drive only the fore wing, the rear wing trails on the fore wing via the coupling at the fold and hamuli. These indirect muscles only provide up and down movement to the wings.
- There are direct muscles attached to all 4 wings, 4 muscles on each fore wing and 3 on the rear wings. These direct muscles are used only for furling/unfurling and for 'trimming' (i.e. twisting) the wings to correct for yawing, rolling and pitching during flight.
- Vibrations while in flight = c. 200/250 c.p.s.
- Speed of flight = c. 15 m.p.h. but can increase to 25 m.p.h. for short periods.
- Blood sugar content for flight = c. 2% (1% cannot fly, 0.5% cannot move).
- Rate of fuel (sugar) consumption = 10mg/hr during flight; this is c. 50 times greater than at rest.
- Range = 4/5 miles (c. 15 mins.); can be extended by resting while glycogen stored in body is converted to sugar.
- Note the use of the scutal fissure for operating the wings during flight.
- The venation in the wings is used as a biometric aid in the identification of various strains of bee (taxonomy).

4.9.4 Legs.

The bee has 3 pairs of legs; appendages to T1, T2 & T3. They are used for: standing, walking and clinging to a variety of surfaces at any angle or upside down. The most important use, however, is for cleaning, comb building and the collection and transportation of pollen and propolis. See diagram 4.10.

- Each leg has 6 major divisions which can be articulated separately by internal muscles; these are:

  - coxa
  - trochanter
  - femur
  - tibia
  - tarsus (divided into 5 tarsomeres)
  - pretarsus (consists of 2 claws for rough surfaces and an arolium for smooth surfaces) or foot.

- Forelegs: are small and close behind the head (ALL CASTES). Hairs on the 1st tarsomere (basitarsus) are used for cleaning dust/pollen, etc. from the head. Circular notch in basitarsus and spur (fibula) on the tibia form the antenna cleaner. The circular notch is lined with fine hairs to provide a comb.
- Middle legs: Single spine on tibia has no known use. This leg has no specific function except for the pollen brushes on the inner surface of basitarsus for cleaning pollen from the thorax and passing it to the rear legs.
- Rear legs: Pollen press and basket (WORKER BEE ONLY). The harvest of pollen collects on the pollen brushes of the basitarsus. While hovering, the bee rubs her hind legs together and the pollen is raked by the rastellum of the opposite leg on the distal end of the tibia. The pollen falls into the auricle and the tibio-tarsal joint is closed and pollen is squeezed and forced to emerge onto the outer side of the leg to be caught in the long hairs of the corbicula on the tibia. Back in the hive, the pellets of pollen are disengaged by the middle legs and dropped into cells. Propolis is bitten off with the mandibles and also carried back to the hive in the corbicula but unloaded by another bee. Wax plates are removed from the mirrors of the abdominal sternites by the rear legs. The drone and the queen have no specialised functions for the use of the rear legs.

4.9.5 The sting.

The actual sting consists basically of 3 parts: stylet and 2 lancets (barbed). There are other associated parts namely, bulb and umbrella valves, the rami, oblong plate (fixed), quadrate plate (moveable), triangular plate (moveable), muscles connected to the oblong and quadrate plates, acid sac, acid gland and alkaline gland. See diagrams 4.2 and 4.14. and section 4.3.

4.10 The functions and behaviour of the worker honeybee throughout its life, including foraging behaviour and orientation.

4.10.1 Description of the work undertaken by worker bees.

The work undertaken by the worker bee is generally dependent on the age of the bee and the development of various glands:

- 0 – 3d   House (hive) cleaning, eg. cells for q. to lay in.
- 3 – 9d   Feeding larvae / nursing.   *
- 9 – 18d   Ripening honey.   *
            Wax making / comb building.   *
            Ventilation / evaporation.
            Temperature control.
- 18 – 21d   Guarding / defence.   *
- 3 – 6w   Foraging.

* – these activities require a glandular activity in the bee; 1st the hypopharyngeal and mandibular glands develop for producing brood food / royal jelly and enzymes for processing nectar into honey, 2nd the wax glands become operative at about 12d. and finally the sting produces venom at about 18d.

It should be noted that the bee works for 8 hours, patrols for 8 hours and rests for 8 hours, although these activities are not performed in 8 hour stretches. The tasks undertaken by the worker bee at its various ages are generally referred to as the 'division of labour'.

4.10.2 Note rule of three!

3 castes q., w., d.
Egg 3d to hatch.
Egg to worker emerging 3w.
Duty as house bee 3w.
Field bee 3w.
Life of drone c. 3m.
Life of queen c. 3y.

4.10.3 House cleaning.

This includes:

- Cell cleaning – removal of excreta, larval moults and then polishing cells ready for laying.
- Hive cleaning – removal of dead bees and debris from the floor. These are menial tasks undertaken by the youngest bees with no experience of other duties; they are performed instinctively and start more or less immediately the bee emerges from its cell.

4.10.4. Feeding / nursing.

- Feeding older larvae   3 – 6d.
- Feeding young larvae   6 – 9d.
- Capping brood cells   9 – 12d.

At 3d. old the hypopharyngeal glands start to become active and the nurse bees take up feeding duties for about 6d. (3–9d. old). At about 9d. old the wax making glands become active. Note very young and very old bees do not secrete wax. From about 9–12d old the nurse bees (now secreting wax) start brood capping duties. Note the colour of the cell cappings; they contain pollen mixed with beeswax to make them porous allowing the larvae/pupae to breathe. Cells filled with honey are capped with pure wax.

4.10.5 Processing nectar into honey.

For a complete description see section 2.2.2.

4.10.6 Wax making/comb building.

- Wax secretion generally occurs in bees 12–18 days old at relatively high temperatures 33°–36°C (91.4° – 96.8°F). The wax is secreted in small flakes from 4 pairs of wax glands on the last 4 visible segments on the ventral side of the abdomen (colloquially known as the waistcoat pockets), ie on the sternites A4 – A7.
- Large honey consumption is required in order that the bee may produce wax. In the literature various estimates are given; however 8lb of honey for 1lb of wax seems to be a realistic mean.
- When building comb, workers gorge themselves with honey and hang in festoons for c. 24 hrs. before the wax secretion and building process starts.
- A wax scale is removed by one hind leg and transferred to the mandibles by the two fore legs. The wax scale is thoroughly masticated before fixing to the comb and moulding it in place. When it is first deposited it is spongy and flaky and is later manipulated again making it smoother and more compact. Removing, masticating and fixing one scale takes about 4 minutes. It is not clear whether any secretions from any of the glands are used in comb building (mandibular, salivary, etc.). Some books indicate that the mandibular glands are used. On the basis of one scale taking 4 minutes to manipulate, 66,000 bee hours are involved building 77,000 worker cells using 1kg of beeswax.
- Bees can detect gravity (sensilla at the petiole between the head and the thorax) and the festooning chains (catenaries) play an important role in the parallelism of the combs.
- Queenlessness and bright light inhibit the bees to build comb and secrete wax.
- According to Dadant, the thickness of the wall of newly built comb is approx. 0.0025in thick and in naturally drawn comb without the use of foundation, the base is 0.0035in thick; Hooper gives 0.006in for the cell wall thickness and Winston 0.073mm (0.003in).

4.10.7 Evaporation.

- The sugar content of nectar varies considerably depending on temperature, humidity, sunshine, wind speed and direction, etc. If the incoming nectar contains 40% sugar then there is c.60% water. After manipulation by the house bees, the ripened nectar will contain c.15% less water, ie. 45% water. Ripe honey contains c.20% water; the difference between 45% and 20% is due to evaporation as warm air is passed over the combs by fanning bees.
- Nectar is first manipulated by the bees (gorging and regurgitating), causing both a physical as well as a chemical change before it is hung up in droplets in empty or partially filled cells (ie. largest surface area). It is spread over a large area of comb and later gathered up and concentrated into a smaller area of comb. For this reason it is very important to provide adequate comb space during a nectar flow.
- On average it takes about 4/5 days to ripen nectar from 60% water content to honey of c.20% water content.
- During the journey back to the hive, the water content remains virtually unchanged.
- Evaporation is dependent on:

- storage cells (space) available
- temperature (directly)
- humidity (inversely)
- ventilation

- There is a need for a continuous stream of air from outside to inside as the air inside becomes saturated. The RH inside the hive varies from 20%–80%. In the brood nest it is fairly constant, 35%–45%RH.
- As an example during a heavy flow with a strong colony c. 2.5kg of water are evaporated in 24 hrs. or 50% of the gross gain per day. c.2/3 of this total loss occurring during the day.
- For each field bee (forager) there are approx. two bees in the hive for house duties which include the ripening and storage of honey. The importance of good hive ventilation is clear; it being important to allow top ventilation through the crown board and roof ventilators as well as the hive entrance at the bottom.

4.10.8 Ventilation.

- Ventilation of the hive is always necessary in order to expel CO_2, to expel water vapour when the colony is ripening honey and for cooling purposes in hot weather. This can be achieved by the bees but assistance can be given by the beekeeper so that the colony is put under minimum stress.
- When the temperature of the brood nest (93°–95°F) tends to rise above its normal limits, there is a colony response. The bees sense the need for ventilation to control both the temperature and the humidity (35–45%RH). Temperature control is necessary to incubate the brood and control of RH is required so that brood food and royal jelly, when present, does not dry out.
- By evaporating water from nectar or from water actually brought into the hive, the heat is 'used up' thereby cooling the hive. When water evaporates there is a drop in temperature (known as the latent heat of vaporisation). The bees do this by fanning; it is a very economical and efficient air conditioning system.
- Fanning: bees collect to one side of the entrance and face inwards and fan vigorously creating an outward flow of air. Others are doing the same thing further in on the floorboard. There can be up to hundreds fanning and the draught created can easily be felt with the hand near the entrance. If the conditions become extreme, a further group will start fanning on the other side of the entrance but facing outwards and setting up in inward current of fresh cool air. Fanning is normally undertaken by older bees who are muscularly strong to perform this task.
- The beekeeper can assist in hot weather by:

    - providing sufficient space within the hive,
    - providing shade over the hive at noon and/or pm,
    - ensuring the crown board feed hole is open and the roof
    - ventilators are not blocked,
    - keeping undergrowth trimmed around the hives,
    - in extreme conditions:- staggering supers, off setting crown boards and roofs, raising hive above the floor (say 25mm or 1in).
    - Note that late in the season to prevent robbing the hive must be beetight and only have one entrance which can be guarded.

- When bees are being moved the temperature increases very rapidly due the disturbance and travelling screens are essential, particularly in summer.

- Ventilation in winter: The degree of ventilation required for successful wintering is not agreed among the experts and the literature can be confusing on the subject. The amount is determined by the sizes of the openings top and bottom and the convection currents (warm air rising around the cluster). The variables are:

  – size of entrance (nb. mouse guards),
  – size of top ventilation
      a) raised crown board (matchsticks)
      b) Morris board
      c) crown board completely removed
      d) size of roof ventilators.

It is generally agreed that greater ventilation is required in warmer and damper regions cf. colder and drier regions. However, it should be noted that about 4 gallons of water have to be dispensed with by evaporation due to the consumption of c. 30lb of winter stores.

4.10.9 Temperature control.

- Individual bees have no means of controlling their body temperature and quickly assume the ambient air temperature (they are said to be poikilothermic). Their activity, both physical and physiological, quickens with a rise of temperature and slows as it falls. This automatic effect of temperature on metabolism may serve to stimulate equally automatic social actions to adjust the temperature of the hive. It should be noted that the bee is capable of sensing temperature, if it could not do so it would be unable to survive.
- Temperature is lowered by:

  – fanning at entrance and inside the hive,
  – water evaporation,
  – dispersion through the hive (as opposed to clustering),
  – clustering of bees outside the hive entrance.

- Temperature is increased by:

  – muscular activity (thorax muscles),
  – clustering tightly,
  – manipulating a colony or moving a colony (muscular activity).

- Activity temperatures:

  – all activities occur between 10°–38°C (50° – 110°F) ,
  – brood nest 35°C (95°F),
  – unable to fly at 10°C (50°F)*,
  – becomes immobile at 7°C (45°F),
  – clustering starts at 14°C (57°F),
  – thorax T = 20°–36° (68°–97°F) normally 29°C (84°F).

- The lower the temperature, the tighter the cluster (physically smaller) thereby providing a

---

* Very often bees can be seen flying at air temperatures lower than this; the actual temperature of the bee is therefore above 10°C. Water collecting in the spring can be a very hazardous occupation for the honeybee; it must not allow its body temperature to fall below the critical 10°C while it is taking water or it can never return to the hive.

smaller surface area and less heat loss. At very low temperatures the bees bury their thoraces in the cluster and spread their wings (also to reduce heat loss) with abdomens out. The connective cluster under these conditions merges with the main cluster.
- The old adage that bees never freeze to death, only starve to death, is very accurate. With an adequate supply of stores they can survive very low temperatures by generating sufficient heat in the centre of the cluster to maintain the outer surface of the cluster at just above 7°C. This stops the bees on the outside from becoming immobile and falling off. Note that, contrary to popular belief, the bees in the cluster do not continually change position to keep warm.

4.10.10 Defence.

- Defence generally occurs at the hive or within a few metres of it. The defensive vigour of a colony depends on the genetic 'make up' of the strain, some bees being much more aggressive than others.
- No guard bees are likely to be found at the entrance of a colony during a nectar flow. Conversely, during times of dearth, many guard bees will be seen.
- Guard bees exhibit a typical stance – standing on their 4 rear legs, forelegs raised and antennae outstretched. If some become alarmed, they open their mandibles and spread their wings ready for attack.
- Each guard bee 'patrols' a particular area. They check incoming foragers and challenge drifting bees by touching with their antennae (1–3 sec).
- Robbers (both bees and wasps) have a distinctive flight noticeable to guard bees who will always attack in defence rather than challenge first.
- Stinging is a defensive mechanism, not an attacking one. In an undisturbed colony less than half % of the bees in a colony are likely to sting (200 in 40,000).
- Guard bees are sensitive to:

  – vibrations,
  – visual stimulus (fast movements),
  – odours (animals, humans and pheromones).

Once the guard bees have been alerted, they will fly round the area outside the hive, the distance they guard depending on the strain of bee. The Africanised bee in S. America will guard at distances greater than $\frac{1}{2}$ mile. Many bees in UK (usually bad tempered stocks) will follow for a few hundred yards. A few yards is typical for a reasonably tempered colony.

- Bees from the same colony have the same smell due to the food sharing and transmission among all the bees in the colony. For these reasons Bro. Adam believes there is a hive odour. Dr. Colin Butler on the other hand maintained there is a colony odour which is genetically produced. Whatever the reason it is generally agreed that guard bees can recognise bees from another hive whether they be drifters or robbers.
- Colonies working the same flower (eg. rape) would be expected to develop the same hive odour and recognition would be through colony odour. However under these conditions, where a flow exists, there are usually no guard bees present and it is clear more work is required on colony versus hive odour theories.
- Stimuli that elicit stinging behaviour are:

  – exhaled breath,
  – smell of hair, leather and many cosmetics,
  – violent vibrations and bumps,

– rapid movements,
– most important – alarm pheromones (bee venom and isopentylacetate from the sting and 2–heptanone from the mandibular glands).

• Guard bees are usually 18d. old prior to becoming foragers. When the guards are alerted and pheromones are distributed around the hive, foraging tends to stop and the foragers become guard bees; many more bees are noticeable at the hive entrance under these conditions.

4.10.11 Foraging.

In a well balanced colony in the season c.$^1/_3$ worker bees are foragers, the other $^2/_3$ are house bees. Workers normally start foraging at c. 21 days old and continue until they die (away from the hive) c. 3 weeks later. They forage only in the daylight hours and in favourable weather; $T \approx 55°F$ (13°C) and above, flying 6–10ft above ground in winds below 15mph (24 km/h). Flying at 15mph, they consume honey at a rate of 10mg/hr.
They forage up to c. 2.5 miles from the hive. They forage for nectar, pollen, propolis and water. When $T=43°C$ (109°F) and above they only forage for water. A small number of the foragers (about 2%) act as scout bees, a very important activity; however it is virtually impossible to determine the exact number.

• Foraging is stimulated by:

– presence of the queen and brood (both produce stimulating pheromones),
– the needs of the colony indicated by food exchange in the colony and the speed foragers are unloaded by house bees,
– scout bees dancing on the combs providing information on distance, direction and quality of the source. The most stimulating dances attract the most foraging activity.

• Foraging bees collect nectar, pollen, water and propolis.

Nectar: this is collected from the nectaries and extra floral nectaries of suitable flowers providing they are yielding nectar and the bee's proboscis is long enough to reach it.

– Nectar is sucked up by the proboscis, the average load being 40mg and the maximum load c. 80mg.
– The returning forager unloads by passing the nectar load to a house bee for manipulation and subsequent ripening.
– The speed of unloading by the house bee indicates the colony's needs (note that high sugar content is preferable to low sugar content).
– Foragers are constant to a particular species of flower and will rest in the hive if it is not yielding at a particular time.
– The number of trips per day is an average of 10 and generally range from c. 7–13 trips.
– The average time per trip is c.1 hr, half this time is spent flying and the other half collecting and unloading. When unfavourable conditions prevail, trips as long as 3-4 hr have been reported.
– Number of flowers visited per trip to obtain a full load is very variable (50–1000) and depends on all the variables associated with the secretion of nectar.
– It should be noted that bees also forage for honeydew, the sugary exudate of many species of aphid.

Pollen: this is collected from the anthers of flowers either intentionally or by chance when foraging for nectar. It is collected by the plumose hairs covering the exoskeleton and transferred to the corbiculae by the 3 pairs of legs.

- The average load (weight of both pollen pellets) ranges from 11–29mg.
- The pollen collecting trips are completed more quickly than nectar collecting trips. Range is reported to be 3–18 minutes.
- The pollen forager returns to the hive and deposits the load directly into a cell adjacent to the brood nest without assistance from house bees. Later, house bees come along and pack the pollen loads into the cells and finally, for storing, they are sealed with a layer of honey and wax. This pollen is known as 'pickled pollen'.
- Open brood provides a pheromone which induces foraging for pollen in addition to queen substance.
- The number of pollen foragers is controlled by the needs of the colony and the number of cells prepared by the house bees for pollen. It has been reported that they can vary from a few % to as high as 95% of the total foraging force.
- The number of foragers collecting mixed loads of both nectar and pollen is c. 3% of the foraging force.

Propolis: this is a resinous exudate from the bark or buds of trees which is collected by the bees for filling cracks in the hive, reducing openings (eg. entrances), smoothing the interior of the hive, varnishing the interior of brood cells, strengthening comb attachments and embalming objectionable objects too large to remove from the hive. It is antibiotic and is known to have an inhibiting effect on about 30 bacteria. For this reason the brood nest would be a most unhealthy environment if the bees did not use it for re-varnishing each cell every brood cycle. It is collected with much difficulty and transported back to the hive on the corbiculae.

- It takes a long time to collect and has to be unloaded with assistance from house bees, again taking a long time (1–2 hr.)
- Some strains of bee collect more propolis than others (eg.Caucasians) and therefore have a larger % of the foraging force collecting at the expense of nectar and pollen.
- In times of dearth, foragers will seek and use alternatives (eg. tar from roads).

Water: this is the only item which is collected and not stored in the hive. It is collected in the same way as nectar with the proboscis and transported to the hive in the crop.

- Water is required for diluting honey so that it can be metabolised, diluting honey for brood food for larval feeding, for humidifying the brood nest and for cooling the hive in very hot weather.
- The average load is 25–50mg. and the foraging trip is very short, most are completed in under 10 minutes.
- The average colony in the spring requires c.150g. per day and a strong colony in hot drought conditions requires c. 1kg per day.
- Reception by the house bees indicates the colony needs; if unloading takes longer than 3 mins. then water collection activity ceases.
- Water foragers mark favourable sites with Nasonov gland and fanning.
- At times water is stored, not directly in the hive but in the crops of the receiving house bees (reservoir bees); this happens when supplies are not readily available.

4.10.12 How the bee orientates to the hive.

The dictionary defines 'orientation' as applied to birds and insects as a faculty of finding their way home from a distant point or place.

- Orientation in the case of the honeybee involves:

    – the use of landmarks (in close proximity to the hive),
    – position of the sun (both altitude and azimuth),
    – ability of the bee to detect polarised and ultra violet light.

  Note also the ability of the bee to fly round obstacles to and from a food source.

- Young bees (during the time they are house bees) take short flights around the hive noting the landmarks in the very close vicinity (eg. large stones, a bush, a tree, etc.).

    (a) Occasionally much activity may be noticed at the hive entrance; these are young bees on initial orientation flights (popularly known as play flights). It is curious that quite a large number do this simultaneously. Successive flights are longer and further afield and occur about the time the bee is converting from a house bee to become a forager.
    (b) By the time the bee starts to forage it has a very precise knowledge of its immediate environment (say half mile radius from the hive). Moving the hive only 2 or 3 ft. disorientates the homecoming bees for a few hours until they re-adjust. It is for this reason that hives may only be moved 3 feet or 3 miles (the normal limit of their foraging range). Experiments conducted by the authors seem to indicate that when a hive is moved, the bee can only remember its old surroundings for c. 2 weeks; after this time it has completely forgotten its old hive vicinity.
    (c) With no immediate local landmarks, young bees tend to drift into other hives. Young bees drift more than older bees. Drifting is more pronounced when the bees have been confined in the hive for long periods (eg. winter); nb. the 2 week memory. It is therefore important when siting colonies in an apiary to have:

        – hives painted different colours,
        – hives facing in different directions,
        – plenty of local distinctive landmarks.

  Note that drifting can spread disease between colonies.

- All the above are visual; there is one other local orientation system frequently used (particularly after disorientation) and that is scent fanning, using the Nasonov pheromone, at the hive entrance.
- The honeybee only flies during daylight hours using its eyes for navigation; it is not equipped for night flying. The ocelli (simple eyes) are incapable of focusing an image and are used solely for measuring light intensity. The compound eyes do produce an image (albeit a poor one by our own standards); they are however capable of detecting polarised light and ultra violet light (UV). It is this capability which not only enables the bee to return to its hive but allows it to communicate the direction and distance to a source of forage to other bees in the hive.
- The sun is an extremely powerful source of UV being a maximum in the sun's direction. At other angles to the sun, the strength of the UV decreases as the angle increases. If the sky is

overcast and completely covered in cloud, the UV radiation still penetrates the cloud layer and the bee can detect it. The strength of the radiation is still a maximum in the direction of the sun; therefore the bee always knows in what part of the sky the sun is to be found.

- The light from the sun becomes polarised as it passes through space and the earth's atmosphere. The plane of polarisation being different in any particular direction (altitude above the horizon and azimuth). The compound eye of the bee can detect the plane of polarisation. Knowing the plane of polarisation and the direction of the sun, it automatically knows the angle between the two and can communicate this angle to the other inmates of the hive. The plane of polarisation defines the forage source which the bee flies to and it returns on a reciprocal course by the same means.
- Bees have another inbuilt mechanism; they can allow for the movement of the sun in the sky (15°/hr.) when calculating the angle to fly or to dance on the combs.
- When they reach the source of forage the foraging bee goes from flower to flower and finally returns to its starting point at the forage before setting a final course back to the hive. How the zig-zag course in the forage is calculated is still a mystery, although it has been proved that the sun is required.

4.10.13 Communication dances of worker honeybees.

- The main dances for communicating nectar and pollen sources, discovered by von Frisch, are:

    – Round dance   –   sources up to 100 m
    – Wagtail dance   –   sources over 100 m

- Round dance: contains little or no information except that the source is close to hand (within 100 m). Bees (newly recruited foragers) responding to this dance search in all directions from the hive. This dance is most apparent if wet supers are replaced on a colony after extraction during daylight. The colony very quickly (a few minutes) goes into a state of agitation with many bees 'milling around' the neighbourhood of the hive looking for the source which of course is on the hive above the brood chamber. This important 'deficiency' in the bees' communication system is the reason why wet supers should ONLY be returned to the hive after dark when the bees cannot fly.
- Wagtail dance (see appendix 14): provides very precise information on the direction and distance from the hive to the source of forage and the time it is available.

    – Direction is given as an angle between the food source and the sun. This angle is translated as the same angle between the vertical and the 'wagging direction' on the comb. The bee can determine the vertical by gravity sensors (between the head and thorax). The top of the comb always represents the sun. If the source, when viewed from the hive, is to the right of the sun, then the dance on the comb will be to the right of the vertical. For sources to the left of the sun, the dance will be to the left of the vertical.

    – Distance information is given by the number of 'straight runs' (centre of the pattern) every 15 seconds as follows:

        100 m = 9–10 runs/15 sec.
        600 m = 7   ditto
        1000 m = 4   ditto
        6000 m = 2   ditto

– Wenner (1962) discovered that during the wagtail portion of the dance, a series of sound blips are made ($\approx$250 Hz) which are inaudible to the human ear. The number of blips also correlate with distance. It is generally agreed that the number of runs per 15 sec is probably the most reliable indicator of distance.
– Time the forage is available is the time the bee is dancing on the comb. It should be noted that bees have the ability to 'remember' time (when the sun is in a particular direction).

• Other types of dances (which are poorly understood):

      – Alarm dances (eg. poisoned food) – spirals or zig-zag.
      – Cleaning dances – stamping legs + swinging body side to side.
      – DVAV* ('joy') dances – front legs on another bee + 5/6 shaking movements.
      – Massage dances – starts by bending head in curious way (sickness).
      – Vibration dances – just before a swarm departs.

* = Dorsal – ventral – abdominal – vibration

4.11 The mating behaviour of the honeybee queen and drone.

4.11.1 General.

• Queen mates on the wing between 5–20 days after emergence.
• If she has not mated in c.3 weeks she is no longer capable of mating properly and is known to be 'stale'. Sperm cannot migrate through the duct leading to the spermatheca.
• Bees in a colony with a virgin queen become more and more aggressive to her until she mates.
• This aggressive behaviour may be responsible for driving out the virgin queen before she is too old to mate and becomes stale.
• After mating, the bees are very attentive to the queen, grooming her and forming a court around her.

4.11.2 Drones.

• Drones often have collecting points where they tend to congregate. Such a congregation point attracts drones from a wide area ensuring drones of varying strains and thus minimising inbreeding. It has been observed that mating only occurs at heights of greater than 10m (33 ft) and less than 40m (130ft) above the ground. Also, the height of mating is inversely proportional to wind speed.
• There are drone congregation areas (DCA) where drones collect to mate. How these are chosen is unknown but some sites are used year after year.
• Drones in the area release a pheromone from their mandibular glands which not only attracts queens but also attracts other drones into the area ensuring a good mix of drones and genetic material from other colonies and other apiaries in the area. When many drones have congregated the pheromone density is high ensuring a good attractant to queens and the recruitment of other drones.

- When a queen enters the DCA the drones locate the queen initially by sight and then by sex attractant pheromone. They follow the queen in a comet tail formation of as many as 100 drones until one drone catches the queen and mating occurs.

4.11.3 The mating.

We have only been able to locate one description of the actual mating by Koeniger 1984 and the following is our summary of a much fuller account.

- Queen flies to the level of the drones and locates the DCA by the drone pheromones.
- Once in the DCA the queen responds to the drone pheromone by holding the entrance to her sting chamber open whilst in flight.
- The strongest flying drone from the 'comet' reaches the queen and grasps her with his legs. The fore and middle legs on the dorsal side of her abdomen and the hinds legs on the ventral side of her abdomen.
- The drone then bends his abdomen and everts his endophallus which enters the sting chamber. The drone then becomes 'paralysed' loses his hold and swings backwards.
- In this position he is carried along by the queen. The endophallus being shaped to fit in the sting chamber making it impossible to be released while the endophallus is everted.
- The cervix of the drone's penis enters the vagina and after a short pause evertion continues (even in the drone's paralysed state) and semen is ejaculated into the median and lateral oviducts.
- The pressure of the semen into the oviducts also pushes out part of the endophallus which becomes detached from the bulb.
- The drone drops to the ground to die and part of the bulb remains in the sting chamber. Some mucus from the mucus glands of the drone coagulates and forms a sealed plug.
- A second drone will mate with the queen in exactly the same way except that the second drone removes the mating sign first with his own endophallus.
- Perhaps up to 5 matings occur until the oviducts and vagina are full of sperm. This then enters the spermatheca by contraction of the oviduct muscles of the queen.
- Further matings (5–15) occur on 2 or 3 separate mating flights.
- Mating continues until the spermatheca is full of sperm. After mating the queen has sufficient sperm to last her life of 3–5 years.
- The vaginal opening of queens returning to the hive after mating flights often contain the male genitalia which is removed by the bees inside the hive.
- The queen is unable to mate with drones of other species due to the unique structure of the endophallus and the sting chamber of the queen allowing the interlock to take place and the queen being unable to release the drone.

4.11.4 Mating flights.

These normally occur in good weather when there are plenty of drones flying (say noon to 4 pm) at temperatures 20°C and greater. High winds discourage mating flights. Average length of time of mating flights have been observed to be c.20 mins. in April which decreases to c. 12 mins. in June.

4.11.5 The mated queen starts to lay c. 2–4 days after mating is complete. Egg laying is often erratic when the queen starts to lay and more than one egg per cell sometimes occurs. This phenomenon generally soon disappears.

4.12 Parthenogenesis in the honeybee.

4.12.1 Definition of parthenogenesis.

Parthenogenesis is defined as reproduction without fertilisation (as from germ cells and in lower plant life). The word is derived from two Greek words meaning virgin birth (parthenos = virgin and genesis = origin). Note that the queen is fertilised but has the ability to lay either fertilised or unfertilised eggs.

4.12.2 General.

- The theory of parthenogenesis in the honeybee was propounded by Dzierzon in 1845, ie. males (drones) are produced from unfertilised eggs and females (queens and workers) are produced from fertilised eggs. The theory has required a minimum amount of modification during the last 150 years.
- The queen has the ability, at will, to fertilise an egg before laying. Koeniger in 1970 showed that the queen uses her front legs to measure the cell in order to determine whether the egg should be fertilised or not.
- In very rare cases unfertilised eggs can give rise to females. Onions found this to be the case in South African bees in 1912 (*Apis mellifera capensis*).
- Queens and workers from fertilised eggs are diploid (with 32 chromosomes) and drones are haploid (with 16 chromosomes). Queens and workers have 16 chromosomes from the queen (their mother) and 16 chromosomes from the drone. A drone has no father, only a grandfather. The 16 chromosomes from the male side are contained in the sperm and the 16 chromosomes from the female side are contained in the egg. Therefore, if the egg is fertilised it will contain 16 + 16 chromosomes and becomes diploid, unfertilised it will contain only 16 chromosomes all derived from the mother queen.

4.13 The seasonal variation in the population size of a honeybee colony including the effects of external factors and the egg laying behaviour of the queen.

4.13.1 The seasonal variation in the population size of the honeybee colony.

Reference should be made to the graph and the accompanying notes in appendix 7 on the Average Colony Population Cycle. The graph shows the gradual increase in egg laying capacity of an average queen from early January to a maximum in c. June. A gradual decline is expected during July, August and September due to lack of income, shorter days and cooler weather conditions. By the end of October egg laying has almost ceased. Attention is drawn to the idealistic nature of the graph, there will almost certainly be anomalies as follows:

- Young queens ie. current year queens may continue laying longer than older queens maintaining their egg laying after the main flow of nectar is over.
- Some strains of bees eg. Italian, originally *Apis mellifera ligustica*, imported from New Zealand will continue laying despite the lack of income. Having been bred from a line of bees accustomed to a very mild weather and continuous nectar flows.
- On examining a brood chamber in early August it is common place not to be able to note

any eggs present. An abrupt end to the nectar flow causes eviction of drones and a reduction in the royal jelly fed to the queen.

- Conversely, the late flow of nectar from ivy blossom in September and October will stimulate an increase in egg laying. This will vary from the South to the North of UK depending on weather conditions and forage available, eg. heather.
- The increase in brood shown for April (c.28 days) indicates an increase of 10,000 emerging brood from eggs laid 3 weeks previously at a rate of c.360 eggs per day. In May this number is doubled to 20,000 emerged bees indicating a laying rate for the queen in April of c.700 eggs per day.
- By May the old winter bees will have died out, increased activity foraging and tending brood shortens the life of the bee to 5–6 weeks.
- By the first week in May most beekeepers expect to extend the brood and storage space for their colonies by giving additional comb area in the form of supers. In a strong colony with a good queen, 90% of the frames in the brood chamber will contain brood. Indicating that with optimum conditions queens may lay about 1,500 eggs per day. Some literature indicates that this capacity to lay may be doubled by certain 'super' queens.

4.13.2 Queen honeybee's egg laying behaviour including the variation of numbers laid with changing circumstances and time of year.

- Newly mated queens will increase their eggs laying capacity with age, probably reaching their maximum capacity over 1,000 / day during their second year. When a newly mated queen starts to lay about 4/5 days after mating, the laying is on a reduced scale and can be erratic with more than one egg per cell. The erratic behaviour very quickly corrects itself but the orderly pattern of laying persists from the start ie. a concentric pattern.
- Old queens towards the end of the second full year of heading a colony will have a reduction in the rate of egg laying. Queens which are badly mated or defective are likely to become drone layers ie unable to produce viable worker brood. In general, a well mated queen is likely to create a swarming situation or be superseded well before becoming a drone layer.
- The queen's capacity to lay is controlled by the house bees who feed the queen with royal jelly. The supply of royal jelly will depend on the flow and on the genetic make up of the strain of bee eg. thrifty, long living, high or low swarming instincts. Egg production will be curtailed by not feeding the queen this will occur:

    a) Prior to swarming.
    b) At the end of a nectar flow.
    c) Starvation conditions, ie no income.
    d) During the winter months.

- The external factors which affect the egg laying of the queen are:

    1. The weather which in turn effects the flow or prevents the colony from foraging and
    2. The beekeeper who should not allow his colonies to reach starvation point. Alternatively the beekeeper can artificially simulate a flow and queen laying by feeding.

- One final point which will affect the colony population cycle is disease in the colony such as Chalk brood, Nosema etc. The queen herself can also be diseased (eg. Nosema) and this also will reduce the rate of her laying very considerably.

4.14 The differences between summer and winter worker honeybees.

- In temperate regions where the winter dearth of forage is long, the temperate bee has developed to survive by clustering adjacent to a good reserve of food collected in the summer when forage is plentiful. In the winter cluster the metabolic rate of each bee is very low and little energy is being used. This is at variance with the tropical bee where the dearths of forage are much shorter and are not associated with the cold. These climatic differences have brought about a difference in life span of the different races and a difference in life span of seasonal bees in the temperate zones, ie the summer and the winter bee.
- After emergence the life span of a worker bee can range from a few days to almost a year. This range of life span is dependent on the following:

  seasonal factors   food availability   activities performed   race of bee

In the temperate zones the lives can be:

  Short lived (15 - 38 days) in the summer to long lived (c.140 days) in winter with Intermediate lives (30 - 60 days) again depending on a variety of factors

It should also be noted that bees in temperate zones respond more strongly to seasonal factors than tropical bees.

- Just after emergence the young bee consumes large amounts of pollen which causes the hypopharyngeal glands and the fat bodies to develop which provides the bee with a store of protein as brood food in the hypopharyngeal glands and in the fat bodies. Honey consumed is converted to glycogen and is also stored in the fat bodies. These protein stores in the hypopharyngeal glands and fat bodies can be used basically in two ways:

  a) In summer. The reserves are used in brood rearing by drawing down on the stored protein from the hypopharyngeal glands in the form of brood food. Maurizio (1950) showed that the more brood that a worker reared the shorter the life of the bee.
  b) In winter. The bees emerging in late autumn have very little brood to rear and the hypopharyngeal glands remain plump. The worker bees have many fat bodies as a result of the pollen consumption in the late autumn flows, eg. ivy in the UK. Most of the fat bodies in the winter bee are stored in the roof (dorsal side) of the abdomen. It has also been shown (by whom we know not) that the life of the bee is proportional to the amount of pollen consumed. This is evident if a colony suffers a dearth of pollen in the autumn then it is likely to succumb during the winter because of the shortage of fat bodies.

- From the above we can now say that the life of the bee (L) is proportional to the amount of pollen (P) consumed and inversely proportion to the amount of brood (B) reared. This is expressed more elegantly:

  $$L \, \alpha \, P \div B \quad \text{or} \quad L = K_1(P/B) + K_2 \quad \text{where } K_1 \text{ and } K_2 \text{ are constants.}$$

- In many ways the winter bee is similar to the bees in a queenless colony whereby the queenless workers revert to young bee types by consuming large amounts of pollen and re-developing the hypopharyngeal glands and fat bodies. However, there the difference ends because the queen by providing queen substance prevents the enlargement of the workers' ovaries and therefore laying workers do not develop in the winter cluster.

- The winter bee has an important job to do in the spring to ensure the survival of the colony. It is its food reserves and its ability to live longer that makes this possible.
- Reference to diagram 4.4 will show the variation of the percentage of bees in a colony with well developed hypopharyngeal glands and fat bodies during the course of the winter period and how in summer there is only about 20% with well developed glands.
- Taranov (1972) undertook some interesting studies on the lives of worker bees. We have not been able to discover where the work was done but it is stated to have been undertaken in a country with a rather warm winter and a hot summer so it may not be directly applicable to the UK. However, it is indicative of the general situation in our own hives.

EMERGE 3rd week	Average life span-summer	Average life span-winter	Average life span-spring	Average life span-total	% age BROOD cf. APRIL
April	3.5 weeks			3.5 weeks	100
May	4			4	96
June	4			4	83
July	4.5			4.5	56
August	8	17 weeks	4 weeks	29	38
September	5.5	17	4.5	27	21
October	2	17	5	24	5

The results clearly show the extended life of the worker bees from August onwards being related directly to the amount of brood that they have to rear.

- The winter bee cannot depart the hive to take cleansing flights when the weather is inclement. The rectum can fill half the volume of the abdomen and extend throughout its whole length. The rectal pads are thought to be involved in the re-cycling of water from the stored faeces (Wigglesworth, 1932) and the build up of faeces in the rectum acts as an irritant which increases the temperature of the winter cluster. Noticeable drops in cluster temperature have been recorded after cleansing flights in winter.
- The nitrogen content of the winter bee's fat bodies is normally 14 to 23mg when healthy but decreases rapidly to about 6mg in bees infected with nosema.
- Finally, long cold winters are bad news for *Varroa destructor* because fewer infested bees survive until brood rearing starts again in the spring.
- In summary the difference between summer and winter bees are as follows:

  Winter bee – long life – low fat content – high protein content – minimum brood reared – ability to retain high rectum content.
  Summer bee – short life – high fat content – low protein content – maximum brood reared.
  The longevity of queenless bees is due to the absence of brood rearing and the high level of protein in the hypopharyngeal glands and fat bodies.
  The variation of bees as a percentage of colony population with well developed hypopharyngeal glands and winter fat bodies is shown in diagram 4.4.

4.15 The organisation of a honeybee colony including the importance of pheromones, particularly queen substance, Nasonov pheromone and the two alarm pheromones.

4.15.1 General – the organisation of the honeybee colony.

The syllabus calls for the Candidate to be able to give a simple account of 'the organisation of the honeybee colony' while disregarding the controls to achieve the social organisation necessary for it to survive and reproduce future generations. It is a very large bit of the syllabus and it should be appreciated that whole books have been written on the subject of the social organisation of the colony.

Seeley in his book 'Honeybee Ecology' discusses, at some length, the level of biological selection required to achieve such a complex and orderly colonisation and whether this should be at an individual level or at colony level. It is suggested that because selection at both individual and colony level can operate together that the honeybee possesses such an elaborate organisation. However, when such things as the colony's foraging behaviour, nest design efficiency and the precise control of temperature is considered there appears to be strong evidence that the colony is organised as a whole.

Some scientific workers have been addressing selection at the individual level whereby the individual bee has evolved to maximise its own reproduction success even if this creates social colony inefficiency. Using this line of thought such items as co-operative food collection and precise temperature control become statistical summations of many individual's selfish activities.

We are of the opinion that Free's book 'The Social Organisation of Honeybees' contains adequate material to answer any general question on the organisation of the colony. However, his later book 'Pheromones of Social Bees' should, if possible, be studied as most of the colony control and cohesion is attributable to the queen and the pheromones involved as a direct result of her presence.

Ignoring the control mechanisms, we list below the main areas to be addressed:

Structure of the colony – queen + workers/duties + division of labour/use of comb/size of nest cavity/selection of nest site.

Regulation of colony activities – energy intake and expenditure/seasonal growth/annual population cycle/communication within the nest/temperature regulation.

Food collection – colony economics/what is to be collected/recruitment to foraging/dance language.

Reproduction – ratio of queens to drones/caste determination/queen replacement/swarming + supersedure/mating behaviour.

Colony defence – mechanisms/recognition of intruders/aggressiveness/guard bees.

4.15.2 Structure of the colony.

4.15.2.1 Queen and workers together with their duties and the division of labour have been addressed in section 4.10.

4.15.2.2 The use of comb in the colony.

See section 4.10.6 wax secretion and comb building.

Comb is used in the colony for a variety of purposes including the storage of nectar and honey, storage of pollen and brood rearing in that order working down from the top of the nest. Drone comb is built in the active season as required by the needs of the colony; the larger the colony the greater the amount of drone comb built. In the wild the combs in a natural nest can be as long as 1m in length where the colony has added to it from year to year and the old comb is vacated and goes unused, an elegant way of minimising disease in the nest.

Comb building is an extremely important part of the organisation of a honeybee colony particularly when a swarm is to set up a new nest. The swarm carries with it the wherewithal to construct the first comb for initial storage of honey and then subsequent brood rearing. Without the store of honey in the bees' honey sacs, the swarm could never survive.

4.15.2.3 The size of the nest cavity.

Here we have to examine the preference of swarms in respect of differing sized potential nesting cavities. It has been found, and well documented over the last 40 - 50 years that in temperate climates a small cavity is avoided for two basic reasons:

    a) There must be sufficient space not only for the colony when it has grown to full size but it must have sufficient space for the stores that it will require for its survival through the long winter.
    b) There must be adequate space to cool the nest in the summer period.

In the tropical situation the reverse is true because there is no requirement for winter stores and there are many more predators making a large nest difficult to defend.

In temperate climates the average nest volume = 40 litre in the range 20 to 100 litres. The average size standard Langstroth box (42 litres). Nest cavities have been found and carefully measured in the range 12 litres to 450 litres and the largest was 630 litres which contained 200kg honey.

It has been shown by experiment that swarms in temperate climates prefer cavities between 40 litres to 80 litres in volume at a height of about 3 to 5 m above the ground with a south facing entrance below the combs and an entrance area = 23 to 30 cm^2.

4.15.2.4 Selection of the nest site.

- Most of the work on the selection of a nest site by a swarm has been done by Lindauer in Germany who confirmed the mechanism to be the wag-tail dances on the surface of the swarm after it has emerged from the parent colony. The decision making generally takes about 1 to 2 days. See section 4.10.13. communication dances. When the bees are dancing on the surface of the swarm they dance at an angle to the sun whereas in the hive the direction of the sun is taken to be the vertical.
- Scout bees leave the swarm immediately it has settled. However, the searching process more often than not starts about 3 days before the swarm emerges. These scout bees spend a considerable time examining a possible nesting site both inside and out before returning and communicating the whereabouts to the rest of the swarm by dancing.

- The dances are identical with those performed in the hive when communicating the sources of both pollen and nectar except the length of the dances. Foraging dances last only a few minutes whereas the dances indicating a new nest site last 15 to 30 minutes. It is for this reason that they have been particularly easy to observe.
- At first there will be many different dances but eventually it is whittled down to two and then the final decision is made on one. After this happens the scouts perform a buzzing run and the whole swarm takes to the air guided to the new site by the scouts.
- Only very occasionally are they unable to come to a conclusion about a new nest site and the swarm remains where it is and builds comb in the open. Inevitably it perishes in the forthcoming winter.

4.15.3. Regulation of colony activities.

4.15.3.1 Energy intake and expenditure.

- The honeybee collects nectar, pollen, water and propolis but only the first two are collected in quantity by the majority of the foraging force. These two items represent the energy intake to the colony to allow it to undertake all its functions from nest building, all hive duties including brood rearing, foraging etc. Seeley has discussed the matter fairly fully in his book 'Honeybee Ecology' which we agree with in principle but not wholly in detail.
- He makes the point that the energy expenditure in winter in order to survive between October and March is 24kg honey and 1kg pollen. This may be true in his part of the world but is a bit on the high side for say UK south coast. The detail is relatively unimportant it is the principle we are more concerned with in this syllabus. His summer figures are 60kg honey and 20kg pollen for mainly brood rearing of 150,000 bees during the period April to September. We consider this to be a bit on the light side for our part of the world. His calculations and measurements are based on a colony weight (bees only) of 1.25 to 5.0kg and the loss of weight of the hive (2.5kg per week) measured during inclement weather when the bees could not fly to forage.
- Calculating the calorific values he concludes that the energy rate of return is 8:1 for pollen and 10:1 for honey based on 10mg per hour used for flying on trips equal to 2.8 miles, which is very efficient. In his annual calculation, he disregards the energy expended and collected in the foraging operation whereby each forager uses honey at a rate of 10mg per hour. During the course of the flying season this amounts to 2 or 300lb of honey which the beekeeper never sees as it is not stored but used on a continual basis.

4.15.3.2 Seasonal growth/population cycle.

This cycle is dealt with in appendix 7 and has been referred to previously. It is extremely important in understanding the organisation of the honeybee colony and in the day to day management of the honeybee colonies for honey production.

4.15.3.3 Communication within the nest.

Communication within the nest is largely by chemical means but also as physiological behaviour patterns. Some are inter related such as grooming the queen, food transfer and queen substance distribution around the colony. By far the most important is the presence of the queen and the effect that she has on the whole of the colony. It has been pointed out that queen substance contains about 32 substances (not all having been identified) and it is possible for these to elicit behavioural patterns or have a physiological effect on workers in the colony either as single substances or in combinations. It will be appreciated that the number of combinations using only two at a time is a large number of options. The two main substances in queen substance are 9 - keto (E) - 2 - decenoic acid known as 9ODA and 9 - hydroxy (E) - 2 decenoic acid known as 9HDA.

Queen substance, mainly from the mandibular glands of the queen but also from the dermal glands on the dorsal part of her abdomen, inhibits the development of worker ovaries and inhibits the building of queen cells. Pheromone from worker brood has the same effect but to a lesser degree. Brood pheromone also elicits the workers to forage for pollen; brood pheromone glycerol - 1, 2 - dioleate - 3 - palmitate, was discovered by Koeniger and Veith in 1983. If the colony was queenless and brood pheromone was not involved, then laying workers would develop very quickly; because brood pheromone is involved it takes about 3 weeks for the first laying workers to appear if the colony is hopelessly queenless. Each worker requires a threshold amount of queen substance which is ingested during food exchange.

It has been postulated that there are other queen identification pheromones such as footprint odour whereby she leaves a chemical trail on the comb and similarly, queen identification pheromones from the glands in the sting chamber.

The next recognition pheromones are those for identifying worker to worker (sister to sister or sister to half sister) and worker to queen. This is the colony odour identified by Kalmus and Ribbands in 1952 and confirmed by Butler and Free in the same year by trapping pollen foragers and putting them into their own hives and into alien hives. There was a high rejection rate into the foreign hives even though all the hives were working the same crop. Colony odour therefore has a genetic basis. This is the reason for the care required in queen introduction; the workers in the recipient colony will know that the queen is alien and the beekeeper must make every effort to protect her during the introduction stage. The colony odour is the basis for guarding at the hive entrance and the guards being able to differentiate between their own workers and those from another colony.

This naturally leads us to the alarm pheromones originating in the sting chamber and also from the worker mandibular glands, isopentyl acetate and 2 - heptanone respectively. Isopentyl acetate is very much more potent than 2 - heptanone and may be regarded as a recruitment message to other guard and foraging bees.

A bee that dies within the hive undergoes a change of odour shortly after death and undertaker bees will be removing the corpse within about 15 minutes. This is the reason why so few dead bees are seen in the hive during the active season.

Drone brood has its own characteristic pheromone which in some way allows the correct number of drones to be reared in the colony. It is also a kairomone recognised by the *Varroa jacobsoni* which prefers it to worker brood pheromone for breeding purposes.

The worker bee has the ability to recognise changes in CO_2 levels to an accuracy of less than 1%. Relative humidity is measured to within 5% enabling the brood nest to be kept within tolerable limits for brood rearing. Temperature regulation in the colony is dealt with in the next section.

Two other methods of communication are used within the colony namely touch and vibration as opposed to smell. It is too dark within the nest for sight to be used. Antennation (use of the antennae) is used between bees during food sharing, soliciting food and guarding duties. Vibration is used by queens piping during swarming and although it can be heard by beekeepers the bee recognises the messages by responses from sensillae in its feet.

4.15.3.4 Temperature regulation.

Temperature regulation of the brood nest and the whole colony in both winter and summer is extremely important because without the heating in the winter and the cooling in the summer, particularly in temperate climates, the honeybee colony could never survive. The honeybee originated in the tropics and over the millions of years of its development it has adapted in order to survive in northern latitudes. To do this a system of thermo regulation has evolved as a social device rather than any specific function of the individual bee.

Between February and October because of brood rearing the temperature is maintained at 33° to 36°C but between November and January the centre of the cluster ranges from c.20° to 30°C when there is no brood present. High temperatures are important for brood rearing. Brood reared experimentally in an incubator show clearly the necessity to heat the brood nest:

<28°C or >37°C very little brood emerged
28° to 30°C emerging bees had deformed wings and mouthparts
32° to 35°C emerging bees were normal.

During the winter period the colony adopts 3 mechanisms to ensure its survival down to very low temperatures. These are:

a) Ensuring that the nest is draught free. All *Apis mellifera* strains propolise their hives or nest sites to a greater or lesser degree in the autumn before winter.
b) Clustering and c) generating metabolic heat. The heat lost is through the exoskeleton which has a surface area of c. 2cm^2. In a cluster of 18cm diameter 15,000 bees have a surface area of 1000cm^2, equivalent to 0.07cm^2/bee. This is a gain of approximately 30 to 1 in surface area and a very efficient means of reducing heat loss. From about 30°C to 18°C the colony does not cluster or contract but generates metabolic heat by individual bees micro-vibrating the flight muscles in the thorax in opposition to one another remaining static the energy being turned into heat. From 18°C to 10°C the cluster forms and starts to contract to maintain the temperatures but no additional metabolic heat is produced. From 10°C to −10°C the cluster continues to contract but additional metabolic heat is produced. When temperature fall below −10°C no further contraction can take place and temperatures are maintained by bees producing more metabolic heat.

During the summer period cooling is often necessary and this achieved by fanning, water collection and evaporation and finally by expanding the cluster (bees cluster outside the nest or hive often seen by beekeepers). Failure to limit the temperatures inside the hive could result in a melt down of the wax combs which can happen at night under extreme conditions when bees cannot fly for water collection.

It is not clear how the thermoregulation system functions in detail but it seems to function without any apparent communication between individuals in the colony. Each bee seems to act independently reacting to its own environment but producing a coherent overall result.

The other point about temperature is disease containment. It is well known that low temperature is a requirement for the spores of chalk brood to germinate. There is growing evidence that other pathogens (eg. bacteria and viruses) are inhibited from multiplying at higher temperatures. The thermo-regulation of the nest at quite high temperatures may in all probability provide a protective mechanism. Many animals and mammals have this automatic temperature increase to combat viral infections; the influenza symptom of a high temperature is typical in humans.

4.15.4 Food collection.

4.15.4.1 Colony economics.

The energy intake versus the colony energy expenditure was examined in section 4.15.3.1 which dealt with the annual requirements of an established colony. The colony has only a short time during the main flow, in a temperate climate, to gather the stores that it requires to survive the long cold winter. If the weather is inclement or the flow is poor then more than likely the colony will draw on its reserves from previous years. Note should be taken of our comments in section 1.14.3 in connection with feeding colonies for winter and the thousands that starve to death each winter in the UK. This seldom happens to feral colonies where the beekeeper has not had the opportunity of robbing them of their stored honey. Bees left to their own devices manage remarkably well despite the severe temperate conditions they find themselves in.

The most precarious situation in the social organisation of the colony is that of a swarm finding a new nesting place and establishing a new colony. The first few weeks are crucial relying on good weather and the availability of sufficient forage both nectar and pollen but particularly pollen.

Consider an average swarm of 15,000 bees each carrying 40mg of honey in their honey sacs have a total resource of 600g honey to build a new nest. The honeybee is capable of converting this to c.75g of beeswax in the ratio of 8:1. Each 1000g of wax can build comb with 77,000 worker cells, therefore the 75g of wax can provide 5775 cells or about one BS brood frame to start the new colony and this assuming that all the resources the swarm is carrying is converted into comb. Some has to be used for initial foraging and producing enough metabolic heat to allow the wax glands to work. Comb is the highest priority of the newly installed swarm for without it the colony will perish. It is required to allow the queen to start laying quickly to replenish those workers dying a natural death and to establish a strong colony for the forthcoming winter. Winter stores have also to be housed.

Of particular importance is pollen. It is not carried as a resource but it will be essential that stores of pollen are available a few days after the first comb is built, the queen has laid in this new comb and the larvae are requiring to be fed. Until new brood is emerging and some stores are accumulated the economics of the colony are in a state of very delicate balance.

From an organisational point of view the social structure demands economy of resources and then comb building as absolute priorities for survival. Economy is manifested in one very interesting way; swarming bees are very disinclined to sting even if they have a strong defensive trait. If a bee stings it dies and this is a wasted resource, one they can ill afford to lose because of the 'bee power' and the stores it is carrying.

4.15.4.2 What to collect?

The social organisation of the honeybee colony provides interesting mechanisms on what the foragers should be collecting. In section 4.10.11 the methods of collection outside the hive were examined; in this section we are concerned with the organisation inside.

Nectar and water are collected by foragers and are always unloaded to a house bee. This is very important in the communication mechanism because it is the house bee that determines the requirements of the foragers. If, for example, the hive is becoming overheated and fanning cannot reduce the internal temperature sufficiently, then water is required. The incoming foragers then have difficulty finding a house bee who will relieve them of their sweet nectar load. They then change from nectar collection to water carrying until such times as they have difficulty again finding a house bee to relieve them of the water load. They then revert to nectar foraging.

Pollen collection is stimulated by brood pheromone directly to the pollen foragers inside the hive. Here it should be noted that the pollen forager does not pass its load to a house bee, it unloads its two pollen pellets directly into the cells itself. Again it should be noted that pollen is stored adjacent to the open brood just the place to receive the chemical message from the brood pheromone. The number of pollen foragers is more pronounced in the spring when the colony is building up on the spring flow and the number of adult bees is less than the brood being reared. A time when the brood pheromone per bee is maximised.

The communication mechanism inside the hive for collecting propolis is not very clear but is believed to be by dancing. The only information we have been able to unearth is that Meyer (1954) and Milum (1955) reported that returning foragers carrying propolis danced after being unloaded and recruits from these dances quickly appeared at the propolis collecting site. That appears to be the end of the story. We believe that it is one of the aspects of bee biology and behaviour that has not been investigated very thoroughly.

It is well known that some strains of *Apis mellifera* collect more than others, some collecting prodigious amounts. The reason is genetic and if the matter was investigated it is likely that there may be differences in the behaviour pattern inside the hive with respect to recruitment and collection

4.15.4.3 Recruitment of foragers.

All foragers are recruited by dancing, initially by the scouts and then by the returning foragers themselves. The vigour of the dances being performed are directly proportional to the richness of the source. See section 4.10.13 for details of the round and wagtail dances.

4.15.4.4 Dance language.

The language of the bees dances both within the hive and on the surface of swarms was discovered by von Frisch and is discussed in section 4.10.13.

4.15.5 Reproduction.

4.15.5.1 Ratio of queens to drones.

Most colonies produce drones during the active season and most colonies limit the number of drones in the colony. For example, if due to inbreeding the queen lays diploid 'male' eggs, they are very quickly destroyed by the workers eating them. It is therefore clear that there is a mechanism operating inside the colony preventing an excess of drones due to this cause.

It is the workers that build the drone comb and the worker comb; but how do they arrive at the amount of each to build? By observation it is known that the amount of drone comb built depends on the time of the year and the size of the colony. Most drone comb in the UK is built during May and June, the classical swarming time. It is also known, by observation that colonies of less than 6000 bees do not generally build drone comb; ie about the size of a 4/5 frame BS nucleus.

The mechanism controlling the building of drone comb is not understood, ie. how do the comb builders calculate the ratio of drone to worker comb? It has been suggested that it depends on the initial cell base that is built and that drone comb may have its own discrete pheromone. Certainly in a colony with no drone comb some will be built in May or June and when it is built it is used immediately for rearing drone brood. Also in a colony with 'plenty' of drone comb, the amount of drone brood correlates positively with the amount of worker brood in the colony. Free has suggested that there could be some kind of negative feedback mechanism responsible. From graphs prepared Free and Williams it would appear that in May/June the percentage of drone brood is about 30% of the total brood (worker + drone) in the colony. This to us seems high but we have not been able to determine whether the colony was managed for honey production or allowed to determine its own way forward.

This is one of the aspects of the colony organisation where we are still in the dark. Similarly, the mechanism for the expulsion of the drones in times of dearth.

4.15.5.2 Caste determination. See section 4.6.

4.15.5.3 Queen replacement.

Queen replacement can be effected in two ways, that is by swarming or by supersedure. When the colony swarms the old colony has the new queen and the swarm (prime swarm) the old one. The probability of the old queen being superseded later in the season when the swarm has established itself are very high.

If a colony supersedes its queen, it can be achieved in two ways:

Perfect supersedure whereby the newly mated queen continues to lay alongside the old one for a while before the old queen is discarded by the worker bees. It is not clear how the old queen is disposed of, whether she is balled by the workers or evicted from the hive in some way – we have not been able to establish.

Imperfect supersedure whereby the old queen is disposed of before the new queen is mated and laying.

It will be clear from the above that in the long run most queens are replaced by supersedure. The reasons for the replacement are known to be:

a) diminished supply of queen substance (queen getting old, see appendix 5),
b) injury,
c) disease and
d) laying insufficient fertilised eggs.

4.15.5.4 Swarming and supersedure.

The first action associated with both swarming and supersedure are the building of queen cups and these are built during the spring build up of the colony. They may be built around the edges of the combs in the brood nest or even on the face of the combs usually where the comb is irregular. Most colonies will have 20 to 25 such cups. Often a lesser number are likely to be built if the colony is to supersede but this is not infallible and some strains of bee which are genetically prone to swarming may build many more.

When the colony swarms eggs will be laid in the cups (when they have been polished and varnished with propolis) and the larva will be fed appropriately to produce a true female, a queen. The colony usually swarms when the first queen cell is sealed.

A few days prior to swarming the workers will be stop feeding the queen so that she may lose weight and be able to fly, the workers will be generally quiescent, some scouts will be scouting for a new nest site and many workers will be festooning at the bottom of the lower combs in the hive. About 60% of the population will leave with the prime swarm leaving 40% of the work force in the original hive together with the remaining unsealed queen cells, worker brood and stores. It has been suggested but not proven that workers that have a true sister relationship with the queen, rather than a half sister relationship, are more likely to form the majority of workers in the swarm.

Casts with virgin queens may or may not emerge about 8 days later. If they do the remaining colony has virtually decimated itself and will have great difficulty in being able to establish itself for the forthcoming winter. This behaviour pattern is not understood.

In the case of supersedure, this is likely to occur in late spring or early summer but can happen at other times in the autumn. It has been stated that about 20% of all colonies supersede (Allen 1965) but we could not establish how these colonies are managed or whether they were feral colonies left to their own devices. In our own managed colonies we find 10 to 15% supersede every year (with 20 colonies this is a small sample) and these are in colonies which are regularly requeened. Most of the supersedures occur after the middle of August, the last time we inspect our colonies before the next spring. This is the time we put in Bayvarol which is removed later but with no colony inspection. We know of the supersedure next spring when we find an unmarked queen. Again this behaviour pattern is peculiar because at that time of the year there is a dearth of drones. Having said that we recommend supersedure queens except sometimes for their doubtful temper due to uncontrolled mating.

4.15.5.5 Mating behaviour.

This was discussed earlier, please see section 4.11.

4.15.6 Colony defence.

4.15.6.1 Mechanisms.

There are a whole series of mechanisms involved which range across the whole biology of the honeybee. The important ones are: a) the recognition of intruders, b) guard bees and c) alarm pheromones which will be discussed in more detail in the following paragraphs.

- The first mechanism involved in colony defence is in the initial choice of nest site by the scout bees when choosing a new site for the swarm. Left to their own devices a fairly well hidden entrance above 3 m in height will be selected. Other parameters may well enter the equation in connection with the capacity and the robustness of the cavity selected.
- The fact that the colony recognises the requirement for guard bees and that the honeybee undergoes this guard training as part of its development ensures that when strong defensive measures are required the whole foraging force can be relied on in the emergency. This is discussed further below.
- Alarm pheromones are available to recruit this massive defence force if required. Again these pheromones are discussed in detail below.
- Stings are the ultimate weapon in the honeybees armoury and only used in the ultimate as the death of the bee is assured if it is used. It is designed to be painful and lethal. For details see section 4.9.5.
- Large colonies ensure the maximum number of defenders for defence purposes and to ensure that colonies are large they must have a young prolific queen and the colony to be disease free. The amount of queen substance being produced related to the age of the queen ensures young queens. There are a variety of items associated with keeping disease at bay.
- Disease is minimised by the bees dying naturally away from the hive and part of the house bee contingent includes a small percentage of undertaker bees. The method of defaecation away from the hive ensures a clean hive environment in the summer and the honeybee's ability to retain its faeces in the winter until a cleansing flight is possible ensures winter cleanliness also. The use of propolis (antibacterial) in the brood nest for varnishing each brood cell before re-use provides an environment for the new nursery inhibiting the multiplication of damaging bacteria. Finally on this point of disease prevention is the high brood nest temperature again inhibiting viruses and bacteria.
- When honeybees are poisoned by whatever cause they are not allowed into the hive or if they gain entry are very quickly evicted and left to die outside. This ensures that honey stores remain uncontaminated and toxic pollen is not used for brood rearing.

4.15.6.2 Recognition of intruders.

Honeybees recognise large predators such as birds, mammals (eg. badgers), humans, etc. by sight and smell. Each species has its own characteristic odour. Even in humans with our rather poor sense of smell compared with the rest of the animal world can recognise one strain from another. If you can gain the confidence of a Chinaman in the far east he will tell you what you smell like!

The same to a much more acute level exists with the honeybee. There is a hive odour and a colony odour both of which are recognisable to the honeybee. The hive odour is derived from the forage the colony is working, the nectar, pollen and the odour of the combs. The colony odour is genetically derived and is peculiar to the genetic make up of the particular strain. This is important when honeybees start robbing other colonies in times of dearth. All bees at these times of dearth will be examined by the guard bees at the entrance.

Robbing bees for reasons unknown always have a characteristic flight when approaching the hive to be robbed which is immediately recognised by the guard bees. The flight is best described as a zig-zag pattern the bee flying from side to side during its approach run. The reason for the flight pattern is unknown and it seems very odd that they should give themselves away so easily to the guards at the entrance.

4.15.6.3 Guard bees.

- The guard bees are those bees approaching the end of their duties as a house bee just prior to it taking up foraging duties in the field. It is generally about 18 days old and thus has been through it all its glandular development, the last gland to develop is the sting.
- In times of plenty there will be virtually no guards patrolling the entrance to the colony but in times of dearth there will be many. This is the time honeybees will rob other colonies.
- Every returning forager is examined by a guard bee and this takes only a second or two the examination being undertaken by antennal contact with the forager.
- In the case of a robber the guard quickly approaches the robber and it often adopts a submissive behaviour and offers a bribe to the guard. If the robber does not submit the guard bee clamps onto a wing or a leg with its mandibles and then curls its abdomen round to sting the intruder. The same treatment is dealt out to wasps.
- If the guards approach the stage where they have to sting an intruder the pheromones involved in the attack on the intruder serve to recruit further guard bees to the entrance.

4.15.6.4 Alarm pheromones.

- There are two main alarm pheromones (see appendix 10 for definition) namely 2-heptanone from the mandibular glands and isopentyl acetate from the sting gland in the sting chamber of the worker bee. The sting gland is the most important and besides isopentyl acetate, which constitutes c. 70% of the pheromone, there are 5 other acetates plus (Z) - 11 - eicosen - 1 - ol and 5 other compounds that have been identified. As always pheromones are a complex mixture of many substances. Additionally, several other alarm pheromones have been identified from the sting sheath.
- Isopentyl acetate smells of banana oil which is often recognised by beekeepers with a keen sense of smell. We have noticed it inside the car when we have been moving bees and we knew of one beekeeper who could detect it occasionally when manipulating a colony (which he closed down on receiving this warning).
- 2-heptanone is c.20 times less potent compared with isopentyl acetate and appears to be used mainly by guard bees tackling an intruder. However, we have noticed that sometimes with an irritable colony, inclined to sting, the bees attempt to bite the skin of our hands with their mandibles presumably marking the intruder.
- Beekeepers are well aware that the site of a sting while manipulating a colony is likely to attract further stings at the same place. We know of one case where a hive was kept in a chicken run and the bees were pretty 'rotten' (very defensive or aggressive) and the beekeeper after manipulating the colony dressed up for outer space, of course, found two of his chickens dead. They had hundreds of stings around their eyes.
- Take the crown board off a colony very quietly in winter and bees with their abdomens upturned with their stings out will be seen. Around each sting will be a glistening liquid - alarm pheromone. The bees are doing two things; they are warming up their flight muscles to enable them to take off and fly to attack the intruder and the alarm pheromone is recruiting a defence force to do the same thing.

4.15.7 Queen substance.

Queen substance may be regarded as the most important pheromone in the colony for without it there would be no cohesion and the colony could not exist as a social unit. It comes from the mandibular glands of the queen and also from the dermal glands on tergites A3, A4 and A5. It contains c. 30 pheromones the most important are:

9 - hydroxy - 2 - decenoic acid known as 9HDA and
(E) - 9 - oxo - 2 - decenoic acid known as 9ODA.

It has the following effects in the colony:

1. Inhibits worker ovary development
2. Stimulates workers to forage.
3. Stimulates workers to release Nasonov pheromone.
4. Inhibits the building of queen cells (9HDA), albeit only weakly
5. Queen recognition substance for the workers
6. Has a stabilising effect on the retinue of workers grooming the queen.

Outside the colony it has the following effects:

a) Attracts drones to queen on mating flights (9ODA).
b) Regulates worker cohesion in swarms and attracts workers to it (9HDA).

It is produced at a maximum in young queens and the output decreases with age. See appendix 5.

4.15.8 Nasonov pheromone.

• The Nasonov gland or scent gland in worker bees only is located at the base of abdominal tergite 7 and is normally covered by tergite 6 when not in use. The scents from the gland are released when the bee arches its abdomen upwards with the tip of its abdomen (segment A7) curved downwards thus exposing the gland, the canal of which runs laterally across the base of the exposed tergite. It is always distributed by the bee fanning air over the exposed gland.
• The pheromone from this gland is extremely attractive to all casts and has been given the name of 'come in and join us' pheromone. It contains a mixture of terpenoids as follows:

Terpenic aldehydes:	(Z) – citral
	(E) – citral
Terpenic alcohols	nerol
	geraniol
	(E,E) – farnesol
Terpenic acids	geranic acid
	nerolic acid

• It is used by the worker honeybees under the following conditions:

a) To attract other workers into the colony from outside.
b) To attract swarms into the new cavity or wherever the queen may be resting (eg. after a swarm has been taken in a skep).
c) After a colony has been disturbed.
d) For use as an orientation aid particularly with young bees after orientation flights.
e) Whenever any disorientation occurs.
f) To mark food and water sources.

• Some of the components are synthesised and used in swarm lures. Our limited experience with them indicate that they are very effective and attractive to bees.

- To illustrate how attractive the real thing is we quote the following experience. One warm sunny day in spring we had completed a Bailey frame change on a colony in our home apiary and the bees were disorientated as a result of the entrance position being changed. Two over wintered 4 frame nucs 15m away were attracted lock stock and barrel to the colony that had many workers fanning and distributing the pheromone. We saw the nucs abscond to the colony and enter the hive and two hours later we found two dead queens outside. These queens were scheduled to requeen two other colonies.

4.15.9 Alarm pheromones. This has been discussed in section 4.15.6.4 above.

The alerting of the colony and triggering the release of alarm pheromones are dependent on the genetic make up of the bee and have been attributed to the following factors:

- Environmental: rain and humidity changes, low temperatures, electrostatic charges (electric storms and thunder storms), magnetic fields (under high tension power lines), light and lack of food supplies (or when a flow ceases abruptly).
- Other stimuli including: scents (foreign colony odour, other animals and mammals breath and sweat, many types of cosmetics and hair shampoos), mechanical vibrations (transporting a hive), fast movements (when manipulating a colony) and colour and texture of clothing.
- The alarm pheromones themselves.

4.16 Methods of communication used by the honeybee including food sharing, dancing and scenting.

4.16.1 The stimuli, senses and the sensors.

All communication methods are the transfer of stimuli from one animal or place to another and is a typical behaviour pattern in a social society. The honeybee colony is no exception and communication has been developed in the honeybee to a high degree because of its closed nest environment and its special requirements to survive in adverse winter conditions.

Any one form of communication is very often associated with another, eg. food sharing (taste) and antennae tapping (smell) making it very difficult to isolate the separate forms of communication.

Both inside and outside the hive, the transfer of stimuli is associated with the appropriate sensillae used by the honeybee which are listed below:

touch	sensilla trichodia	hairs
taste	sensilla basiconica	pegs
smell	sensilla placodea	plates
CO_2, RH, T	sensilla coeloconica	pits
stress / strain	sensilla campaniformia	bells
vibration / hearing	sensilla scolopophora	complex formation

There are other stimuli such as electrostatic charge and magnetism which the honeybee responds to but are outside the scope of this syllabus. The queen and drone presumably must also be able to measure atmospheric pressure in some way in order to determine the correct height for mating. The force of gravity is detected by special sensors at the petiole between the head and thorax. None of these are used as methods of communication between honeybees. Similarly, sight and the simple and compound eyes of the honeybee is essential for its existence but is not a form of communication.

4.16.2. Methods of communication.

The methods of communication used by the honeybee colony are as follows:

1. Food sharing – chemical communication, taste, smell and touch used.
2. Dancing – auditory and vibration.
3. Scenting – olfactory
4. Vibration – hearing

4.16.3 Food sharing.

This is the exchange of nectar or honey from one bee to another. It goes on continually 24 hours / day 365 days / year. The process is at a much reduced level in the winter while the colony is clustering.

The mechanism of food transfer (trophallaxis) is as follows:

1. Begging – the bee attempts to thrust its proboscis between the mandibles of another bee.
2. Offering – the bee opens its mandibles and moves its folded proboscis slightly downwards and forwards exposing a small droplet of nectar or honey.
3. Antennal contact occurs during food transfer which appears to be important to the process but the reason is unknown. It probably elicits some form of stimulus. There is no known information on a possible antennal language.
4. Young bees (1-2 days old) obtain all their food from other bees by begging and this has been observed to happen even up to 2 weeks old.
5. It is usually the older bees that are offering and this is always true in the case of foragers returning to the hive.

The average sugar content in the honey sac of a bee is 50%, the level at which the carbohydrates can be metabolised. This is an important point as it forms the basis of the transfer of a vast amount of information in the internal management of the social structure as follows:

1. The type of nectar / honey by taste.
2. The need for water for the dilution of stores (to 50:50) or for cooling. In either case the house bees will be reluctant to unload high sugar content nectar from foragers.
3. The general availability of food and water.
4. The selection of the best source of forage (ie. highest sugar content)
5. The state of queenrightness of the colony by transfer of pheromones derived from queen grooming.

As a result of food sharing the following activities are prompted:

• Egg laying rate of the queen increases when there is abundant income with the resultant increase in brood rearing. The brood pheromone in turn prompts pollen collection.

- Ripening and storing of honey.
- Wax secretion and comb building.
- The transfer of queen substance from the queen providing each bee with a threshold amount to inhibit ovary development and the building of queen cells leading to swarming. The food transfer process is very rapid throughout the colony. A single transfer between two bees takes about half minute (transferring both food and pheromone). If these two bees feed two others, and then the four feed four others ad infinitum a series 2, 4, 8, 16, 32, 64, c.125, 250, 500, 1K, 2K, 4K, 8K, 16k, 32K, 64k is evolved; ie. 15–16 transfers each lasting about half a minute. In 7 or 8 minutes the whole colony is aware of the 'state of play'. This model is very simplistic and in practice the communication is faster than this. It is readily demonstrated by removing a queen from a colony. In about 5 minutes bees are busily searching the entrance area for her. In a matter of an hour or two emergency queen cells are likely to be started demonstrating the effect of shortage of queen substance.
- If foragers are unloaded in less than 40 seconds this nearly always prompts the forager to dance in order to recruit further foragers to the high sugar source of forage.

The high degree of organisation found in the honeybee colony suggests that information is likely to be exchanged by food transfer of the most economic forage to be collected. The optimum energy gain based on sugar content of the nectar and the amount of nectar used for flying to and from the source would be evaluated in some way. The mechanism remains unclear at the present time.

4.16.4 Dancing.

We have identified in the classical literature the following dances associated with the honeybee (ie. Apis mellifera) most of which are poorly understood:

Round and wagtail dance – location of food sources and nest sites.
Alarm dances (Zittertanz, zitter = shiver and tanz = dance) – warning of poisoned food income.
Cleaning dances – expressing that assistance is required to groom.
DVAV or joy dance – associated with an opulent colony.
Massage dance – origin and reasons very vague possibly something to do with sickness.
Humming or whir dance (Schwirrlauf dance, schwirr = buzz and lauf = hum) - occurs just before a swarm leaves the hive.
Washboard or planing dance – possibly for smoothing rough surfaces.

Details of how the above dances are performed by the bees may be found in Dadant – 'The Hive and the Honeybee' and 'Communication among social bees' by Lindauer. For examination purposes their existence should be known but an in depth knowledge of the round and wagtail dance is required.

The length of time that these dances are performed has been examined by Wittekindt in 1961 who found that they were dependent on the environmental conditions in the hive. The more opulent the colony the longer the dances.

Lindauer discovered that there is a variation in the dances (round and wagtail) between races of *Apis mellifera* (ie. say between Italian, Caucasian, Carniolan, etc.) Additionally, the Eastern honeybees (A.florea, cerana and dorsata) have a dance language which is very similar to *A. mellifera*.

The round and wagtail dances are a very important behavioural characteristic and play a major role in scouting for food (nectar, water and pollen) and new nest sites. When the scout bees (about 200 - 500 bees) have decide on a new nest site they lead the swarm to the new site. How this few bees shepherd the very large flock (about 10,000 or more bees) during the flight, which can be over a considerable distance, is not understood. However it is known that on arrival these scout bees Nasonov at the new entrance to lead the swarm in.

4 16.5 Scenting.

In its narrowest sense 'scenting' has been understood to mean the use of the Nasonov gland (the come in and join us scent which is very attractive to honeybees) but we believe for the purpose of this syllabus it has a much wider meaning. The sensilla associated with smell are perhaps the most numerous over the exoskeleton of the honeybee and are associated with a wide variety of communications.

The sensilla placodea are particularly sensitive and are capable of detecting 1 molecule of a particular pheromone. The following communication channels associated with smell have been identified:

1. The type of forage – scent of flowers on the bee and the aroma of the nectar.
2. Presence of the queen – queen substance from the mandibular and dermal glands of the queen.
3. Requeening by swarming or supersedure – queen cells give off their own pheromone.
4 Alarm pheromones – isopentylacetate, $(CH_3)_2CHCH_2CH_2OCOCH_3$, from the sting chamber and 2-heptanone, $CH_3(CH2)_4COCH_3$, from the mandibular glands. These also have the effect of inhibiting foraging in favour of guarding thereby providing a much greater defence force.
5. Mating information – 9-ODA attracts drones outside the hive.
6. Swarm cohesion – 9-HDA holds swarms together.
7. Foraging – presence of queen elicits foraging generally. Open brood also gives off a pheromone which elicits foraging particularly for pollen.
8. Guidance information – fanning the pheromone from the Nasonov gland.
9. Queen recognition – pheromones from the Koschevnikov gland in the queen's sting chamber and from her Renner Baumann glands on the distal edges of the 3rd to 5th abdominal segments.
10. Marking – by footprint odour (Arnhart glands) and water with a pheromone from the Nasonov gland.

The pheromones of the queen are extremely complex. Considering only queen substance, it is known to have 31 constituent parts with 13 of these identified. Only two effects of this pheromone have been proven ie. the inhibiting of worker ovary development and the inhibiting of queen cell production. There are likely to be many more channels of communication discovered as research continues.

Footprint odour is left by the worker bees at all places where they forage. Little is known about the chemical nature of the pheromone but it persists for at least 4 hours at 23°C and for at least 4 days at 5°C. The honeybee marks the sources of water with a combination of footprint odour and with an additional pheromone from the Nasonov gland because of the odourless nature of water.

We, and others, have noted that aggressiveness is apparently often directly associated with the queen and not from her offspring. We have swapped queens in good and bad tempered colonies and the temper of the bad tempered colony has within a day become good tempered and vice versa with the other colony. Change them back again and the reverse happens. We have no idea which pheromones from the queens concerned are responsible for this behaviour pattern.

Work continues to be undertaken at Rothamsted investigating the use of synthesised pheromones to be applied to crops with other sprays to attract or repel bees in order to improve pollination or protecting the honeybee from toxic insecticides. Pickett in particular has been responsible for much original work on the pheromones connected with the Nasonov gland.

The general all round knowledge about pheromones is scanty due to the difficulty in identifying the very small quantities involved and in different circumstances the pheromones may have different meanings, eg. queen substance. Pheromones can act synergistically (working together) thus providing innumerable possible effects and forms of communication. The persistence of pheromones is important, some are highly volatile and some are not. There are 3 ways in which pheromones may be transferred:

in the air
by physical contact (eg. antennal contact)
in the food (eg. food exchange)

All pheromones contain only carbon, hydrogen and oxygen which are all readily available in the bees diet and do not require special collection.

Colony activities which are regulated by pheromones are provided by:

Fertile queens
    inhibit rearing of queens
    stimulate building of worker comb
    stimulate cell cleaning, brood rearing, foraging, honey + pollen storage
Immature queens and queen cells
    inhibit production of laying workers
Workers
    guiding (Nasonov), guarding (alarm pheromones)
Comb (incorporated in the wax)
    attractive to workers (eg. bait hives)
Worker brood
    stimulates pollen collection
    inhibits the development of worker ovaries
    encourages drone production
Drone brood

To conclude this subsection on scenting mention must be made of the drone brood pheromone which is classed as a kairomone as it benefits the receiver varroa mite to the disadvantage of the donor bee. See appendix 10 - Semiochemicals.

4.16.6 Vibration.

It is the sensilla scolopophora that detect vibrations and are attributed to the hearing senses of the bee. There are some found in the bees head attached to the articulation of the antennae and also in the pedicel of the antennae (Organ of Johnson). Four occur in each leg, one in the femur, two in the tibia and one in the tarsus. The main organ of hearing is regarded as the largest sensilla in the tibia near its joint with the femur capable of detecting vibrations in the substrate upon which the bee is standing.

Sound is, of course, a vibration of air causing pressure changes which our ears can detect. Es'kov (1972) has shown that two or three rows of hairs situated behind the back margins of the compound eyes respond to airborne sound but whether this constitutes hearing as we understand remains to be answered. It is not clear what frequency and intensity such sounds may be detected. The honeybee colony is continually producing sound but how much if any of this comprises communication messages is unknown.

The best dissertation on the sounds made by the honeybee is in the Encyclopaedia of Beekeeping and divides it up into 3 main groups, flight and fanning sounds, colony background roar and calls and pulsed sounds. Appended below are those sounds which may or have been associated with behavioural communications:

Flight and fanning sounds.

    No known sound communication.

Colony background roar.

    1. When the bees become irritated during a colony manipulation the background roar changes to a louder higher pitched sound. It is not clear whether this is a communication between the bees but it is certainly a warning to the experienced beekeeper.
    2. A colony that has been queenless for a few days always has a characteristic roar which is at a much greater level than a normal queenright colony. Is this another way of communicating queenlessness?
    3. Woods 'Apidictor' (basically an audio amplifier with variable bandpass filters – not now marketed) could detect a warble between 225 and 285Hz 10dB below the background hum when a colony was preparing queen cells. Sound communication between bees?

Calls and pulsed sounds.

    1. Wag tail dances. During the waggle part of the dance, the bee produces a sound derived from a carrier frequency of c. 250Hz modulated with pulses (pulse width c. 20 ms, pulse rate c.31/sec.) The pulse frequency is very low to the human ear. It is not proven that this sound is a form of communication.
    2. Queenlessness (after a few hours). The sound is described as 'bubbling' or 'popping'. Carrier 250 to 300Hz, pulse width c. 27ms, pulse rate c.20/sec. Is this a form of communication?
    3. Grumbling colony. Carrier frequency c.250Hz, variable from 15 to 75ms, pulse rate 40/sec. Level quoted to be high and can be heard up to 3m from the hive. Behaviour quoted as uncommon and if this is so it cannot be a regular form of communication.

4. Squeaks by workers observing dances. Observed by von Frisch, squeaks at c.300 Hz and suggested that it is a request for a sample of the forage.

5. Workers piping after colony disturbance. Piping c.500 - 600Hz and claimed to calm the colony after being disturbed.

6. Queen quacking and piping. Perhaps the best known of all the sounds. Young queens still in their cells 'quack' before the exit of a swarm – frequency c.1000Hz, rate 3/sec., call lasting 4 to 5 seconds. Thought, but not proven, to be a message that colony will be left with a viable virgin after the swarm departs. The other form is 'piping' produced by virgins after emergence – frequency c.1200Hz starts with a long burst about 1 second in length followed by a number of shorter bursts of 0.3 to 0.4sec separated at 0.2sec intervals. Piping is thought to be a challenge to fight.

The beekeeper's hearing requires to be quite acute to hear the piping and quacking and these sounds are at a higher level than others produced by the bees. For those that have never heard them, the time signal pips from the BBC have a frequency of 1000Hz.

It is still a matter of conjecture how the bees make the sounds but the popular explanation is by the indirect flight muscles when both the wings are either furled or unfurled.

4.16.7 Tactile.

It is not certain whether there is any form of communication by touch which occurs during buzzing runs prior to swarming, while receiving information about forage dances and antennal contact during reciprocal feeding.

4.16.8 Other points.

There are other scalars such as distance and time that bees are able to communicate one to another but the way they do this has not been proven. It is suggested that distance is conveyed by the amount of nectar consumed to undertake the trip or round trip. Bees are certainly aware of time and indeed observe it but whether they can communicate it one to another is doubtful.

It will be clear that there is still much to be researched and discovered about the bees communication systems.

4.17 The collection of nectar and water and their use by the colony.

4.17.1 The way nectar (and water) is collected and conveyed back to the hive.

a) The factors which encourage nectar collection have, surprisingly, been little studied. It is not known whether the amount of nectar collected is related to the amount of honey stored; it is obvious that collection extends far beyond the colony's actual requirements.

b) The presence of a queen and brood stimulates the collection of nectar in much the same way as it stimulates pollen collection. Unlike pollen which is deposited directly by the forager into a cell, nectar foragers pass their load to a house bee. After unloading the foragers can if necessary perform a wag-tail dance to recruit more foragers.

c) Scouting and finding the source of forage occurs first. About 2% of the bees in a colony actually scout for forage. The scouts return with a load and communicate the source by dancing. The forage selected by the colony is likely to be the best in quality (highest sugar content) and quantity.

d) Returning foragers are likely to repeat the wag-tail dances. The number of foragers in a balanced colony is about one third of the population (ie. two thirds of the adults are house bees).

e) The bee collects nectar by sucking it up the food canal of the proboscis (see section 4.9.1) and thence to the honey sac in the abdomen via the pharynx and oesophagus. Average load is 40mg. (cf. the weight of bee = 90mg.) taking approx. 100 – 1000 visits to flowers on the one foraging trip. Foragers make c. 10 trips per day ranging in time from 30 – 60 minutes.

f) The enzyme invertase from the hypopharyngeal glands gets added to the nectar as it transits the pharynx to the oesophagus and the conversion of sucrose (disaccharide) to fructose and glucose (monosaccharides) starts on the flight back to the hive. The process is continued after reception by the house bees receiving the load.

- The behaviour of the foraging bees and the house bees receiving the foraging loads is very similar whether nectar or water is being collected. The crucial factor in the determination of whether the foragers should collect water or nectar is the 50:50 ratio of sugar to water maintained in the bees 'stomach' to enable it to metabolise the sugars. This was first discovered by Simpson in 1964.
- Additionally the honeybee produces a liquid excrement and must consume water regularly in order to survive. This water requirement is mainly derived from nectar but under certain circumstances the colony requires to actually collect water. This need arises when the average sugar content of the food exchange starts to become unbalanced and has a concentration greater than 50:50.
- When this happens the foragers have greater and greater difficulty in finding house bees to unload them and they transfer to water foraging. Water has no taste and no smell so when the foraging dances are performed by a water carrier giving distance and directional information, the dance is usually interspersed with the dancer providing small tastes of the water foraged. Clearly the lack of sweetness forms part of the communication system.

Park in 1928 did a lot of original work on water foraging, some of the more important points are listed below:

a) The honeybee spends c. 1 minute taking up water at the point where it is being collected and the site is often marked by pheromones from the Nasonov glands and the footprint odour around the water source.

b) 67% of the field trips are completed in 3 minutes and 90% in 10 minutes.

c) The time spent unloading and dancing in the hive is c.2 to 3 minutes.

d) A water carrier makes c.100 trips/day and the average load is 25mg (max. load = 50mg).

e) Water is the one commodity that is collected but is never stored.

The collection of nectar by the honeybee colony is to secure the colony's only source of carbohydrate to provide energy for its day to day activities. The process starts by the scout bees finding forage and returning to the hive where they recruit foragers by dancing routines. The most vigorous dances recruit the most foragers who in turn recruit further foragers upon their return to the hive. The more vigorous the dances the better (higher sugar content) the forage.

Bosch, von Frisch and more lately Seeley have conducted experiments with different strength sugar solutions both at the same distance from the hive and measured the rate of recruitment of additional foragers. With dishes containing solutions of 2.25 and 1.50 mol/litres the recruitment in 8 hours was found to be 79 and 10 respectively.

Sources of equal strength but at different flying distances will attract the greatest number of new recruits to the nearest source to the hive.

4.17.2 The use of nectar, honey and water by the honeybee colony.

There are two inputs to the hive, nectar and water (ignoring propolis and pollen):

a) water – used for cooling and humidity control of the brood nest and the dilution of honey.
b) nectar – used for converting to honey for food and storing.

Food transfer from bee to bee is a continuous process within the colony and the average honey sac content is 50% sugar and 50% water. This average content is important. It is the right mixture for digestion by the bee. The use of nectar, honey and water is shown in the 'Honey Usage' diagram 4.15. Points of interest on the diagram:

1. A balance of 50/50 is always maintained in bee's 'stomach'.
2. When nectar is flowing in: no water required: manipulation ('ripening') loses 15% approx. of water. Excess above colony requirements is stored after the full ripening (evaporation).
3. When no nectar is flowing in: honey reserves must be used and water is required for dilution of the honey from 80/20 to 50/50. Foragers will then convert from nectar to water carriers.

During wintering water is required to dilute stored honey. Where does this come from? Winter water flights are very limited (cold weather). Other sources of water are:

– CO_2 + water vapour from trachea. H_2O from this water vapour condenses on cold surfaces within the hive,
– honey uncapped and being hygroscopic it absorbs some water on the surface,
– re-absorption through the small intestine and rectal pads; note that there is no definitive proof of this.

There are three principle uses of water in the honeybee colony as follows:

For diluting high concentrations of honey or nectar in order that it is capable of being metabolised.
For nutritive purposes, as previously mentioned above.
For cooling purposes in the event that fanning is an insufficient form of cooling.

The use of water in a colony may be summarised as follows:

The average colony requirement = 150g/day. 200g/day was calculated by Michailoff in 1961 for temperate climates.

The annual requirement of an average colony = 44lb excluding nectar (Weipple 1928) mostly collected during the spring breeding period.
A strong colony under drought conditions needs c. 1kg/day for cooling and nutritive purposes.

The use of nectar and honey during the course of a year is enormous and is used mainly for foraging, brood rearing and wax making which is never seen by the beekeeper. The calculation is as follows:

Flying bee uses 10mg/hour
Forager flies for c.5 hours/day, therefore the consumption = 50mg/day for 21 days
Queen lays 1500 eggs / day for 100 days, therefore produces 150,000 bees / year
Honey required to rear one bee = 50 to 150mg say 100mg
∴ The annual colony consumption:-

Foraging = (150,000 × 50 × 21) ÷ (1000 × 1000) = 157.5kg = 346.5lb
Brood rearing = (150,000 ×100) = 15kg = 33lb
Wax making (for say 1lb of wax) = 8lb

∴ TOTAL BEFORE SURPLUS = 387.5lb which is unseen by the beekeeper.

Any surplus collected will be in excess of the amount shown above. It will be clear that the foraging activities represent a very large percentage of the overall expenditure and the larger the colony the higher the figure is likely to be. Note the difference in the prolific Italian yellow bee that continues rearing brood irrespective of weather conditions and produces enormous colonies compared with the more thrifty black bee of northern latitudes. The balance is redressed when the flow starts and there is a much larger foraging force to utilise it to advantage. The large yellow colony usually wins hands down on surplus and repays the sugar bill to keep it alive for the occasion.

• In general the foraging behaviour may be summarised as follows:

  • The number of foraging trips that a worker makes per day is between 7 and 13 with the maximum about 24 and an agreed average of 10/day.
  • The average load is between 40 and 50mg.
  • Time foraging per trip = 27 to 45 minutes.
  • Time unloading and dancing in the hive = c. 4 minutes.
  • Number of visits to different florets = c.100 and depends very much on the flow and the flower being worked.

4.18 The conversion of nectar to honey and the inter-relationships of nectar, honey and water in the honeybee colony.

4.18.1 Constitution and types of nectar.

Nectar is the sweet secretion from the nectaries and extra floral nectaries of flowers and plants. It consists of sugar (5 to 80%) and water plus very small quantities of the following substances that give it its characteristic colour and flavour when converted into honey:

proteins	mineral ash
amino acids	salts
enzymes	vitamins
lipids	mucus
organic acids	gums
vitamins	ethereal oils
alkaloids	dextrin
antioxidants	alcohols

Other external agents are always found in nectar such as pollen, fungi, yeasts and bacteria. It has a pH ranging from 2.7 to 6.4 (ie. acid to neutral) and is seldom alkaline.

Generally there are 4 types of nectar collected by the honeybee which are classified by the major constituent ie. the sugars:

Sucrose dominant   (disaccharide $C_{12}H_{22}O_{11}$)
Glucose dominant   (monosaccharide $C_6H_{12}O_6$)
Fructose dominant (monosaccharide $C_6h_{12}O_6$)
Balanced with equal amounts of sucrose, glucose and fructose.

Generally the composition of the nectar does not change with the age of the flower, between flowers or with variations in climatic conditions. It is also to be noted that glucose was formerly known as dextrose and fructose known as levulose. Fructose tastes twice as sweet as glucose and fructose can be tolerated by diabetics.

4.18.2 The conversion of nectar to honey.

The conversion involves two basic changes which are:

Chemical change – breaking down the sucrose with invertase the predominant enzyme in nectar and which is also provided by the honeybee. The conversion process requires water which is present in the nectar as secreted:

$$C_{12}H_{22}O_{11} + H_2O \quad\quad \xrightarrow{\text{invertase}} \quad C_6H_{12}O_6 + C_6H_{12}O_6$$

sucrose + water $\rightarrow$ glucose + fructose

Physical change – evaporation of the excess water content to reduce it to about 18% for an average honey.

4.18.3 Conversion process by the honeybee.

- While the field bee is collecting nectar it adds invertase (= sucrase) from the hypopharyngeal glands. This secretion travels down the salivary canal of the proboscis where it mingles with the nectar and is then drawn up through the food canal and stored in the honey sac.
- The foraging field bee transfers its load to a house bee usually below and on the periphery of the brood nest.
- The house bee then moves its position away from the brood nest and manipulates the nectar by regurgitating and swallowing again a large droplet of nectar. This operation takes about 5/10 seconds and during the process more invertase is added. It does this for about 20

minutes (say about 100 times). This manipulation process evaporates c. 15% of the water.
- The house bee then spreads the manipulated nectar to dry, on the upper surface of empty cells or into partially filled cells above the brood chamber.
- Fanning by other house bees removes the moist air from the hive to be replaced by dry air from outside. When the moisture content is down to c. 18% the cells are then sealed with wax cappings.
- Reference to section 1.16.1.2 shows the amount of space required in the colony to convert nectar into honey.
- Other chemical processes are occurring during the conversion to honey and after it has been sealed. Higher order sugars are produced mainly from the glucose and the glucose oxidase reacts with the glucose to produce gluconic acid and hydrogen peroxide. The hydrogen peroxide acts against any bacteria that may be present and is the substance in honey responsible for its efficacy in the treatment of open wounds.

Note: The description by Gary and the drawings of the proboscis of the honeybee ripening honey by Janson under the direction of Park are, in our opinion, unsurpassed. They may be found in 'The Hive and the Honeybee' by Dadant.

4.18.4 Honeydew honey.

The syllabus for module 4 omits reference to honeydew which the honeybee can collect and store in the hive. A much fuller and detailed account will be found in section 2.27. However, we believe for completeness that mention should be made of the subject here; accordingly we have appended below from our manuscript notes some basic facts.

Insects, primarily of the order hemiptera (aphids) feed on the phloem sap from the phloem tubes of forest trees, notably *pinus sylvestris* but also other conifers. The large quantities ingested are quickly secreted as a sweet sticky substance called honeydew and if allowed to dry on the living parts of the plant is called 'manna'. Mixed in the honeydew and manna are the secretions from the salivary glands of the aphids which contain many more enzymes than nectar from floral sources and additional higher order sugars, examples shown below:

Enzymes – invertase, diastase, a peptidase, a proteinase, etc.
Sugars – melezitose, melibiose, erlose, raffinose, etc,

- The additional enzymes breakdown sugars such as sucrose, maltose and trehalose to produce sugars discrete to honeydew honey.
- Organic acids are always present (eg. citric and more rarely malic acid) and many amino acids (up to 22 have been identified in one sample of honeydew honey).
- In general, the honeybee converts honeydew and manna (usually collected early morning as it is diluted with dew) in the same way as floral nectars. The resulting honey can vary from a golden colour to nearly black; it would never be classed as light honey and the flavour is mild to very strong. The protein content is also higher. It fails to granulate evenly and is always marketed as a run honey. It is prone to deterioration due to the moulds on the honeydew before collection.
- The difference between honey from floral plant and honeydew and manna can be determined by the following formula:

$Q = -8.3x_1 - 12.3x_2 + 1.4x_3$ where
$x_1 = pH$, $x_2 = \%age$ ash content and $x_3 = \%age$ reducing sugars

If Q < 73.1 the sample is honeydew honey and
If Q > 73.1 the sample is honey from floral plants

It is well established that nectar from Rhododendrum ponticum contains the toxin and-romedotoxin acetylandromedol which is dangerous if consumed by man. Similarly there are honeydews which are also toxic to man and to quote one well known one from New Zealand ie. the secretions of the *Scolypopa australis* found on the *Coriaria arborea*.

In some countries honeydew honey is highly regarded and in others it is considered inferior. Most countries recognise it in their regulations regarding honey for sale.

4.18.5 Other points for consideration converting nectar to honey.

• It will be clear from the above that plenty of space is required and there is much sense in the old adage 'over super early in the season and under super late in the season'.
• It is important to provide conditions in the hive to allow the bees to ventilate and ripen their honey easily. The authors believe that by providing top ventilation it assists the bees to ventilate via the hole in the crown board and roof ventilators. In a nectar flow if the roof is raised there are always bees fanning around the open feed hole; we notice many beekeepers keep this hole closed for no apparent reason. It must be hard on the bees to move the air from the 3rd or 4th super down to the bottom entrance.

4.18.6 The interrelationship of nectar, honey and water in the honeybee colony.

Reference should be made to the honey usage diagram 4.15 which shows diagrammatically the inter-relationship between water, nectar, stored honey and the honey sac of the bee. See also section 4.17.2. The honeybee can only metabolise a sugar : water ratio of 50:50 to satisfy its own requirements and it strives to maintain this concentration continually throughout its life.

When nectar is being collected (sugar content varying from as low as 10% to as high as 60%) the house bee ripens this and then hangs it up to 'dry' by evaporation and fanning before sealing as honey with a sugar content of c. 80%.

If nectar is not coming into the hive then the colony must rely on its honey stores and these have to be diluted with water to 50:50 in order for them to be metabolised. Foragers start collecting water under these conditions.

Nectar. The 50:50 ratio is required to provide the energy for feeding, heating, muscular energy for walking, etc., synthesis of wax and the production of brood food and royal jelly.

Water. There are two uses for water by a colony, one for diluting honey stores and the other for cooling purposes (latent heat of vaporisation) which is deposited on top bars and crevices around the hive. This is the only commodity that is collected and not stored in the hive for future use.

a) The annual consumption is c. 44lb (4.4 gallons).
b) Large amounts required for brood rearing (c. 200g/day)
c) Only small amounts required when over wintering.
d) Water foraging trips are short (c.50 to 100/day with loads of c. 25mg)

4.19 The processes of swarming and supersedure and the distinguishing features of swarm, supersedure and emergency queen cells.

4.19.1 General.

MAFF booklet published in 1969 entitled 'Swarming of bees' is necessary reading for this part of the syllabus; unfortunately it is not in print and only old second hand copies are available. Its opening remarks liken a colony of honeybees to an immortal river whereby the dying bees are represented by the loss to the sea and the emerging bees to the tributaries maintaining the level. The life of the bee is finite and the colony is infinite which of course is untrue. Colonies perish for a variety of causes and it must reproduce; swarming is the way this is achieved to enable the species to continue to exist.

4.19.2 The origin of swarming.

Researchers have recognised that there have been (are?) two types of swarm as follows:

1. Mating swarms whereby the colony or part of it accompany the queen on a mating flight and presumably never return to the original nest.
2. Hunger swarms whereby the whole colony departs with the queen in times of dearth to find better foraging areas.

There are pros and cons for both being the origin of swarming of the subfamily of Apinae which contains Apis, Melipona and Trigona. The consensus of expert opinion is that the hunger swarm appears to be the most creditable but more detailed knowledge of the African bee and the stingless bees of S. America is required.

It is interesting to note that if the *Apis mellifera* from the temperate regions of Europe is compared with its present day ancestor from Africa there are some important differences related to swarming.

a) The European bee invests much of its colony resources in collecting and storing large quantities of honey and has developed the ability to cluster for long periods in order to survive a winter climate.
b) Survival in the tropics is considerably easier than in a temperate climate. The African bee invests much of its resources in swarms and drones and still swarms en masse to find forage, often travelling large distances to find it and clustering overnight en route. This swarming instinct has been calculated as ×16 > than that of the European bee. The African bee does not cluster for long periods and does not have the same thermo-regulatory ability which, of course, is unnecessary in a warm climate.
c) The African bee has a preference for a nesting cavity of about 10 litres capacity whereas its European counterpart prefers 20 to 80 litres possibly because of winter storage requirements.
d) Its last major difference is its defensive trait the African bee guarding and stinging at distances > 100 metres. The natives in Zambia, for example, are very cautious when a swarm of bees is seen to be on the wing which happens very often after the jacaranda trees in that area stop blooming.

It will now be clear why the Africanised bee has spread so rapidly in S. America and has caused such alarm because of its defensive traits. The propensity to swarm is part of the genetic make up of the African bee and this characteristic may be found in the old Heath bees of Holland which has been derived from the old African ancestors many millions of years ago.

4.19.3 Swarming theories and other causes.

After Langstroth discovered the concept of bee space in 1851 and the moveable frame hive came into widespread use throughout the world, practical beekeepers have endeavoured to minimise the swarming in their colonies in order to maximise their honey yields. Various theories have been advanced and the three which have received much attention are as follows:

> **Gerstung** (The brood food theory). This theory propounded by Gerstung of Germany in 1890 assumed that when a colony built up and became opulent there was an excess of brood food produced by an excess of nurse bees. Accordingly they built queen cells to use up this excess and swarming occurred.

> **Demuth** (The overcrowding theory). Demuth, a very famous American beekeeper, postulated this theory in 1921 and it received wide acclaim. Relieving congestion in the hive minimised swarming and this was extended by Demaree to congestion in the brood nest and hence his system of control to relieve this condition. From a practical beekeeping point of view the congestion theory was hailed as a great breakthrough in the management of colonies for honey production.

> **Butler** (Queen substance theory). The discovery of 'queen substance' was made by Dr. Colin Butler at Rothamsted in the 1950s probably 1953. It simply postulates that pheromones are produced by the queen and required by the worker bees to inhibit the development of worker ovaries and to inhibit the building of queen cells in the colony. His experiments proved both these hypotheses and are extremely well documented in his book 'The World of the Honeybee' which also contains descriptions of some of the more important experiments that he undertook to prove the theory.

Butler's theory put paid to both the previous theories, in fact it explained the overcrowding theory. Queen substance is passed around the hive to each worker by reciprocal feeding one with another and any congestion would interrupt this process to a greater or lesser degree.

There are other factors which are attributed to swarming and said (thought) to be a trigger in the process. These are listed below:

> **Season.** There seems to be little doubt by general observation that swarming is more prevalent during some years when compared with others.

> **Weather.** Similarly, some weather patterns appear to be associated with the issue of swarms.

> **State of the flow** is said to affect the propensity of swarming.

> **Shade / ventilation** is also said to be a contributory factor.

> **Strain of bee**. There is little doubt about this factor; some strains are inveterate swarmers while some hardly ever swarm.

> **District or area**. It was shown that during one year with a reasonably settled weather pattern over southern England that more swarming occurred in one county compared

with another where statistics were being recorded. This was a one off sample and the sample is a small one and not too much credence can be given to it.

Manipulations are said by some to trigger swarming. The beekeeper who leaves his colonies alone will never be certain the extent of swarming and the authors are not convinced about this one.

Comb space. This is directly related to congestion and is a contributory factor.

4.19.4 Queen substance.

4.19.4.1 Discovery of queen substance (QS) was due to the work of Dr. Colin G. Butler at Rothamsted in the early '50s and contains:

(E)-9-oxo-2-decenoic acid	(or 9-ODA for short),
(E)-9-hydroxy-2-decenoic acid	(or 9-HDA for short),
13 other identified substances,	
?? unidentified substances,	

mainly derived from the mandibular glands of the queen which are larger than the mandibular glands of the worker. It is extremely attractive to worker bees and, as a pheromone, elicits the following effects on worker bees:

Inside the hive:	– inhibits worker ovary development,
	– inhibits queen cell production.
Outside the hive	– acts as a drone attractant for mating,
	– holds swarms together as a cohesive unit.

QS is also produced from dermal glands on a queen's abdomen and possibly the Koschevnikov glands in the sting chamber. It has been shown that each worker in a normal colony requires a minimum threshold amount of QS per day. Various estimates can be found in the literature but 0.15 to 0.2μg / day seems to be an accepted figure. The total amount produced by a healthy queen seems to be about 5000μg / day (see appendix 5) in her first year and which reduces with time according to the exponential law of decay. This gives a colony size of about 33,000 to 25,000 bees which could be a bit low in many cases if all the bees are included. One third of the total will constitute the foraging force and these bees are understood to require less queen substance (QS). We have been unable to find any work undertaken on the amount of QS produced by queens of different races of bees, eg. yellow Italians cf. black bees of N. Europe. Since the yellow races are more prolific with larger colonies, the question must be asked whether yellow queens produce more QS than black queens? On the other hand if all queens produce roughly the same amount then do yellow bees require a lower threshold amount per day? There is still much to learn about colony activities and associated pheromones which was initially broached by Butler. Butler's book 'The World of the Honeybee' is not only essential reading for this examination, it is compulsive reading.

It is now known that the pheromone queen substance is a complex mixture (c. 31 found) of mainly fatty acids of which 13 have been identified. It is produced by the mandibular glands of the queen and also from other dermal glands on the abdomen. It has not been possible to synthesise it successfully to prevent swarming although it was attempted by Glaxo some years ago. The following points in relation to the pheromone are important in relation to the swarming behaviour of the colony:

a) Butler showed that the behaviour pattern of the colony depended on the actual amount the colony received, ie. it is a quantitative problem.

b) J.B.Free has stated that a young (new) queen produces about $5000\mu g$ / day.

c) A minimum threshold amount is required by each worker bee to prevent the building of queen cells. It is unclear whether the threshold amount is the same for all races and strains of bee. Similarly, it is unclear whether different queens produce the same amount per day. Compare the large prolific yellow colony with the smaller less prolific black colony; does the yellow queen produce more QS or do the yellow workers require a lower threshold? Conversely, does the black colony require a greater threshold or does the black queen produce less?

d) QS produced by the queen decreases with time and obeys the exponential law of decay. If she produces an average of $5000\mu g$/day during her first year then this will halve ($2500\mu g$/day) during the second year and halve again ($1250\mu g$/day) in the third year, etc. See appendix 5. The importance of maintaining a young queen to prevent swarming will be obvious.

e) QS is believed to be distributed around the colony by food sharing and the food is contaminated with the QS after the worker has groomed and licked the queen. Again, Butler endeavoured to identify the distribution mechanism but was only able to deduce by observation. It seems that after workers have groomed the queen their next work task is offering food and feeding other workers, often well away from the queen and to the extremities of the hive thereby ensuring a widespread distribution. Unless other evidence comes to light we must assume that this is how it is done.

4.19.4.2 Quantitative effects of queen substance. Before looking at the effect of QS on the various types of queen cells (QC) it as well to note one of Butler's experiments. A colony of about 12,000 bees was split into 3 units each of about 4,000 bees and each with roughly equal amounts of eggs and open brood. The queen, in a Butler cage, was put into the colonies for the times shown below over a period of 48 hours:

4000 bees queenless all the time	-27	emergency cells built
4000 bees queen – 52 minutes/hour	-3	ditto
4000 bees queen – 6 minutes/hour	-10	ditto

Butler shows, very elegantly, that QS is a quantitative requirement in a colony and is reflected in the amount required by each worker bee and the number of QC built. It should also be noted that genetically some bees are inveterate swarmers and build many more QCs when swarming than other strains.

4.19.4.3 Speed of communication. If a queen is removed from a colony or if the queen becomes injured, the normal supply of QS is interrupted and the colony will start to build emergency queen cells, usually in about 3 or 4 hours. Complete queenlessness is detected by the bees in a matter of 10 minutes or so. Queen substance is distributed around the colony by the food transfer process or reciprocal feeding. The distribution is very rapid. A single transfer between two bees takes about half a minute (transferring both food and pheromone). If these two bees feed two other bees, and then four feed four others ad infinitum a series 2, 4, 8, 16, 32, 64, c.125, 250, 500, 1 k, 2 k, 4 k, 8 k, 16 k, 32 k, 64 k is evolved; ie 15 - 16 food transfers each lasting about half minute. In 7 or 8 minutes the whole colony is aware of the 'state of play'. This model is very simplistic and in practice the communication is faster than this. It is readily demonstrated by removing the queen from a colony. In about 5 minutes bees are busily searching for their queen around the entrance area. In a matter of an hour or two emergency queen cells are likely to be started demonstrating the effect of shortage of queen substance.

4.19.5 Emergency queen cells.

As demonstrated by Butler, the number of emergency QCs will be variable but their construction will be quite unique and different from either swarm or supersedure QCs. Emergency queen cells are always built from remodelled worker cells and the inhabitant always started life as a worker. These emergency QCs can be built in any part of the brood nest where suitable eggs or larvae can be found. The authors have noted that quite often many emergency cells are started and then, depending on the prosperity of the colony, some may be torn down by the bees. This is readily demonstrated in a small mating nucleus where the queen has been lost on a mating flight and a frame of eggs and larvae are introduced.

There is no mistaking emergency queen cells; they are always right angular in shape starting in the horizontal plane and the turning at right angles downward on the face of the comb in an area of worker brood or eggs. The other signs, dependent on when inspection takes place after the colony becomes queenless, are the amount of freshly laid eggs or their complete absence. Depending on the size of the colony and the strain of bee there may be only a few or very many emergency queen cells.

4.19.6 Swarm and supersedure queen cells.

Swarm and supersedure queen cells are quite different from emergency queen cells and are always built from queen cups that the queen has laid in. There is no way of distinguishing between a supersedure QC and a swarm QC, they are both built from queen cups and are in close proximity to the brood nest. It is quite normal for all colonies to build queen cups and not use them until swarming or supersedure occurs. They are built in places where there is sufficient space for a QC to be constructed completely in the vertical plane or where the comb is uneven. When a colony starts swarming preparations more queen cups are built. Contrary to many books, there is no scientific evidence to show that eggs are placed in these cups by worker bees; the queen lays in them herself.

4.19.6.1 Supersedure QCs are built when the queen fails to satisfy the need for QS. In the case of swarm QCs the lack of QS is generally caused by congestion or too large a population for the threshold for each worker to be satisfied assuming that the colony has a young queen (first or second year)

4.19.6.2. The number of QCs built can be an indication of supersedure or swarming but this cannot be relied on. It has been suggested that 1 to 5 is supersedure and 5 or more is swarming. The time of the year may also give a clue but again this cannot be relied on. In the authors' experience supersedure queens are often discovered in the spring (because the queens are not marked or clipped) and these supersedures occur after about mid August, the last inspection of the year before wintering when the known marked queen was in residence.

4.19.7 The commencement of swarming in the colony.

When the supply of queen substance is below the threshold required for colony cohesion the queen's egg laying in profusion will rapidly decrease. The eggs which have been laid in the queen cups, which are a part of every normal colony, will not be removed but will be allowed to hatch out into larvae. Queen cells will result and the colony will be on its way to swarming. Other signs will be apparent as follows:

a) House bees will be reluctant to accept nectar loads from foragers.
b) Foraging diminishes and redundant foragers become scouts and start to seek a new nesting site.
c) The queen ceases to be fed and decreases in weight by c. 30% to enable her to fly.
d) Egg laying virtually stops.
e) The decrease in foraging and brood rearing results in physiological changes to the worker bees. Because of the reduced level of QS, worker ovaries start to develop and also because of lack of brood rearing the hypopharyngeal glands also develop producing additional fat bodies and an additional protein reserve.

The number of queen cells appears to depend very much on the strain of bee; those strains prone to swarming and genetically inclined that way will build very large numbers. We have counted as many as 70 in such colonies. For the more normal colony it is likely to be between 10 and 20.

By the time the first queen cell is sealed there will be no freshly laid eggs in the colony and the queen will be physically able to fly. Assuming the weather to be favourable the swarm will emerge at about noon. The following events are pertinent:

a) The emergence is preceded by the 'whir' or 'buzz' dance where the bees run backwards and forwards across the combs in horizontal lines buzzing with half spread wings every 0.5 to 3.0 seconds. Buzz frequency is c. 180 to 250 cps.
b) The dancers touch other bees (for up to 5 seconds) buzzing at 400 to 500 cps when touching.
c) The disturbance and excitement multiplies and soon leads to the emergence of the swarm. Exactly which bees go is unknown and some return very quickly back to the hive.
d) We have not been able to trace at what stage the bees gorge themselves with honey before departure from the hive.
e) The prime swarm with the old queen will settle usually within 10 to 20 metres of the hive. This is to allow the scouts to determine the new nest site. Clearly these scouts could not dance within the hive when forage dances are being undertaken otherwise confusion would occur. The decision making has to be left until the swarm is clustered outside appears to be the most reasonable explanation of this behaviour.
f) Queen pheromone and Nasonov pheromone are vital to co-ordinate the swarm while in flight and during the settling process.

4.19.8 The colony behaviour after the prime swarm has departed.

a) The colony, with decreased numbers of worker bees, ceases to forage avidly without a queen.
b) The remaining queen larvae are nourished and the queen cells sealed.
c) The emergence of the first virgin either produces the first cast or the destruction of other virgins to establish sovereignty.
d) It is unknown how the colony decides to proceed and some colonies if left to their own devices throw a continual stream of casts and virtually decimates itself by not being large enough to be a viable unit.
e) Fighting between virgins is preceded by piping. There are two types as follows:

1. By an emerged virgin – c. 450cps in the range 435 to 493cps (piping).
2. By virgins in their cells – c. 320cps measured as 323cps (quarking).

f) These sounds are produced by the contracting and expanding of the wing flight muscles at the frequencies quoted and are the precursors of fighting between rival virgins. Ones hearing has to be quite acute to hear this phenomenon.

4.19 9 The conditions leading to supersedure.

The definition of supersedure is the requeening of the honeybee colony without the colony swarming. There are two types of supersedure as follows:

Perfect supersedure – whereby the new queen becomes mated and starts laying in the colony together with the old queen before the bees dispose of the old queen. Occasionally the two queens are seen. We have only observed it once or twice.
Imperfect supersedure – whereby the bees dispose of the old queen before the new queen is laying.

• The signs within the colony are often very similar to swarming but the number of queen cells tend to be less than with swarming. They use the same queen cups built during normal colony development.
• Note the difference in the position of swarm and supersedure cells which are identical compared with emergency queen cells which are built on worker larvae amid worker brood. Some books indicate that the queen cells are at the top of the brood nest for swarming and at the bottom for supersedure; we do not consider this to be a useful guide.
• Similarly, the number of queen cells has been quoted as being a guide with 1 to 10 for supersedure and 5 to 20 for swarming. Again we believe reliance on such figures can be unreliable.
• It is impossible to tell whether the bees will swarm or supersede or indeed destroy the cells altogether and do neither. The beekeeper must always assume that swarming is the colony intention.
• The number of colonies that supersede is, in our opinion, about 10%. We base this on the number of new queens that we find at our first spring inspection; ie. unmarked and without clipped wings. The beekeepers who never mark and clip their queens will be unaware of this state of affairs.

Many reasons have been suggested for supersedure; some are as follows:

a) Presence of Nosema disease (Farrar 1947). There is no doubt that queens are affected by the disease and we have dissected queens and checked for positive signs of nosema and then found the spermatheca to be abnormal with a dark black colour instead of the shiny silvery colour of the surrounding glistening trachioles. We have never ascertained what this condition meant.
b) An inadequate supply of eggs (Wedmore 1942 and Root 1948). It is not clear how these two came to this conclusion.
c) Physical damage to the queen (Wedmore 1942 and Snelgrove 1946). In our opinion highly likely but no proof can be offered to substantiate the statements.
d) High drone population and shortage of sperm (Snelgrove 1946). Again no proof offered; in our opinion shortage of sperm usually manifests itself in a drone laying queen rather than a supersedure all other things being equal.

e) Shortage of queen substance (Butler 1954 – 56). Which seems to be the most realistic of them all as it will lead to the production of queen cells but how the bees deal with them is still unknown.

We are of the opinion that all old queens are eventually superseded when one considers that the old queen in a prime swarm heads a new colony in a new site. Initially, because of the reduced number of bees, compared with those in the parent colony, the queen is able to supply the threshold amount of queen substance for each worker bee. This may continue until next year when she may swarm again. In reality there must come a time when the colony decides to supersede in order to replace the failing queen.

It would be interesting to know the incidence of supersedure in the African bee which is a more prolific swarmer compared with its European counterpart.

4.19.10 Other points about swarms.

- The swarming period is usually between April and June at a time when the colony is in an opulent state.
- Swarms have been recorded very early in the season and very late (October and November). Much depends on the weather and the colony.
- The size of swarms varies widely but generally about 50% of the bees in the colony leave with every swarm.
- If a bee weighs 90mg and each bee is carrying 50mg of honey then there will be c.3250 bees per lb in a swarm. A swarm of 20k bees weighing c. 6lb is likely to have originated from a colony of c.40 k bees.
- The temperament of swarms is usually good immediately after swarming irrespective of the characteristics of the parent colony.
- If the weather has delayed the departure of a swarm it may contain more than one queen; ie. 1) the old queen plus one or more virgins or 2) one or more virgins.
- Perhaps mention should finally be made of the conditions associated with the swarming of the honeybee which are:

  Mating
  Hunger and
  Reproduction leading directly to swarming and two types of supersedure already discussed in detail above.

- Mating swarms are comparatively rare in temperate climates and are usually associated with very small broodless mating nuclei. It is not known why the bees join the queen and none return.
- Hunger swarms are virtually unknown in Europe but still remain a feature of the African bee.

4.20 One method of rearing queens suitable for use in an apiary of five to ten colonies.

4.20.1 General considerations. Every beekeeper should rear his own queens, whether he maintains one or two colonies or more. We believe that spare queens should also be available in case of an emergency. With these two thoughts in mind a few criteria can be developed, as follows:

- If spare queens are to be available throughout the year, then they will have to be reared and kept in overwintered nuclei. The emergency may occur in the spring (eg. a drone laying queen is found in one of the stocks) when it is impossible to raise another queen because of the absence of drones at that time of the year for mating.
- One of the biggest problems in UK beekeeping today seems to be the large number of colonies that are bad tempered. If a queen is overwintered in a nuc it is very easy to determine whether her offspring are suitably tempered for use in a large colony. If not, the queen can eventually be culled. Bad tempered nucs are very easy to handle; bad tempered colonies are very difficult to handle and a nuisance to the beekeeper and his neighbours.
- Queens can be reared from a good tempered line (as they always should be) but due to the mating, a bad tempered strain can result. Mating is out of the control of the beekeeper and he can only monitor the end result. We consider that all queens should first be tested for temper before introduction into the honey producing unit. If all beekeepers followed this advice, their beekeeping would become more enjoyable, neighbours would not be stung and the amount of personal protection could again be reduced to a simple veil.
- Any queen rearing should be planned and this must include consideration of the following:

    - Timing – ready to start at 2nd or 3rd week in May.
    - Selection of the breeder queen.
    - What method of larval transfer is to be used?
    - Selection and preparation of the cell building colony.
    - How many queens are required?
    - Mating nucs.

Each of the above points will be examined in some detail with a view to evolving a suitable approach for the small hobbyist beekeeper.

- Before setting out to rear any queens it is absolutely essential to fully understand the life cycle and natural history involved from the laying of the egg by the breeder queen to the new queen actually laying (see section 4.5.3).
- Once the timing schedule has started, there can be no variation; come hail or shine each operation has to be done on time. Opening a colony under an umbrella in the rain is not too easy on one's own and in this sort of situation good tempered bees are definitely preferred.

4.20.2 How many queens? A method for a use in an apiary of 5 to 10 colonies. The wording is very ambiguous and it would be better to define the number of queens required. 5 to 10 queens would, in our opinion, be a small number and suitable for an apiary of this size. 10 to 50 queens would be a medium number and 50 to 500 would be in the commercial queen rearing class. The number is important because to rear good queens, the larvae have to be well fed and the more there are the bigger and stronger the cell building colony has to be. There is, of course, a finite limit to the capabilities of the strongest colony in respect of the number of queen cells (QCs) it can successfully raise. Depending on the method used, so the skill and experience of the beekeeper will influence the success rate. This is particularly true if grafting is adopted. It is therefore prudent to allow a safety factor for this 'success rate' and 50% success is quite realistic for the moderately dextrous operator. So if you want 10 aim at 20. It is always best to use simple methods until more demanding techniques are learnt.

4.20.3 Timing. The critical factors in queen rearing are:

a) Mature drones are required for mating (12 days after emergence).
b) Optimum conditions are those associated with the time that colonies swarm naturally.
c) A flow is virtually essential and this can be simulated by feeding.
d) There must be an abundance of nurse bees for feeding the larvae.
e) Royal jelly is synthesised from pollen and this is required in quantity.

Considering all the above factors, they indicate that, in UK, the month of May is generally the time that they all occur naturally. We always aim to have the cell building colony ready by the 2nd or 3rd week in May. If bad weather occurs the start date can slip a few days but once started there can be no slippage. At the first inspection in the spring, the cell building colony should be selected (the breeder is likely to have been chosen the previous season) and this colony must be built up until it is teeming with bees and brood by mid-May. Queen mating nuclei will be required 9/10 days after larvae are introduced into the cell builder and provision for making these must also be included in the timing schedule.

4.20.4 Selection of the breeder queen. This is the queen which is selected for her good characteristics which hopefully will be reproduced in her protégé daughter queens. There are many characteristics, but the important ones, in our opinion, for the hobbyist beekeeper are as follows:

• **Temper** must come at the top of the list. It is essential for the breeder queen to come from a colony which produces good tempered bees which can be handled without gloves and with a minimum of smoke. If this requirement cannot be complied with, it will be necessary to buy in a queen of known good temper to breed from. Having ensured the temperament of the breeder queen it does not follow that success is also ensured; the mating of the young virgins finally casts the die.
• **Nervousness.** This trait is exhibited by bees that move quickly and run all over the comb during inspection, finally clustering in a bunch at the bottom of the frame and falling off leaving the comb virtually bare of bees. It is extremely difficult finding a queen in such a colony and they are usually difficult to requeen by normal introduction with a Butler cage. When a frame is removed from a colony during a normal inspection, the bees should remain quiet and completely cover the frame while it is out of the hive. If they can't meet this test, then don't use the queen as a breeder.
• **Swarming.** Do not breed from a strain which swarms prolifically (producing a large number of queen cells). The Heath bees brought into this country after the I.O.W. disease (Acarine now Acariosis) are inveterate swarmers and the strain is still with us in our mongrel bees. Some years ago we acquired a queen from a fellow beekeeper which passed on the above traits but turned out to be a swarmer when we bred from her; it was impossible to stop them swarming and we had to dispense with them in the end.
• **Disease.** Some strains of bees are more resistant to a particular disease than others. It goes without saying that the breeder queen should come from a colony with a disease free record.
• **Fecundity.** A prolific egg layer means a large colony and lots of bees which in turn means a larger foraging force for honey production. It is to be noted that the very yellow coloured bees (Italians originally) now brought in from New Zealand are very prolific and convert every bit of food into bees. They often require feeding when other strains can survive on their own resources and they tend to be prone to Acarine infection; a pity because they are delightful bees to handle.

After a season has been completed, most beekeepers are well aware of the colony which is headed by a queen with the least undesirable characteristics (unlikely to be the most desirable!) and selection is therefore very easy. One characteristic which is not mentioned above is the tendency to collect propolis in large quantities. With one or two hives it never seems to matter very much but when 20 or more colonies are 'propolisers' it does become a little irksome during manipulations.

4.20.5 Selection of the cell builder. The cell building colony will receive the 12 to 36 hour old larvae and build them into queen cells after a period of queenlessness. The colony has to be very strong and teeming with bees and is to be opened at fixed times irrespective of the weather. It is therefore important that this colony should also be of good temper. A further factor for consideration is whether to work a single brood chamber or a double one. With hives using BS frames (eg. British National) a double brood chamber system is likely to be the most popular format for most beekeepers. For the hobbyist beekeeper it is probably more convenient to do his queen rearing at home rather than at his out apiary. In such a case, there could be advantages initially preparing the cell builder at the out apiary and moving it to the home apiary on to a site just previously occupied by another colony so that the cell builder is further reinforced by the flying bees from the stock moved in the home apiary. It should be noted that the cell building colony and the breeder can be one and the same stock if required.

4.20.6 Larval transfer. There are a variety of methods of introducing larvae from the breeder queen's colony to the cell builder; some of the more well known approaches are listed below:

a) Grafting (something of a misnomer) is physically transferring the larva with a small tool (a grafting tool, another misnomer) from a worker cell in the breeder colony to an artificially made queen cup which is then put into the cell builder.
b) Double grafting – a larva is transplanted into a queen cell and then 1 or 2 days later before it is sealed it is replaced with a new young larva.
c) Punching out the whole worker cell containing the egg or young larva. The punched out cell is then attached to a suitable bar in a standard frame for insertion into the cell builder. Examples are the Barbeau method and the Stanley method. The advantage is that the actual larva is not touched and therefore reduces any likely damage and hence failure.
d) Transfer of a whole frame of eggs and larvae from breeder to cell builder direct. There are variations on this eg. Miller method of cutting the comb in 'Vs', the line of the cut being adjacent to larvae of the right age. A frame can be put over the top of the cell builder horizontally (about 1 in above the cell builder frames) allowing the cells to be formed vertically from the lower comb face (popularly called the Australian method supposedly because the frame is the wrong way up!).
e) A more recent approach is to use the Jenter method. These methods prevent physical damage to the larvae and require little dexterity as the larvae are selected by the bees.

A simple method of raising 5 to 10 queens would certainly rule out grafting methods which are essential for raising large numbers of queens and require good eyesight, a steady hand and some experience to have a fair degree of success. When we undertake grafting, we do 10 grafts each to provide a total of 20 in 2 separate rows to check our own dexterity one against the other (so far there has been no clear winner or loser!) which is a useful monitor.

4.20.7 Mating nucs. Provision will have to be made for the mating nucs and be part of the overall plan. Because of the vagaries of the UK weather it is probably better to have the nucs made up prior to the day that the ripe queen cells are transferred. If it is pouring with rain the transfer is quite enough to do. See section 1.19 for details on nucs.

4.20.8 A simple method: based on double brood chambers with BS frames and using the breeder colony as the cell builder. 5 to 10 queen cells may be expected. The steps in the process are listed below:

- Prepare the cell building colony for queen rearing, aiming to have the largest population and brood by mid May when there are likely to be mature drones for mating. The stock would be 2 full brood chambers, QEx and 2/3 supers.
- Draw out a programme (like the top part of the diagram in appendix 4) with actual dates incorporated below the natural cycle from egg to emergence.
- Re-arrange the colony for queen rearing using a spare empty brood box. Into the spare brood box put all the frames of open brood and eggs and as much sealed brood and pollen as possible but with no queen. The queen and the balance of frames are placed on the floorboard with QEx over. Add the supers and the box of brood with no queen with crown board and spare eke and feeder (1pint size adequate). Feed approximately 1pint per day. As a result of this rearrangement all the nurse bees (or most of them) will join the brood in the top box and in 24 hours queen cells are likely to be started; this must be checked. If not, insert a screen board with entrance under the top brood box. There can now be no possibility of any queen substance reaching the bees in the top box and QCs will be started.
- After 3 days examine the top box and destroy all sealed QCs (these will have been built on larvae 2 or more days old). Count and leave all other open QCs which should be sealed in another 1 or 2 days time. There are two problems with this system of queen rearing which are as follows:

  1. When destroying the sealed QCs most of the bees will have to be brushed off the frames to ensure that all the sealed ones are destroyed. Do not shake your future queens.
  2. One can never be quite sure when the remaining open cells are sealed. It is therefore very important to mark up the programme and be ready to remove the ripe QCs on day 14 approximately 2 days before the theoretical emergence. If one or more emerge earlier than your calculated day 16 it will not ruin the whole programme; they will be safely in their mating nucs and the first one out will not be capable of destroying the lot in the cell builder.

- Four or five days before the ripe QCs are to be distributed, nucs can be prepared and left queenless for 4/5 days if they are permanent nucs. This means de-queening them and then destroying all emergency QCs just before introducing a ripe QC on day 14. All frames must be shaken to ensure no scrub QC is left in the nuc.
- On day 14 new nucs can be made up with only sealed brood (no eggs or open brood) and the ripe QCs distributed to them.
- The top box can be left with one ripe QC and when this new queen is mated and laying the top and bottom boxes can be united after removing the old queen in the bottom box. Alternatively, the top box can be used to make 3 good nucs for some of the ripe QCs.

4.20.9 Other points of interest.

- Queens are expensive to buy and after travelling they are not in the best condition for introduction. They are only available at the wrong time of the year. The beekeeper with a small number of colonies can produce queens the equal of those at top prices with the material he has available on his own door step if he is so inclined.

- In order to get rid of bad temper it is essential to maintain overwintered nucs to test the new queens from the time they are reared to the following March when they should be introduced. Our own experience with mongrel strains amounts to culling approximately 10% of those reared.
- For 20 stocks we maintain approximately 15 permanent nucs for re-queening purposes. The nucs are virtually self supporting.

4.21 Methods of queen introduction itemising necessary precautions.

4.21.1 General considerations. In order to introduce a new queen it is essential that the colony is queenless; this may be stating the obvious but there are numerous queens lost each year on this count. Young queens are generally nervous and do not behave sedately until they have reached a certain stage of maturity. Bro. Adam believes that this maturity is reached about 8 weeks after the queen starts to lay and it is unwise to introduce a queen until after this stage has been reached. Some of the known facts about queen introduction, mainly empirical and not proved theoretically, are as follows:

- The greater the population in a colony the more difficult it is to requeen.
- Therefore it follows that requeening before April and after August are the best times and this is borne out in practice.
- Requeening in a honey flow is easier than in times of dearth.
- Requeening in the spring has many advantages particularly as finding queens in small colonies is easy and quick.
- Spring requeening is virtually 100% successful.
- Requeening with a queen of the same strain is easier than with a queen of a different strain. Yellow queens into black colonies are particularly difficult.
- Queens should be in the same physiological condition (ie. laying normally) for successful introduction. Queens that have travelled through the post are not in normal laying condition.
- Bro. Adam maintains that 'colony odour' plays no part in the success of queen introduction, it is the behaviour of the queen. If the behaviour of the old and the new queen is the same then it is not an introduction but a substitution.

4.21.2 Introduction by cage.

The general principle involved is to place the queen into a cage (with a mesh of about 7 or 8 per inch) with some kind of barrier that prevents the queen from escaping but which can be slowly broken down by the bees, thereby releasing the queen. Various types of cage have been designed but most beekeepers these days use the Butler Cage (due to Dr. C. Butler nb. Queen Substance) which is made of wire mesh and plugged at one end with a piece of wood. The dimensions are approx. 4in × 0.75in × 0.5in. In use, a small piece of newspaper is placed over the open end and secured with a small elastic band. It is usual for 2 or 3 pin holes to be made in the paper before placing in the colony. All our own cages have a slight modification by driving a 1.5in panel pin through the wooden plug; this leaves 1in of pin proud which is a useful fixing device for pushing into the wax comb. Another popular barrier is a plug of candy which is eaten away by the bees (candy = honey with icing sugar mixed in to a stiff paste); we consider this messy and more complicated than the newspaper. It is important that the mesh is not too small, if it is it will prevent antennal contact with the queen by the workers. Release is generally effected in 12 to 24 hours. The salient points of this method are:

- The queen only should be imprisoned in the cage without any attendant workers.
- The cage should be placed in the brood nest, and if possible, on a frame with brood at all stages of development. The queen should start her normal laying duties virtually as soon as she has been released.
- Remove the cage the following day.
- The method is virtually 100% successful if undertaken in the spring.
- During the active season if a large colony has to be requeened it is more reliable to plug the open end of the cage with wood and leave the queen imprisoned for 2 days. After this time, open up the colony and remove the frame with the queen cage and then remove the wooden plug and let the queen walk out. If she is unmolested after a couple of minutes replace the frame, with her on it, back into the colony. If she is molested and workers start collecting round and over her, put her back in the cage for another 2 days. If a yellow queen is being introduced into a colony of black bees, we leave the queen a full week before supervising the release which should be a sedate and unruffled affair.

The two other cages which are commonly used are:

- The plastic hair curler, used by ladies, suitably plugged at one end and newspaper over the other end.
- The combined travelling/introduction cage, which usually has candy already incorporated in it. They are mostly made of plastic these days whereas in days gone by they were wooden blocks bored out and wire cloth tacked on. The wire cloth is considered unsuitable, the mesh being too fine. It is important to remove the attendant workers before introduction, so that the queen is fed by the receiving colony and not by the attendant workers from her original colony. See 4.21.3 below for queens received by post or other means of delivery.

4.21.3 Uniting method.

Methods of uniting are described in section 1.22 and cover all the main points of interest. The only other uniting method that requires discussion is for dealing with a queen that has been travelled and out of her colony of origin for a few days. Such a queen is not in a physiological condition for immediate introduction; she must be in lay. If she is to requeen a large colony, the following points should be observed:

- Make up a nucleus from the colony to be requeened and sited adjacent to it ready to receive the new queen. Do not dequeen the colony at this stage.
- Remove the attendant workers and introduce the new queen in a Butler cage to the nucleus. Note controlled and supervised release if considered necessary.
- Once the new queen is accepted allow 1 to 2 weeks for her to start laying normally in the nuc; the longer the better.
- Unite the nuc with the colony immediately it has been dequeened. The usual way for this is by direct introduction back into the space in the brood chamber created when the nuc was made. As a further precaution the new queen can be caged again for a day while the uniting settles down.
- Any uniting should, as stated previously, be done as it is getting dark and the bees have

finished flying; it prevents any fighting by guards at the entrance challenging bees from the other colony.

It will now be clear that because queens can only normally be purchased from the suppliers from May onwards, they are only available at a time least favourable to them being introduced to another colony. The moral must be clear, every beekeeper should not only rear a few queens but should always have a spare one on standby.

4.21.4 Direct introduction.

There are a variety of methods claimed for direct introduction from shaking the dequeened colony out in front of the hive and, in the resulting confusion, running in the new queen with the bees to dunking the queen in a variety of substances (eg. water, honey, etc.). None are now recognised as modern methods and generally are considered a bit cranky even though some have been advocated by eminent beekeepers (eg. Simmins). After dunking, the advocates then run the queen in via the entrance or the feed hole at the top. During 1989 there was some serious work undertaken in France on direct introduction by bathing the queen in a mixture of royal jelly and water (70% & 30% respectively). Trials were carried out on both fertile queens and virgins into nucs, colonies and colonies of laying workers. The success rate was high for all permutations and it is expected that more will be heard of this approach in the future.

See 1.11.2 for requeening bad tempered colonies using the chloroform method which is the only method we know where there is a high success rate running a queen directly into the colony.

4.22 The signs of queenlessness and a method of confirming the condition.

4.22.1 The signs (not symptoms) of queenlessness in a colony can be readily seen by the observant beekeeper both outside the hive and also inside. The beekeeper with only a little experience can generally tell, by looking at the entrance and studying the bees' behaviour patterns, whether the colony is normal or abnormal. It is a sound practice to have 2/3 stocks in the garden and to study the entrances for a few minutes 2 or 3 times a day while the bees are out, both in the summer and in the winter through to spring. With practice it is generally possible to say whether a colony is normal or abnormal by observing the entrance without recourse to examining the interior; this is particularly useful in the early spring as winter is drawing to a close. The art should be developed by all beekeepers. Colonies seldom become queenless of their own accord, it is usually due to an error or series of errors on the part of the beekeeper and his manipulations which cause this condition. A very small percentage of colonies become queenless during the winter due to the death of the queen at a time when the bees do not have the ability to produce a replacement.

4.22.2 The signs of queenlessness are as follows:

• If a queen is removed from a colony, within about 10 to 15 minutes, signs of queenlessness are likely to be observed at the entrance. Bees are wandering around the outside of the hive 'looking for' the queen. These bees crawl up the front and sides of the hive and appear to be in an agitated state. Conversely, if the queen is returned to the colony, it takes about the same time for it to return to normality (see section 4.19.4.3)

- If the colony has been queenless for some time (say 24 hours or more) the foraging will be greatly reduced, there will be apathy among the workers, some of which will be running around somewhat aimlessly.
- The colony will give a distinctive roar when opened which is very different from the normal colony sound.
- The colony will become more aggressive than usual and difficult to handle.
- The first signs inside the colony are no eggs and eventually no brood and the possible appearance of emergency QCs built over worker brood.
- If the colony has no means of re-queening itself it is said to be 'hopeless', for example, when there is only sealed brood or no brood at all in the colony.
- The colony starts to dwindle in size, and if it is left queenless for 3 weeks or more laying workers will start to appear and eggs will be found in an erratic laying pattern. More than one egg per cell is common and drone brood in worker cells starts to appear. At this stage the colony has a 'dispirited air' (difficult to describe in words) about it.

4.22.3 Confirmation of queenlessness.

A colony, of course, should not be allowed to get to the stage of laying workers. Before this stage, a virtually infallible test is to put a frame of eggs and brood of all ages into the queenless colony. If there is no queen (either fertile or virgin) then queen cells will be started on the introduced larvae within 24 hours. If this test is undertaken too late (ie. laying workers present), it may not work. There is only one situation when this test comb may not give a reliable indication and that is after a colony has just swarmed and has a young mated queen. QCs may be built still under the swarming urge. This is not a very common occurrence.

4.23 The methods of marking and clipping queens and the advantages and disadvantages of these practices.

In order to mark or clip a queen it is necessary to keep her still and in such a position that the operation may be effected without damaging her. It is an aid to bee management but our own observations reveal that marking and clipping are not widely practised by hobbyist beekeepers in the UK. Some beekeepers object to clipping on ethical grounds, a point of view we cannot understand and seemingly those who hold such views cannot explain them.

4.23.1 Queen marking cages.

There are two basic types of queen marking cages, namely the press on cage which imprisons the queen in the cage on the comb and the glass plunger type whereby the queen is gently pushed to the end of the tube with a soft foam plunger until she is just in contact with a plastic grill through which she is marked.

There are two types of press on cage one made of plastic and the other called a Baldock type which is prefabricated. Both are about $1\frac{1}{2}$in diameter with a mesh on top having about $\frac{5}{32}$in squares. The bottom has a series of spikes which can be pushed into the wax comb. The only difference between them is the Baldock type has finer wires forming the top mesh making it easier to mark the queen and it has finer pointed spikes making it easier to push into the comb.

We recommend the Baldock type, the plastic one is somewhat crude and more difficult to use.

The Plunger type requires the queen to be handled. She has to be put into the glass tube at one end and pushed gently up to the other end. It unfortunately has a plastic grill and suffers from the same defect as the plastic push on cage, the plastic mesh of the grill is too coarse. We have never used one but have seen queens damaged by them not being used carefully enough.

4.23.2 Holding the queen in the fingers.

Many beekeepers, including ourselves, never use cages for marking. We find it easier to pick the queen up and hold her while clipping and marking. The recommended way is to pick the queen up by her wings in the right hand (assuming you are right handed) and place her on the ball of the thumb of the left hand and hold her between the thumb and forefinger while preventing her slipping down with the second finger beneath the queen. She is held by the head and thorax not the abdomen.

We use a different method which was shown to us many years ago by Brian Palmer of Kent. We have used it ever since and we have shown many beekeepers how to do it; to our knowledge we have never seen mention of it in print. The queen is picked up in the same way by the wings and placed on the ball of the thumb of the left hand. The three legs on one side are smoothed down until all three are trapped between the thumb and fore finger. When she is safely held by the legs the hold on the wings may be released. It is surprising the amount of pressure that can be used to hold the three legs without damaging the queen. We suggest that practice is first gained with a few drones.

4.23.3 Marking queens.

4.23.3.1 Reasons for marking.

These are the advantages of marking and listed in order of popularity:

    a) To make the finding of the queen easier
    b) To identify the age of the queen
    c) To identify different suppliers and strains
    d) Research and studying queen behaviour.

4.23.3.2 Materials used for marking queens.

Clearly the colour is important particularly with dark bees where the queens are much more difficult to find compared with the lighter coloured bees. White and yellow are particularly good. Most bee suppliers can provide a set of colours in quick drying paints or enamels which are normally used for model aeroplane or motor cars. It is important that emphasis is put on the quick drying and here the solvent is important. Any use of amyl acetate (which smells of pear drops) should be avoided as it has similar effects to iso pentyl acetate (which smells of bananas) the alarm pheromone from the sting chamber. Most nail varnishes fall into this category. We do not colour code our queens and we always use white Tipp-Ex (as used by stone age typists) which uses trichloroethane an industrial degreasing agent.

If colour coding is used indicating the year the queen emerged then there is an internationally agreed colour code as follows:

COLOUR	LAST DIGIT OF YEAR	READ DOWN
White	1 or 6	Which
Yellow	2 or 7	Year
Red	3 or 8	Reared
Green	4 or 9	Great
Blue	5 or 0	Britain

Paints, enamels or other marking fluids can be applied in a number of ways with a small brush (Tipp-Ex comes complete with brush in the lid), head of a match stick, pin stuck in a cork, etc. With all marking it is important that the marker is sufficiently fluid to penetrate the small hairs on the queens thorax and adhere to the exoskeleton of the thorax, the only place a queen should be marked. The amount used must be just right and must not run down into the petiole or into the queen's eyes.

Small numbered discs are available which are attached to the queen with a small dab of quick drying glue. These are also available in the colours quoted above.

Another variation is the Eckhart marker which cuts out a small circular disc and is ejected and stuck onto the queen with glue by an internal plunger. They are not often seen these days but were the 'in' gadget 50 years ago.

Fluorescent paint has been used in conjunction with UV light and radio active paint in conjunction with a Geiger counter. It is unlikely that the hobbyist will have any interest in these two methods which are much more research orientated.

It is important that the queen is held for a short time after marking for the paint to dry or the glue to set before she is released back into the colony.

4.23.3.3 The disadvantages of marking.

There are a few disadvantages in marking which are as follows:

a) Whenever the queen is handled or touched there is always a small danger that she may be damaged. The moral is handle her very carefully.
b) Marking with the wrong type of marking material can prove fatal (nb.amyl acetate).
c) Badly marked with an excess of marking fluid will prompt the bees to supersede the queen.
d) One source we consulted indicated that marking a queen leads to supersedure. We have marked hundreds and this has not been our experience.

4.23.3.4 When to mark a queen.

It is our belief that all queens should be marked. There are two reasons for saying this:

1. Practically all methods of swarm control require the beekeeper to find the queen and a well marked queen makes the task so much easier and more reliable particularly if the bees are a bit sharp.

2. If a colony becomes bad tempered and the queen has to be changed. To do this quickly and efficiently great concentration is required to find an unmarked queen particularly if the bees are also runners.

There is only one time to mark the queen, in our opinion, and that is when the colony is small and easy to handle. This means in the spring just after the first inspection. We never touch or handle a queen from the time she emerges (usually about May) until about March when she is both marked and clipped before introduction to a colony from an over wintered nucleus. Bro.Adam advocated never touching a queen until she was at least 8 weeks old; very sound advice.

4.23.4 Clipping queens.

4.23.4.1 The reasons for clipping queens.

The primary advantage is in connection with swarming. Using a clipped queen it is possible to have 14 day inspections up to the time swarming preparations are detected and then the beekeeper must revert to 9 or 10 inspections. If a swarm issues with a clipped queen the queen falls to the ground and the swarm of worker bees returns to the hive. Using the aforesaid inspection times saves losing the bees which are the motive force for collecting a crop of honey. The secondary advantage is to provide an indication of the age of the queen by clipping a particular wing for odd years and the other for even years. This is a form of marking.

4.23.4.2 Clipping.

About $\frac{1}{3}$ of the wing (s) is cut off. Single wings or both on one side or both on both sides may be trimmed. The important point about clipping is to have a very sharp pair of scissors with very fine points. Surgical scissors are by far the best.

Be very careful about the queen curling one of her legs over the top of her abdomen when the clipping operation is being done. It is very difficult (nearly impossible in our opinion) to clip a queen in a queen marking cage. Beekeepers try it and we suspect that the queens are damaged in the process. We believe that to clip a queen it is necessary to hold her in one hand and clip with the other.

It is very important that ones fingers are not sticky with propolis when picking up a queen by her wings; if they are really sticky it will be very difficult to release her with out damaging her at the wing roots. This is the only time gloves are permissible; wear them until the queen has been found and then remove them to do the clipping. At these times we adopt a single role, one looking for the queen and the other doing the marking and clipping with a clean pair of hands. A much better arrangement.

4.23.4.3 Other points.

- Clipping does not hurt a queen, it rather like having a hair cut. We have met some beekeepers who will not clip their queens and say it is wrong to do so but the reasons why it is wrong are never forthcoming.
- Often clipped queens walk back into the hive after swarming. As long as one is alert to this it should be no surprise to find a clipped queen and sealed queen cells in the colony.
- Sometimes if the queen does not get in the hive she will be found with a swarm under the hive depending of course on whether she can gain access to the underside.
- Once a queen has been clipped it is difficult to pick her up if she has to be transferred to another place. In such cases we always use a Butler cage put over the queen on the comb and wait until she walks up into the cage before plugging it with the queen inside.

Diagrams for section 4:

Candidates sitting for the examination in Module 4 should be able to sketch all the above diagrams. Questions can be set on any of the biology topics covered and diagrams may be a mandatory part of the question. Being able to reproduce the sketches will indicate to the examiner an understanding of the subject.

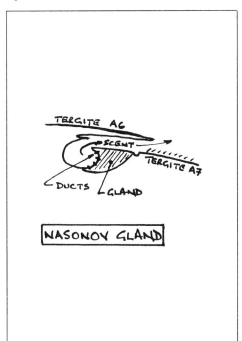

Diagram 4.1

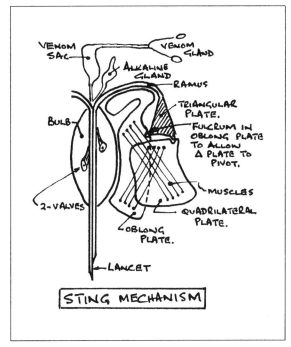

Diagram 4.2

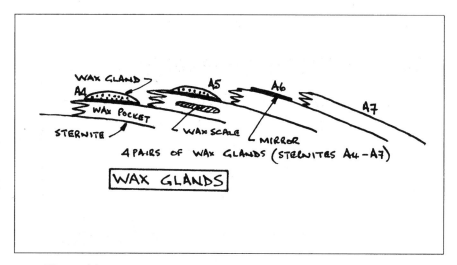

Diagram 4.3

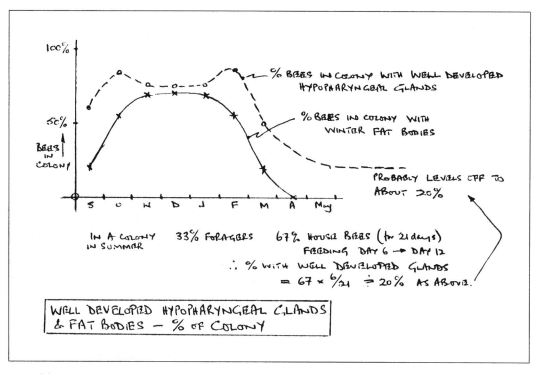

Diagram 4.4

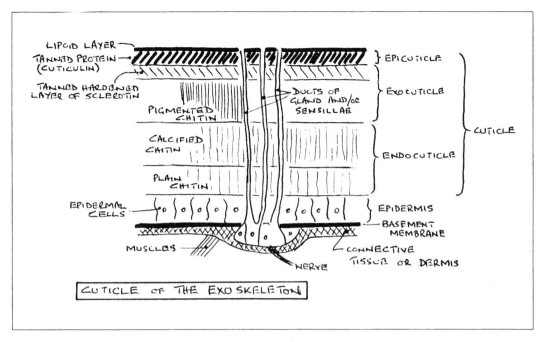

Diagram 4.5

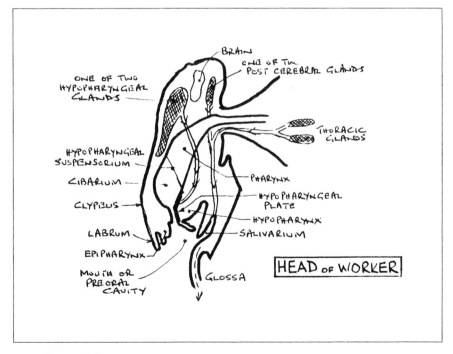

Diagram 4.6

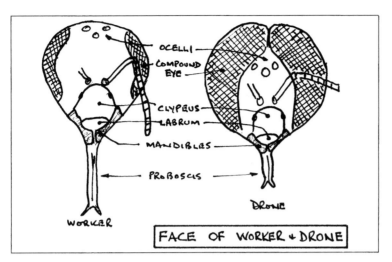

Diagram 4.7

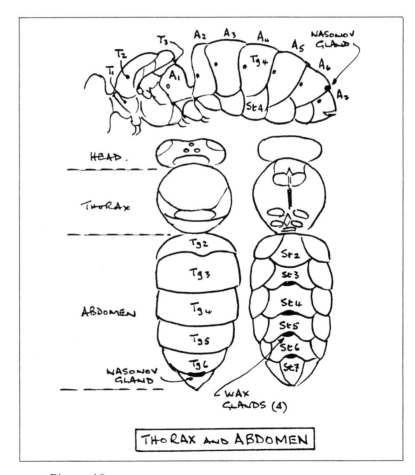

Diagram 4.8

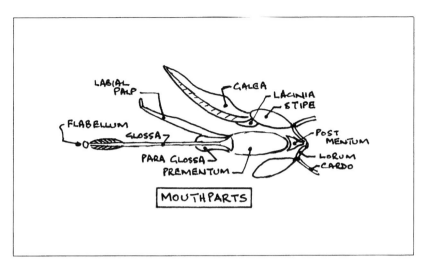

Diagram 4.9

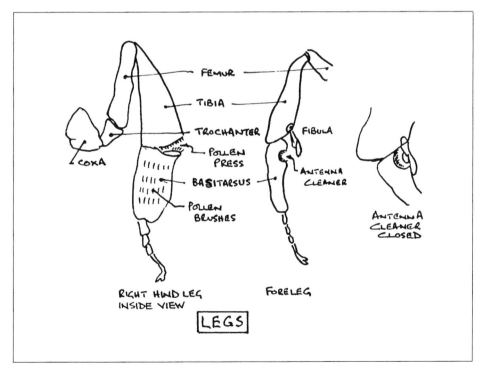

Diagram 4.10

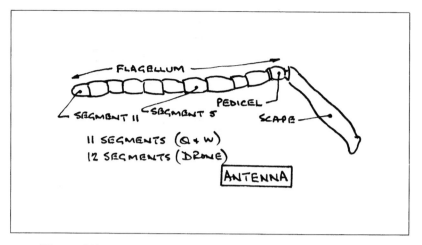

Diagram 4.11

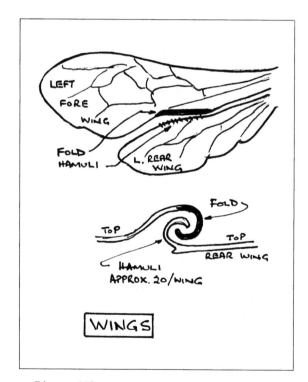

Diagram 4.12

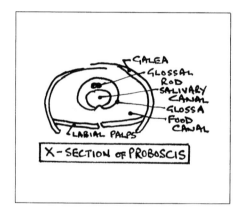

Diagram 4.13

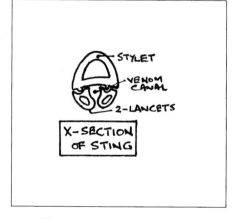

Diagram 4.14

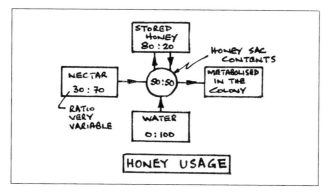

Diagram 4.15

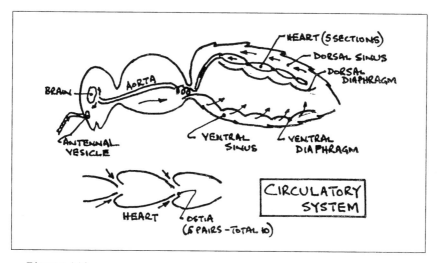

Diagram 4.16

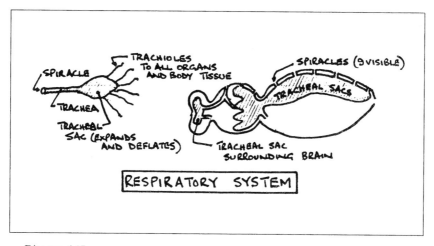

Diagram 4.17

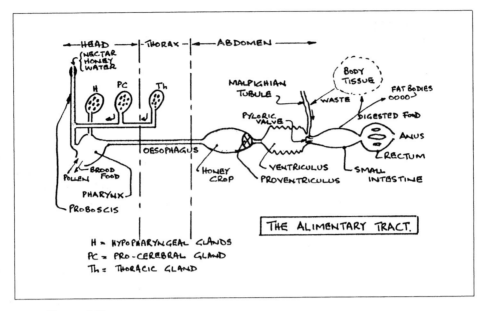

Diagram 4.18

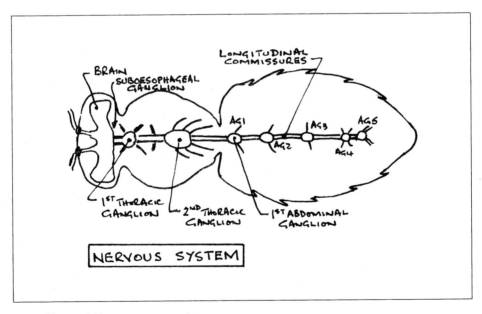

Diagram 4.19

APPENDIX 1 – **FRAMES**
(Copy of an article written for Beekeeping Quarterly – Autumn 1994)

In September / October 1984 the following British Standards were withdrawn:

1947 – Bees (colonies and nuclei)
1950 – Honey grading glasses
1960 – Bee hives, frames and wax foundation

with the result that the beekeeping fraternity, if that is the right word, has no nationally recognised standards. The only ones that I know of are the BBKA definitions of a nucleus and a stock. This unfortunate state of affairs arose, so I was told by the British Standards Institute (BSI), because of lack of interest on the part of BBKA who used to provide representatives on a special BSI committee dealing with the subjects quoted above.

There seems to be a case for a motion at the ADM asking the BBKA Executive to examine the feasibility of getting the working committee at the BSI reconvened (or should the Husbandry Committee be approached?) as there is a mountain of work to be done to standardise the equipment we use. In this short article I will deal only with frames to illustrate why it is one of things that has puzzled me and why it would be to the good of beekeeping in the UK to rethink the whole design of frames that fit into our hives. Most of the frames are so horrendous in design that it puzzles me why so many beekeepers continue to use them. Note that the last standards were dated 1960, 34 years ago and the standards actually lapsed in 1984 now 10 years ago. We should not be talking about a British Standard (BS) frame as there is no standard!

Let us look at the brood chamber first to see what is required. In a wild colony if the brood comb is examined carefully it will be found that the distance from septum to septum of adjacent combs is $1\frac{3}{8}''$ and the length of 2 worker cells, with a common septum, measures $\frac{7}{8}''$. This gives a space of $\frac{1}{2}''$ between the comb faces; ie. 2 bee spaces each of $\frac{1}{4}''$ with the bees working back to back on the adjacent comb faces. All this is fact and Hoffman got it right with his spacing method moulded into the frame end bar shoulders giving exactly the correct spacing of $1\frac{3}{8}''$. Surely the $1\frac{1}{2}''$ spacing provided by metal and plastic ends should be shelved by any standards committee working on the topic? William Broughton Carr (WBC) was a great beekeeper but I have yet to meet the dedicated beekeeper who would thank him for the metal ends which were conveniently dimensioned to fit 10 of them into a WBC brood chamber (10 x $1\frac{1}{2}''$). I'm not sure which came first the frame spacing or the brood chamber. The Hoffman frame has its faults; the flat part of the spacing shoulder on the RH side of the frame, with the top bar uppermost, is fine, but the $2''$ knife edge on the LH side spells disaster for bees when frames are closed up during the final stages of a manipulation. It is splendid device for chopping bees in half and I actual cut a queen in two when giving a demonstration at a branch meeting on one occasion – carelessness on my part I know. However, it doesn't happen with my frames where the knife edge has been replaced with a small brass round head wood screw. To my knowledge I have never damaged a bee with this arrangement and my frames are all Hoffman compatible to accommodate those people to whom I supply nucs each season. So far we have only considered frame spacing; what about the size of the woodwork? There is no justification for using $\frac{7}{8}''$ wide top and side bars. With $1\frac{3}{8}''$ spacing the distance between the woodwork of the frames is $\frac{1}{2}''$ which is greater than a bee space, with the result that brace comb is built between them. If $1\frac{1}{16}''$ wide top and side bars are used the spacing becomes $\frac{5}{16}''$ which is the 'accepted bee space' exactly in the middle of the range $\frac{1}{4}''$ to $\frac{3}{8}''$ where the bees do not build brace comb. Next, look at the space between the two bottom bars which is very narrow and quite useless for fitting new foundation after the frame has been assembled and used for a few years. My own frames have a space of $^5/_{16}''$ making the job extremely simple. I think I have said enough about brood frames to illustrate the nonsense that prevails at present; a committee could start to rationalise the problem.

Let us now take a look at frames for supers and here we find a situation that is no better. Manley, the farmer turned bee farmer responsible for the Manley frame, found by trial and error that a $1^5/_8''$ spacing is the maximum that can be used for foundation to be pulled out evenly. 10 fit nicely into a National super with $^3/_8''$ to spare. The $1^1/_{16}''$ width of the top and bottom bars make excellent guides for uncapping and the comb thickness is fine for cut comb. These frames are the best available on the market except for one major fault, mentioned by the Editor in his 'Hints for the month' in the August issue; the bees always propolise the side bars together and if the frames are not well levered up to one end of the super the propolis build up is quite spectacular. The propolis builds up very quickly and uses up the spare $^3/_8''$. The remedy is simple. Cut off $^9/_{32}''$ from the LH side of each side bar and put in a brass round head wood screw and the problem disappears. It seems a pity to have to 'butcher' a manufactured side bar but it will make your management a whole lot easier. The space between the two bottom bars is better on a Manley frame, when compared with a Hoffman in the brood chamber, but it could be larger to advantage. Other super frames using $^7/_8''$ top bars and metal ends or plastic spacers, which have to be removed for extracting, are not even a starter in my book and castellated spacers preclude the flexibility of opening up super frames to obtain really fat chunks of honey which can be obtained on the flows that we have experienced this summer.

It was my intention just to discuss frames but I must include a warning about extractors particularly the 10 frame variety. They are still manufactured today taking 10 frames with $^7/_8''$ side bars; 10 Manley frames won't fit in unless a bit of the woodwork at the bottom of both side bars is cut away. I still have such an extractor and I still have some of the Manley frames that I had to modify. Anyone buying an extractor should approach the purchase with extreme caution. With a BS committee in operation the frames and the extractors would have to fit in order to receive a BS. The manufacturers solved the problem by making a nine frame extractor which will take Manley frames! Has anybody out there got 9 frame supers?

I have to make all my own frames because I cannot buy frames to suit my simple trouble free beekeeping. It puzzles me that with the wealth of experience and knowledge we have in the craft that so many beekeepers put up with so much inconvenience. Discuss the matter in your branches and perhaps your county may wish to put up a motion to the ADM to resurrect the BSI committee. JDY.

APPENDIX 2 – CALCULATION OF THE ANGLE OF TILT FOR A SOLAR WAX EXTRACTOR

We have included the calculations because we have heard beekeepers state incorrectly, so many times, that the angle of tilt should equal the latitude where the extractor is being used. This is not so and the following calculations will show the fallacy of such statements. We must stress that the formulae and their derivation are not required for examination purposes. Diagram 1 shows the earth's annual orbit round the sun, the altitude of the sun at a given latitude and the required angle of tilt.

The first part of Diagram 1 shows the earth's annual orbit round the sun with its 'wobble' of approximately ± 23° which is the angle of declination for the sun. The earth passes through

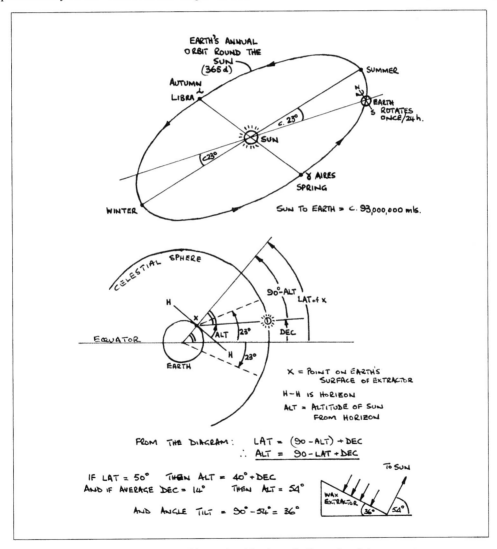

Diagram 1 – Earth's orbit, sun's altitude and tilt angle of the extractor.

the first point of Aires each March when the declination is = 0° and reaches its maximum of c. 23° N in mid summer and then returning to zero again in September when the earth passes through Libra. A similar cycle occurs during the passage from autumn through winter to spring but this time the declination is southerly making the sun low in the sky in our northern hemisphere.

The second part of the diagram shows a point 'X' on the earth's surface with a line through it tangential to the earth, the horizon. The sun shining on point 'X' is at an altitude of 'ALT' above the horizon; this could be measured with a sextant and is the basis of celestial navigation. The diagram shows that the angle of declination is northerly above the equator. The angle of latitude is also shown cutting the celestial sphere vertically above point 'X'. The angle between the vertical at point 'X' and the sun = 90° -ALT. It will be clear from the diagram that LAT = 90 − ALT + DEC and thus ALT = 90 − LAT + DEC.

The third part of the diagram at the bottom of the sketch shows the wax extractor and its angle tilt.

ie. ANGLE OF TILT = 90° − ALT = 90° − (90° − LAT + DEC)

Therefore, **ANGLE OF TILT = LAT + DEC.**

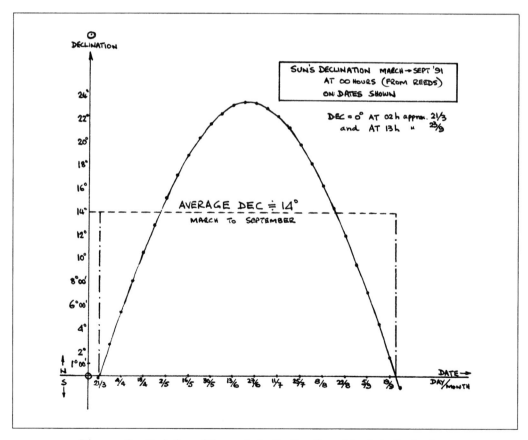

Diagram 2 – Variation of the sun's declination from March to September.

The declination is changing daily and reference to Diagram 2 shows this variation plotted for the year 1991. Subsequent years are virtually identical and so is the second half of the year in the southerly direction. The average value can be calculated (approximately 14°) for the period of the year from spring to autumn when the beekeeper is likely to be using a solar wax extractor. This is the angle used together with the correct latitude to set the extractor for nominal efficiency.

It has been suggested at various times that the beekeeper should continually adjust the extractor for maximum efficiency. Each day the extractor must start its daily cycle facing east and finally end up facing west requiring it to be turned again ready for the next morning's sunrise in the east. The sun will travel across the sky at a rate of 15° per hour from east to west. During this time the altitude will vary from zero to maximum and back to zero. During the six month time span the altitude will also vary by ± 23° from the mid summer value. The suggestion is somewhat nonsensical unless one has nothing else to do except optimise the setting of a solar wax extractor!

Many years ago a device called a 'solar eyeball' was developed at STL to track photovoltaic arrays to keep them always normal to the sun. It worked well but was an expensive bit of apparatus and has never been produced commercially. Interestingly most, if not all, photovoltaic arrays are optimised using the best declination for maximum output for the conditions required. As an example, in order to provide maximum output in Scotland throughout the year the arrays are tilted to obtain maximum in winter when the sun is very low in the sky.

APPENDIX 3 – BBKA STANDARD FOR BEES, COLONIES AND NUCLEI.

The following is copied directly from the BBKA 1986 Year Book. We believe that it should be more widely promulgated and used in everyday beekeeping.

These Standards apply to bees, colonies and nuclei offered for sale with or without a hive.

1. (a) Colony. This term shall denote bees, including healthy normal brood in all stages and a fertile laying queen, occupying a minimum number of combs:
British Standard (14″ x 8½″) 6 combs.
All others, 4 combs.
The number and size of combs must be stated.
1. (b) Stock. This term shall denote a colony of bees together with the hive it occupies.
1. (c) Nucleus colony. A colony occupying not less than three combs of the size in 1(a).

2. Diseases. Nucleus colonies, colonies and stocks shall be free from visible signs of diseases and pests when despatched.

3. The Queen. For each nucleus colony, colony or stock sold the age of the queen shall be stated.

4. Brood area. Not less than half the total comb area shall be occupied with eggs and worker brood in all stages and all combs well covered with bees. Not more than 5% of the total comb area shall be of drone cells.

5. Frames and combs. The frames shall be securely pinned or glued together and properly squared. The combs shall be fully built and wired. A maximum of a bee space may be permitted between the comb and the side and bottom bars.

6. Food. At least one side of combs adjacent to the brood shall have not less than half its area comprising cells with stored pollen and liquid food.

7. Bees sold without combs. Swarms and package bees shall be sold by weight which shall be that at the time of despatch. They shall include a mated and laying queen and shall include a container attached within the package holding sufficient food to ensure survival.

The BBKA recommends purchasers of Bees, Colonies and Nuclei to obtain from the respective vendor a statement preferably in writing, that the goods supplied conform to this standard.

Any complaint that bees, colonies or nuclei do not meet these standards must be made to the seller within seven days of receipt.

Note: The authors believe that 5 should read ... securely pinned and glued together ...

APPENDIX 4 – COLONY INSPECTIONS (TIMING)
(See section 1.17.4)

From the diagram below is possible to determine the timings for swarm control inspections which are:

Unclipped queen   Every 7 days
Clipped queen   Every 14 days – when the last inspection showed no swarm preparations
                               Every 9 / 10 days – after queen cells have been destroyed.

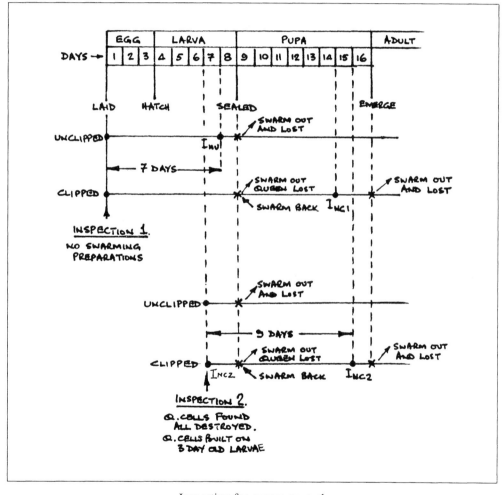

Inspection for swarm control.

APPENDIX 5 – QUEEN SUBSTANCE

Queen substance is produced and secreted by the mandibular glands of the queen and to a lesser extent by dermal glands on the dorsal side of the queen's abdomen. Queen substance is a complex mix of fatty acids in varying quantities. It was discovered by Dr. Colin Butler at Rothamsted in the early 1950s.

The secretions contain:

(E) – 9 oxo 2 decenoic acid............... popularly abbreviated to 9-ODA
(E) – 9 hydroxy 2 decenoic acid.................... abbreviated to 9 - HDA
13 – other substances which have been identified.

The amount secreted varies with the age of the queen as shown in the diagram below.

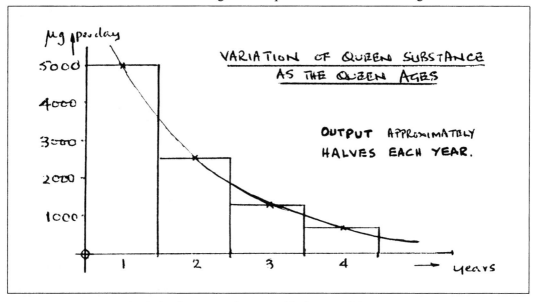

Variation in queen substance with the age of the queen.

- The effects of the queen substance which is distributed around the hive to all workers by reciprocal food exchange are as follows:
  Inside the hive: inhibiting queen cell production and inhibiting the development of worker ovaries.
  Outside the hive: drone attractant for mating and enabling a swarm to act as a cohesive unit.
- Each worker in the hive requires a minimum threshold level of the pheromone and it would appear that this level varies with the strain of bee or queens of different strains produce varying absolute levels. Compare prolific yellow bees with less prolific black bees. Queen substance is the most important factor in swarm control considerations.
- In some cases it appears that the aggressiveness of the bees is controlled by the queen substance of the queen in other cases this is a genetic trait.

APPENDIX 6 – CONSUMPTION OF STORES DURING WINTER

Many years ago we weighed the colonies in our apiaries throughout the year. This was done for a number of years and the results were very informative, for example, in the summer it showed that the main flow consistently started on virtually the same date every year. In winter it showed how the consumption of stores was directly related to the weather. Shown below is a graph of the stores consumed from October to March in a typical year and is typical of all the measurements made on our colonies. The results are actual and were obtained by measurements made with a steelyard.

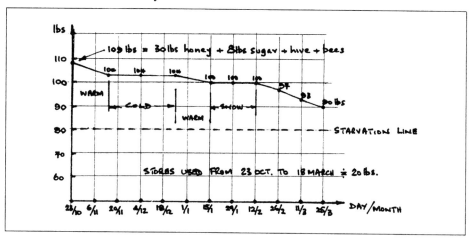

Graph showing the use of winter stores by an average colony.

Some points of interest from the graph:

• This particular colony overwintered on a BS brood box and one super with no queen excluder.
• The colony was fed 8lb of sugar which is equivalent to 10lb of honey, ∴ total stores = 40lb in October.
• The starvation line has been drawn in to indicate when the stores in the colony have reached 10lb. We regard this as the critical point and if there is no income, the colony may require to be fed.
• The autumn was warm up to mid November and c. 6lb of stores were used.
• Then the weather was cold (40°F and below) up to Christmas and hardly any stores were used (ounces not pounds). Many beekeepers find this surprising.
• Christmas to mid January the weather was warmer (45°F+) and bees were flying on cleansing flights. Stores are being used.
• Come February when it gets warmer and brood rearing is increasing, stores are starting to be used very rapidly.
• From the beginning of March the beekeeper must be alert to possible stores shortage in his colonies. If the colony has 40lb of stores in October we have never experienced the necessity to feed in the spring.
• The graph demonstrates the nonsense of feeding candy on Christmas Day.
• Further, removing the roof alerts the colony, puts up the temperature of the cluster, shortens the life of the bees and induces them to use more stores.

APPENDIX 7 – AVERAGE COLONY POPULATION CYCLE

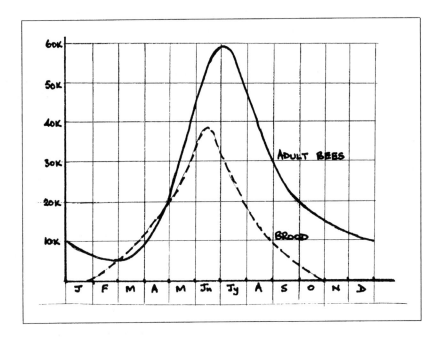

- Brood = adult bees twice per year.
- Brood > adult bees from February to April. This is a very critical time in the annual colony cycle (nb. the danger of chilling brood and not having enough adult bees to incubate this brood).
- Brood peaks in early/mid June.
- Adult bees peak end June/start July (3 weeks after brood peak); this is the time the main flow usually starts when the maximum foraging force is required.
- After the main flow the population starts to decrease, rapidly at first (old foragers dying off) then more slowly as the winter bees (6 month life) start to appear in the colony.
- The minimum adult population occurs c. end February (c. 5000).
- The maximum population will vary from 40,000 to 60,000 depending on the fecundity and strain of the queen. Dr Jeffrees considers a colony of 47k to be massive.
- The population builds up on the 'spring flow' often using all the income and storing very little.
- The maximum adult population stores very large amounts in a short time for winter (much less brood to care for).
- The reduced population allows adequate reserves for winter.
- Brood rearing ceases in late autumn and starts again after the winter solstice when the days start to lengthen.
- There is a continual decrease in population throughout the winter so dying bees are not abnormal at this time. The healthy colony removes any that die in the hive.

It should be noted that the graph is a representation of average conditions and the local flora and climatic conditions will modify it accordingly. Similarly, these local variations mean a peaky graph and not a smooth curve as shown.

APPENDIX 8 – THE SIZE OF THE COLONY FOR WINTER

Experimental and theoretical work on this subject was undertaken in the early 80's by Dr.Jeffrees at Aberdeen University. He determined by photography that a BS frame, well covered with bees, has c.1500 bees, ie about 750 on each side. Thus a 10 frame colony has c. 15,000 bees.

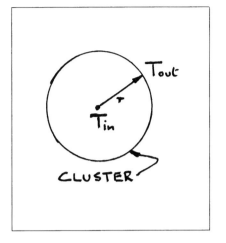

He found also that:

The average number of bees in the winter cluster = 21cu.in.
Temperature gradient in the cluster = 8°F/in.

Noting that:

The volume of a spherical cluster = $V = \frac{4}{3}\pi r^3$, and
The surface area of such a cluster = $SA = 4\pi r^2$

Therefore, if the colony has 700 bees then the volume of the cluster, $V = 700 \div 21 = 33.3$ cu. in. Thus, if $V = 33.3 = \frac{4}{3}\pi r^3$, then $r = 2$ inches. If $T_{out} = 45°F$ Then $T_{in} = 45 + (2 \times 8) = 61°F$

Using the same reasoning for other sized colonies we have:

NUMBER OF BEES	RADIUS of CLUSTER (inches)	T_{in}(°F)
700	2	61
3800	$3\frac{1}{2}$	73
11000	5	85
24000	$6\frac{1}{2}$	97
45000	8	109

The usual variation in the temperature of the winter cluster is from about 68°F to 86°F (20°C–30°C). From the table above it will be clear that a colony can be too large for successful wintering. Conversely, optimum sized colonies winter well while small colonies have to consume more stores to maintain a survivable temperature in the centre of the cluster.

The bees do not allow the outside temperature of the cluster, T_{out}, to fall below 45°F otherwise the bees become immobile and they would fall off the surface of the cluster.

It is interesting to apply Dr. Jeffrees findings to a 5 frame nucleus on BS frames:

It has 7,500 bees, a cluster radius of 4.4 inches giving an inside temperature of 80°F when the outside temperature is 45°F. This is a virtually ideal temperature for wintering and partially explains why nuclei of this size overwinter so well.

APPENDIX 9 – **BAILEY FRAME CHANGE**

This is a method of transferring a stock of bees on to sterilised comb or foundation. It is recommended for use in the spring or early summer for a stock of bees which has been infected with *Nosema apis, Malpighamoeba mellificae* or *Ascosphaera apis* (Chalk Brood). The spores of these diseases remain dormant on the comb and will be re-cycled by the house bees cleaning the cells of the brood nest, infecting the larvae in the case of Chalk brood or the adult bees during the exchange of food in the case of Nosema or Amoeba. During a period of fine spring weather when the bees are foraging daily and the brood nest is expanding, (a weather pattern which we are likely to experience during April/May) the colony should be re-arranged on the original site as follows:

- The queen plus the brood frame and bees on which she is found is placed in the middle of a clean brood box complete with frames of comb or foundation. Mark this frame with a drawing pin.
- The gap in the frames of the bottom brood box is closed and the dummy board moved up.
- The queen excluder is placed on top of the old brood box.
- A 'U' shaped spacer 18in × 18in × $\frac{7}{8}$in thick (the same as the entrance block) is placed on top of the queen excluder thereby providing a space for a new entrance in the same direction.
- The clean brood chamber is placed on top of this spacer with a clean crown board, feeder and the old roof.
- Now close the original entrance and reduce the new entrance.
- Feed the stock the same evening with a gallon of syrup (eg. strength 1kg sugar to 1 litre water) into which is mixed 166mg Fumidil 'B' (for Nosema infected colonies).
- Keep an accurate record card and destroy any queen cells if they appear in the bottom brood box after 7 days.
- After 3 weeks all the brood should have emerged from the bottom brood box. It can be removed together with the queen excluder, 'U' spacer, old floor board and entrance block.
- A clean floor board and entrance block should be given to the new brood box.
- The marked comb in the top box should be moved to the side of the brood box for removal when empty of brood.

Other points to note:

- After the first re-arrangement the bees will orientate to the new entrance by exposing their Nasonov glands and fanning vigorously. This may attract bees from other hives in the apiary. During such a procedure on a fine sunny day in 1985 our re-arranged colony attracted two overwintered nuclei complete with queens which were promptly killed on entry!
- Splitting the brood nest does put the bees under stress especially if it is a small colony and it may cause chilled or chalk brood.
- If foundation is used for the new brood box it may be necessary to continue feeding. Care must be taken to avoid robbing.
- Always check that the Fumidil 'B' is not time expired and has been stored in a cool dark place.
- Follow the maker's instructions when mixing the Fumidil 'B', its activity is lost if the syrup is hotter than 120°F (49°C).
- The queen is likely to be infected with Nosema and the colony should be re-queened as soon as possible after the change of combs has been completed.
- A sample of bees should be taken in the autumn before the winter feeding to monitor the success of the frame change.
- All the old combs will need to be disinfected before re-using, the other contaminated hive parts should be scraped clean and flamed with a blow lamp before re-use.

APPENDIX 10 – **SEMIOCHEMICALS**

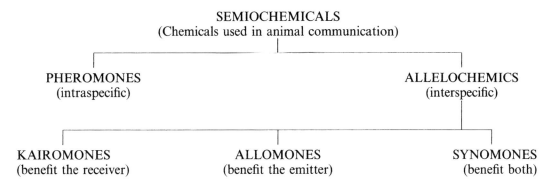

SEMIOCHEMICALS
(Chemicals used in animal communication)

PHEROMONES
(intraspecific)

ALLELOCHEMICS
(interspecific)

KAIROMONES
(benefit the receiver)

ALLOMONES
(benefit the emitter)

SYNOMONES
(benefit both)

- Note that intra = within and inter = between. Therefore pheromones are used within a particular species and allelochemics between different species.

- **The definition of a pheromone**. A pheromone is a chemical, secreted from the exocrine gland of an animal, that elicits a behavioural or physiological response by another animal of the same species and so acts as a chemical message. It is secreted as a liquid and transmitted as a liquid or a gas.

- There are many examples of pheromones associated with the behavioural pattern of the honeybee but kairomones are at present relatively rare and are new to the beekeeping scene.

- **The definition of a kairomone.** A kairomone is a chemical, secreted from the exocrine gland of an animal, that elicits a behavioural or physiological response by another animal of a different species and so acts as a chemical message which benefits the receiver of that message. It is secreted and transmitted in the same way as a pheromone.

- Kairomones generally advantage predators or parasites enabling them to find their prey or host respectively. This appears to be a disadvantage and the question may be asked why kairomones have survived during evolutionary selection? The answer is probably that the chemical has some advantage to the producer, eg. as a pheromone.

- It is now known that honeybee brood pheromone which elicits foraging for pollen is also a kairomone attracting *Varroa destructor*. The attraction of the *Acarapis woodi* to the first thoracic spiracle may also be a pheromone / kairomone mechansim at work and perhaps some scientific research may one day be directed in this area.

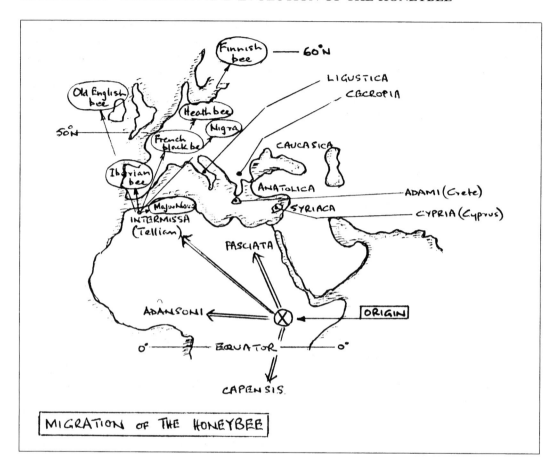

The above diagram shows the migration of the honeybee, from its origin in what is now Kenya, during the last 30 million years. All the major races shown by double arrows may be considered primary races and the one of importance to the UK situation is the *Apis mellifera intermissa*. It is from this bee that migrated northward into north west Europe that all the other sub-species have evolved, such as the French Black Bee and the Old English Bee shown with single arrows emanating from north west Africa on the diagram, ie from the area of Tunisia and Algeria. It migrated as far north as north latitude 60° in the Arctic circle and became the Finnish Bee, a bee that is characterised by its ability to tolerate long periods of confinement in very cold conditions without cleansing flights. A truly remarkable evolution from an ancestor derived from the tropics.

The western honeybee, *Apis mellifera,* was transported to America initially by the pilgrims and to Australia and New Zealand by the settlers to these Antipodean countries. Until man took a hand in these migrations there were no honeybees in either of the two regions. The original bees were taken in skeps on the old sailing ships with a voyage time of about 6 months to the Antipodes; quite remarkable and a topic that would be an interesting line of research into the whys and wherefores of these exploits.

APPENDIX 12 – **RECIPES USING PRODUCTS OF THE HIVE**

Beeswax is inflammable with a flash point of 242°C to 250°C. Never leave wax unattended during the heating process. If the contents of the saucepan should boil or spit, wax is sprayed over the oven surface. If this should happen leave the wax to solidify before attempting to remove the mess. Cover the top of the oven with aluminium foil to protect the surface and make the cleaning up easier. The authors have used the following recipes continuously over the last 20 years. All metric measurements have been rounded up or down and are not exact equivalents of the Imperial measure.

Furniture Cream.

½ pint (285ml) turpentine
½pint (285ml) water
3oz (85g) of clean beeswax
1 teaspoonful (5ml) of liquid ammonia

Method.

- Break the wax into small pieces.
- Prepare the containers for furniture cream. This quantity will make just over two 8oz (227g) portions.
- Heat all the ingredients together in a double sauce pan.
- When all the wax has melted. Stir vigorously together. Take off the heat.
- Add 1 teaspoonful (5ml) of liquid ammonia.
- Continue to stir as the mixture cools. Take the saucepan outside onto a cold surface and stir with a rotary mixer. This will help to keep the smell of the ammonia out of the kitchen.
- When the mixture shows signs of congealing on the sides of the saucepan pour into prepared containers.
- When cool seal with lid, weigh and label according to current regulations if for sale to members of the public.

Furniture Polish.

1¼ pint (710ml) of turpentine
12oz (340g) of clean beeswax

Method.

- Break up the clean wax into small pieces.
- Place both ingredients into the double saucepan.
- When the wax has melted stir well and remove from heat.
- As the mixture begins to thicken pour into prepared containers. The polish tins obtainable from bee equipment suppliers hold about 3oz (85 g) if well filled. Weigh tins before and after filling.
- Allow the polish to set before cleaning the lips of the tins, closing the lids, weighing and labelling (labels can often be purchased with the tins).

Cold Cream – use for chilblains or sore, dry or rough skin.

    1oz (30g) of beeswax
    1oz (30ml) of distilled water
    ½ teaspoonful (1.5g) boracic powder
    5oz (145ml) of light mineral oil (eg. liquid paraffin)
    1oz (30g) of unbleached petroleum jelly

Method.

- Use a 'bain - marie' to melt the boracic powder in the water ie. dissolve the boracic crystals on top of the warm water placed in a small container of hot water.
- Melt the beeswax, petroleum jelly and oil in a double saucepan.
- When all is well dissolved take off the heat and stir well.
- Add the boracic powder and water mixture at approximately the same temperature.
- Stir vigorously.
- As soon as the cooling mixture shows signs of thickening pour into prepared pots.
- Allow the cream to set before closing with lid.
- If producing the cold cream for sale then label showing the weight and contents.

Wax for Show.

The final preparation of the wax for casting.

1st Filtering of the wax cappings:

- Weigh the amount of wax required for filtering into moulds (c. $1\frac{1}{2}$ to 2 times the weight of the final mould).
- Put 1–2in of soft water into a clean dish ready to receive the clean wax. The water used should be free from any salts i.e. rain water or water saved from a dehumidifier or when defrosting a refrigerator and strained before use.
- Use a large clean tin can with both ends open.
- On one end of the tin tie the plain lint fluffy side inside. To the other end attach 2 or three wire hooks.
- Break the wax into small pieces, place it in the tin and hang the tin in the oven over the bowl of water.
- Use a very low heat not more than 194°F (90°C) and allow the wax to slowly drip through the lint onto the water.
- The tin may need to be refilled with clean wax pieces depending on the amount of clean wax required.
- Allow the wax to cool. Remove from bowl and dry.

2nd Filtering:

- Break up the clean wax and filter again using another clean tin and the same method as for the first filtering but use a paper filter supported by a piece of fine nylon net instead of the lint.
- Wait for the wax to solidify as above. This wax is now ready for casting into moulds or candles

The casting of wax.

Cast the wax in the evening prior to retiring so that after the casting there will be no disturbance until the wax has solidified ie. no vibrations from doors, floor boards etc. Basic requirements are:

> Clean wax. Double saucepan or pan with jug, three thermometers (wax, water and oven), spirit level, plate glass to cover the large bowl, two house bricks, two glass bowls, one for the mould and one large enough to hold the mould, detergent, hot water, water proof marker, cling film, waxed paper, weighing scales, soft water and a piece of soft old silk.

Method.

1. Since wax and water have approximately the same specific gravity 0.95 and 1.00 the depth of the wax required to make a mould of a certain weight can be judged by placing the chosen mould on the scales and adding water to the required weight. Mark the level of the water with a water proof marker on the outside of the bowl. All surfaces used should be checked first with a spirit level and made horizontal.
2. The wax mould should be thoroughly cleaned and free from all blemishes. Using soft water and a drop of liquid detergent mixed together and coat the inside of the dust free mould with a little of this solution using clean finger tips. Cover all the surface and rub until the surface feels dry. Cover the prepared mould with a piece of cling film.
3. Meanwhile heat the prepared clean wax, using twice the required amount of wax in a clean jug in a saucepan of hot water or in a double saucepan. Keep the top of the jug or saucepan covered with waxed paper or polythene to avoid any contamination of the wax. Do not heat the wax higher than 194°F (90°C). Have two thermometers to hand one for the wax and one to use for the water.
4. The oven should have been checked with a spirit level to make sure the shelves are horizontal. Light the oven keeping a temperature no higher than 194°F (90°C) and into it place two building bricks on the bottom. Place a piece of thick plate glass onto one of the shelves.
5. Now prepare a second glass bowl with water 151°F (66°C), using sufficient water so that the bowl for the mould just floats on the surface.
6. With the molten wax in the jug at about 158°F (70°C) pour the wax into the centre of the mould, which is standing in the warm water to the required level. Always pour the wax into the centre of the mould.
7. Carefully place the mould in the oven and cover with the warm glass. Close the oven door gently.
8. Turn out the oven and leave the room until the following morning. Do not open the oven door again until the following morning when the mould with the wax should be placed in a bowl of cold water and left for the wax to float out.
9. Should the wax mould not release itself then place the bowl in the coldest part of the fridge for a few hours (Note that molten wax shrinks by approximately 10% when solidified and cold).
10. When the wax floats out take care not to damage the edge of the mould. Avoid marking with your fingers any part of the mould. Carefully dab the water from the surface with a silk cloth.
11. The exposed surface of the mould should be perfectly flat, no cracks or depressions.
12. Keep the mould in a safe place until exhibition time. Place it in a clean polythene bag to keep it free from dust. It may be polished with a very soft piece of silk.

Making mead.

- Preparing the must – all apparatus used must be clean :

  Honey plus water to the correct specific gravity c. 1.070 in a bucket. Then add 2 Vitamin B tablets crushed (Benerva tablets) + 1 tsp (5ml) of yeast nutrient + 1 tsp (5ml) of citric acid + tannin (strained remains of a cold teapot) for every gallon of must. Mix well. Using fresh capping 'washings' it is not generally necessary to sterilise the must to kill wild yeasts. However, to be on the safe side and especially when using 'stale washings' (greater than 2 or 3 days old after uncapping) it is best that the washings be heated to 150°F (66°C) for a few moments to kill any wild yeasts which can give the mead an objectionable flavour.

- Make a starter with your chosen yeast eg. Gervin wine yeast number 3 or 5. Read the instructions on the packet. Must made with rape honey is sometimes slow to ferment. Always use freshly purchased packets of yeast. Add to the prepared must. Stir well. Place in a warm compartment such as an airing cupboard or a temperature controlled brewing box. Temperature should be about 75°F (24°C). Lower temperatures give a slower fermentation. If all the sugar is used in the fermentation process the mead will be dry. The alcohol levels at the finish (SG = 1.000 or less) will be as follows using the starting specific gravities shown:

  SG of 1.070 = sugar 32oz / gallon of must ⇨ after fermentation = 9.2% alcohol
  SG of 1.080 = sugar 38oz / gallon of must ⇨ after fermentation = 10.9% alcohol
  SG of 1.090 = sugar 43.5oz / gallon of must ⇨ after fermentation = 12.6 % alcohol
  SG of 1.100 = sugar 49.5oz / gallon of must ⇨ after fermentation = 14.3% alcohol

- Fermentation:

First aerobic fermentation (violent) in the bucket for 7–10 days. Leave plenty of room in the bucket to accommodate this.

Second anaerobic fermentation (gentle) in demijohns with an airlock for 3/4 months until fermentation complete (when the mead starts to clear and the lees sinks to the bottom of the demijohn). The chemical processes involved in fermentation are extremely complicated and beyond the scope of this appendix. Other alcohols are produced as well as methyl alcohol but in only small quantities together with many other organic compounds (those compounds containing carbon).

Very simply the process is:

sugar	+ yeast	=	carbon dioxide	+ ethyl alcohol
$C_6H_{12}O_6$	+ yeast	=	$2CO_2$	+ $2C_2H_5OH$

- Enzymes in the yeast promote fermentation and transformation.

6C sugar + hexokinase	= 3C sugars (triose)
3C sugar + aldolase	= glycerine + glyceric acid
glyceric acid + enolase	= pyruvic acid
pyruvic acid + carboxylase	= acetaldehyde + CO_2
acetaldehyde + zymase	= ethyl alcohol

- Enzymes are precipitated by alcohol (maximum alcohol c. 12% by volume as most wine yeast is inhibited by increased alcohol levels ie. as the alcohol level increases so the yeast activity decreases).
- The working temperatures of enzymes are best between 86°–104°F (30°–40°C). This is too high a temperature for wine yeast activity.
- Yeast cells are killed above 90°F (32°C) and work best between 70°–75°F (21°–24°C) – slow release of enzymes.
- If the temperature is allowed to go too high, overheating produces acetic acid in lieu of alcohol.
- Finishing Specific Gravity (SG):

> Above 1.000 means some sugar is not converted to alcohol and the mead will be medium to sweet.
> The higher the SG - the sweeter the mead
> Sweet mead has a SG from 1.010 to 1.030 and dry mead has a SG below 1.000.

It is virtually impossible to get alcohol concentrations higher than 10 to 12 % by volume with normal wine yeasts (wild yeasts are lower c. 5%). Therefore it is important to start with the correct SG of the must for whatever type of mead is being produced (dry, medium or sweet). When the alcohol volume reaches 10 to 12 % then fermentation will stop and any sugar unconverted into alcohol will remain in the mead as sugar.

- Rack (removal from the lees) after 3-4 months when fermentation has finished and the must cleared. Check SG.

> Remove the 'clear mead' from the yeast deposit (lees) by syphoning.
> Oxygenating the mead during the transfer process provides the necessary O_2 for the ageing process.
> Two or three rackings per year are required.
> With first racking add 2 tablets of 62% potassium sorbate to each gallon to prevent any secondary ferment.

- Ageing the Mead:

Firstly, during fermentation alcohol, acids (eg. acetic which is volatile and has a strong smell, lactic, citric plus succinic acid with little or no smell), aldehydes (halfway between an acid and an alcohol), glycerol, etc. are produced. Glycerol is sweet and gives the matured mead the 'curtains' in the glass when it is swirled and held to the light.

Ageing is an oxidisation process which is very slow and with complicated chemistry. Combinations of organic compounds take place, the main changes are as follows:

> Alcohols + acids = esters (sometimes they give mead its aroma).
> Aldehydes (have sharp smell and taste) oxidise and produce other acids (some amino).
> Other acids + alcohol = other esters.

The oxidisation process in mead takes about 2–3 years. White wine is fast compared with red wine which is slow and takes 3 to 6 years depending on the wine.

> Age in a dark place at temperature = 50°–60° F (10°–16°C).

Keep the containers full with minimum air space (may be necessary to fill with boiled water).

Do not shake or disturb mead during ageing.

Do not use polythene vessels for long term storage.

- Keep a record of all procedures.
- Important to test and smell when the mead is ready for bottling and drinking. The important points are:

  Type of bottle, cork and label allowed by show rules.

  Filter before bottling. Use paper wine filters.

  Final produce should sparkle.

  Enter the mead into the correct class ie. sweet or dry.

  The judge may finally reject the mead on taste; don't be disappointed if you don't win a prize, judging is very subjective.

  The bottle with the most 'swigged' out of it is usually the winner!

- Specialist wine and beer brewing shops can give good advice if your fermentation stops or must remains cloudy. As ever practice makes perfect and even if the judge turns it down at the show it may well be to your palate.

APPENDIX 13 – MEASUREMENTS and CONVERSIONS (IMPERIAL TO METRIC)

We have had numerous requests from readers of our previous notes to provide a more detailed reference for converting from one set of units to another. We hope that the conversions below will satisfy this request. The units follow the International System of Units (SI system) which is now virtually universal. Many of the units are named after scientists such as, Gauss, Tesla, Kelvin, Ampere, Celsius, etc.

The dimensions associated with hives and frames and their spacing involve a range of fractional imperial measurements which were the basis of the original designs in the UK and USA. For all sizes the nearest metric equivalents are rounded up to the nearest milli-meter except $\frac{1}{16}$in which is too small to be meaningful when rounded up or down. For example the Modified National brood box measures $18\frac{1}{8} \times 18\frac{1}{8} \times 8\frac{7}{8}$in and when converted into metric becomes $460 \times 460 \times 225$mm and not $460.375 \times 460.375 \times 225.425$mm.

Linear measure – inches (in) to milli-meters (mm).

$\frac{1}{16}$in = 0.063in = 1.5mm	$\frac{9}{20}$ in = 0.450in = 11mm	1 in = 1.000in = 25mm
$\frac{3}{32}$in = 0.094in = 2 mm	$\frac{1}{2}$ in = 0.500in = 13mm	$1\frac{1}{16}$in = 1.063in = 27mm
$\frac{1}{8}$ in = 0.125in = 3 mm	$\frac{9}{16}$ in = 0.563in = 14mm	$1\frac{3}{8}$ in = 1.375in = 35mm
$\frac{3}{16}$in = 0.187in = 5 mm	$\frac{5}{8}$ in = 0.625in = 16mm	$1\frac{9}{20}$in = 1.450in = 37mm
$\frac{1}{4}$ in = 0.250in = 6 mm	$\frac{11}{16}$in = 0.687in = 17mm	$1\frac{1}{2}$ in = 1.500in = 38mm
$\frac{5}{16}$in = 0.321in = 8 mm	$\frac{3}{4}$ in = 0.750in = 19mm	$1\frac{3}{4}$ in = 1.750in = 44mm
$\frac{3}{8}$ in = 0.375in = 9 mm	$\frac{13}{16}$in = 0.812in = 21mm	$1\frac{7}{8}$ in = 1.875in = 48mm
$\frac{7}{16}$in = 0.437in = 11 mm	$\frac{7}{8}$ in = 0.875in = 22mm	

Liquid measure - pints (pt) and liquid ounces (oz) to litres (l).

1l = 1000ml	1 gallon = 8pt = 4.546l
1l = 1.76pt	1pt = 20oz = 570ml
1pt = 0.57l = 570ml	1oz = (570 ÷ 20)ml = 28ml

Weight of water.

1 gallon water weighs 10lb	1000ml water weighs 1kg = 1000g
1pt water weighs 1.25lb	1ml water weighs 1g
1 litre water weighs 1kg	1cm^3 water weighs 1g

Temperature degrees Centigrade (°C) to degrees Fahrenheit (°F).

$$x°F = \{(x - 32) \div 1.8\}°C \qquad y°C = \{(y \times 1.8) + 32°F$$

Miles (miles) to kilo-metres (km).
1 mile = 1.6km   1km = 0.625 miles

Yards feet and inches to metres and milli-metres.

1in = 25.4mm;   12in = 1ft = 304.8mm;   3ft = 1 yard = 914.4mm = 0.9m
1m = 39.37in

Area.

1 sq in = 6.45 cm^2,   1 sq ft = 0.093 m^2,   1 sq yd = 0.836 m^2,   1 sq mile = 2.59 km^2,
1 acre = 0.405 hectare (ha),   1ha = 2.47 acres

Mass.

1oz = 28.4g,   1lb = 454g,   1cwt = 112lb = 50.8kg,   1 ton = 20 cwt = 1.016 tonne

Pressure.

1lb/sq in = 6.89kN/m^2 = 0.0689bar = 703kg/m^2 = 51.7mm mercury (Hg)

1mm Hg = 133 Newton(N)/m^2, 1bar = 10^{5}N/m^2

Power.

1 Watt (W) = 1 Joule (J)/s,   1 calorie = 4.187J,   1kWh = 3.6MJ

Note on presentation of units.

We have endeavoured to determine whether there is any standard or regulation in connection with the presentation of numerical values and in particular whether there should be a space between the number and the unit (eg. 454 g) or whether the presentation should omit the space (eg. 454g). Our enquiries at British Standards Institute, Institute of Packaging, reference libraries, etc. revealed that there was no accepted standard. Our local Trading Standards Officer confirmed that there were no regulations or recommendations on this point. Throughout the text we have used no space where the abbreviation of the unit is used (eg. 21mg) but we have used a space where the unit is quoted in full (eg.21 gram). This system falls down with litres (eg. 11 litres) when the abbreviation is used (eg. 11l). Using upper case 'L' would be incorrect as it means inductance measured in Henrys.

In the food industry there will be found a mixture of both types of presentation as also in scientific papers using SI units.

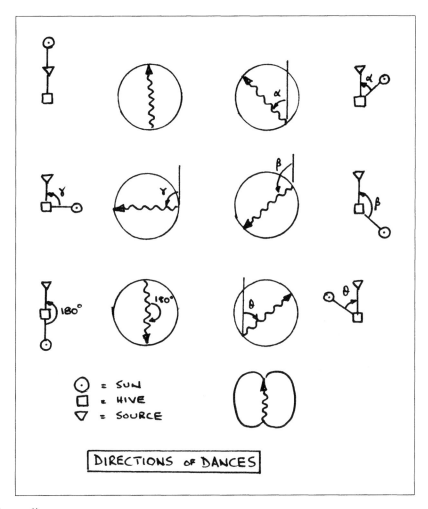

In the above diagram:
- When the food source is to the left of the sun (viewed from the hive), the bees dance on the comb to the left of the vertical.
- Similarly, if the food source is to the right of the sun, the bees dance on the comb to the right of the vertical.
- If the food source is in the same direction as the sun, the bees dance upwards on the comb.
- If the food source is in the opposite direction to the sun, the bees dance downwards on the comb.
- The arrow head in the diagrams indicate the head of the bee and its direction of travel on the comb.
- The wriggley line behind the arrow head denotes the waggle of the abdomen while the bee is dancing.

APPENDIX 15 – CLASSIFICATION IN THE PLANT KINGDOM

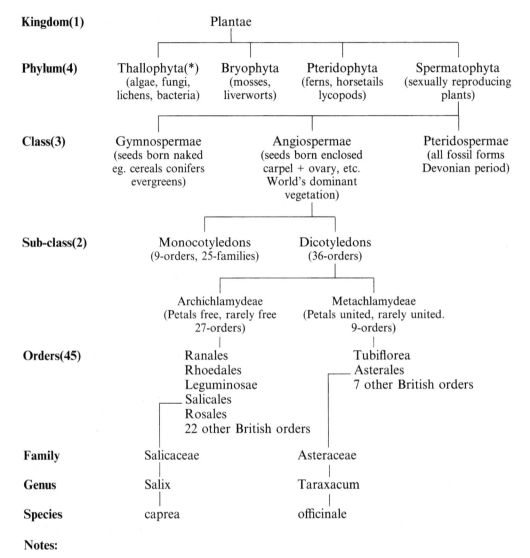

Kingdom(1) Plantae

Phylum(4) Thallophyta(*) — Bryophyta — Pteridophyta — Spermatophyta
(algae, fungi, (mosses, (ferns, horsetails (sexually reproducing
lichens, bacteria) liverworts) lycopods) plants)

Class(3) Gymnospermae — Angiospermae — Pteridospermae
(seeds born naked (seeds born enclosed (all fossil forms
eg. cereals conifers carpel + ovary, etc. Devonian period)
evergreens) World's dominant
vegetation)

Sub-class(2) Monocotyledons — Dicotyledons
(9-orders, 25-families) (36-orders)

Archichlamydeae — Metachlamydeae
(Petals free, rarely free (Petals united, rarely united.
27-orders) 9-orders)

Orders(45) Ranales Tubiflorea
Rhoedales Asterales
Leguminosae 7 other British orders
Salicales
Rosales
22 other British orders

Family Salicaceae Asteraceae

Genus Salix Taraxacum

Species caprea officinale

Notes:

The classification of two examples are shown above:
Goat willow – Salix caprea where all the petals are free and
Common dandelion – Taraxacum officinale where all the petals are joined.
* This phylum has now been abandoned in favour of an additional 12 new phyla. This
state of affairs is not uncommon as more and more research unravels more detailed
information. The new phyla are:

Cyanophyta (blue-green algae)   Chlorophyta (green algae)
Xanthophyta (yellow-green algae) Phaeophyta (brown algae)
Bacillariophyta (diatoms)   Rhodophyta

Chrysophyta   Pyrrophyta
Cryptophyta   Euglenophyta
Myxomycophyta (slime fungi)   Eumycophyta (true fungi)

ORIGIN AGES OF THE PRINCIPLE PHYLA

ERA	GEOLOGICAL SYSTEM	AGE (million years)	APPEARANCE OF THE PLANTS
Cainozoic		present day	
Mezozoic	Cretaceous	70	
		80	angiosperms first appeared
	Jurassic	140	
	Triassic	170	
Paleozoic	Permian	195	
	Upper Carboniferous	220	
		230	gymnosperms develop
	Lower Carboniferous	255	
	Devonian	275	
		280	bryophyta develop
	Silurian	320	
		340	pteridophyta develop
	Ordovician	350	
	Cambrian	420	
		500	algae date from this period
Pre-cambrian		520	

- Note the development of the the angiosperms (70 million years ago) with respect to the honeybee (c.20 million years ago). The flowers appeared first in an elementary form compared with the flowers we know today.
- Note also some of the terminology:

  Phyte – denoting a vegetable or plant-like organism.
  Phyte – plant, eg. phytophagous – feeding on plants.
  Pteridology – study of ferns.
  Bryology – study of mosses.
  Thallus – plant body with vascular tissue not differentiated into root, stem and leaves.
  Spermatophyte – plant producing seeds.

APPENDIX 16 – USEFUL INFORMATION

The following information about bees and beekeeping may well prove useful for examination purposes.

Honey useage.
a) Flying worker bee uses 10mg / hour and flies at 15mph, drone uses 30mg / hour.
b) A colony needs 10lb of liquid stores to next inspection. This is based on a colony size 27 to 30k bees and 10 day inspection periods. For 7 day inspections it would be marginally less.

Blood sugar levels.
a) Flying worker bee: c.3%   b) Unable to fly: <1%   c) Motionless: <0.5%   d) Hive bee: c.2%

Honey requirements versus ambient temperature.
When: T = 52°F (11°C): 10mg / hour, T = 98°F (37°C): 0.7mg / hour,
T = 118°F (48°C): 1.4mg/hour

Brood rearing.
Honey required to rear one worker bee = c.100mg (50 to 150mg)
Pollen required to rear one worker bee = c.120mg (70 to 150mg)

Weights.
a) Weight of an egg = 0.13mg   b) Weight of a worker bee = 90mg
c) Weight of a queen = 130mg. If queen lays 1000 eggs/day, the weight of eggs laid = 130mg
d) Average load of nectar or honey carried by worker = 40mg
e) Average load of pollen carried by worker bee = 10 to 30mg (total of two pollen pellets one on each leg)

Syrup for feeding.
7lb sugar to 5 pints of water will mix cold without becoming super saturated. Stonger mixes leave dried out sugar crystals in the bottom of the feeder which are always difficult to clean. For emergency feeding for immediate consumption (50:50), 1kg sugar to 1 litre water.
Total winter stores required = 35lb (16kg)/colony.

Temperatures.
All activities occur between 10°– 38°C (50°–100°F)
Brood nest: c. 35°C (95°F),   Unable to fly : 10°C (50°F)   Immobile: 7°C (45°F)
Clustering starts: 14°C (57°F)   Thorax: 20°– 36°C (68°–97°F), normally 29°C (84°F)
Range of winter cluster: 20°– 30°C (68°–86°F)
Wax making: 33°–36°C (91°–97°F)   Wax melts: 64.4° ± 0.6°C (147.9° ± 1°F)
                                                  Wax solidifies: 63.5° ± 0.5°C (146.3° ± 0.9°F)
Optimum for honey granulation: 14°C (57°F),   Wild yeasts killed at 60°C (140°F)

INDEX

drone congregation areas, 259
drone laying queen, 242
dummy board, 66
duties of worker, 250–259
DVAV dances, 259
Dyce process, 112
Dysentery, 197
Dzierzon, H.C.J., 261

E

Easy Beesy, 7
EFB (*Melissococcus pluton*),
    15, 66, 77, 159–69, 175, 191–
    4, 201, 208, 210
egg production, 262
eke, 41, 54–5, 204, 208, 301
electric carving knife, 100
emergency queen cells, 243,
    294
endemic disease, 159, 160
endo cuticle, 244
endophallus, 260
Enterococcus faecalis, 162
entrance blocks, 74, 86
Environmental Health
    Officers, 90
enzymes, 117, 229, 284
epidemic disease, 159
Erica carnea, 137
Erica cinerea, 110, 137
Erica spp, 137
essential oils, 182
ethanoic acid, 120
European Foul Brood=EFB
Euvarroa sinhai, 188
evolution,
    bees, 330
    plants, 144
excretory system, 229
exo cuticle, 244
exocrine glands, 235
exoskeleton, 244–5
exponential law of decay,
    293
epicuticle, 244
epidermis, 244
evolution of the honeybee, 330
excluders (queen), 4–5, 9, 34,
    37, 46, 48, 55–6, 65, 67, 167,
    225, 245, 325, 328

extra floral nectaries, 145–6,
    255
extraction of honey, 102–104
extractors, 102–104

F

fanning, 252
Fastac, 216
fat bodies, 196, 239, 263
    storage cells, 239
feeders, 40–41
feeding, 39–43, 75, 325, 342
feeding / nursing, 250
feral colonies, 273
fermentation, 118–119
fertilisation (plants), 142, 157–
    8
    m. & f. gamete, 141
    generative nucleus, 142
Filamentous Virus, 197, 202,
    210
first aid, 88
flabellum, 247, 313
flagellum, 247, 314
flailing machines, 100
flower, f. gamete, 141
    embryo sac, 141
    nucellus, 141
    ovary, 141
    ovules, 141
    polar nuclei, 141
flumethrin, 185
fluvalinate, 184
Folbex & Folbex VA, 83, 178,
    186, 198, 204
Food (Lot Marking) Regs, 92–
    93
Food Labelling Regs, 92
Food Safety Act 1990, 184
food sharing, 277–278, 285
foot print odour, 268, 280
foragers, 98
foraging, 250–5, 283–6
    number of trips, 286
    unloading, 286
    average load, 286
formic acid, 204
frames, 5, 317
    construction of, 10
    British Standard, 7

brood, 6, 317
design of, 8, 317
Hoffman, 6, 317
Manley, 6, 101, 104, 318
other frames, 7
super, 6, 318
Free, Prof. J.B., 272
Frisch K., von, 271, 285
frosting, 111
Frow mixture,198, 204
fructose, 116
Fumidil 'B', 83, 85, 194, 196,
    328
fumigation of comb, 207
furniture cream, 331
furniture polish, 331

G

Galleria mellonella, 192, 208,
    224
ganglion, 233–4
gene, 143
germination (plants), 142
Gerstung, 51, 291
glossary (botany), 142
gloves, 28
glucose, 116
glucose oxidase, 288
glycogen, 239
Glycophagus domesticus, 223
glycosidases, 229
grading glasses, 129
grafting, 128, 298, 300
granulated honey, 107, 111,
    114
Greater Wax Moth, 192
    life cycle of, 224
green woodpecker, 33, 86
guard bees, 255, 273
guarding, 250

H

haemocytes, 239
haemocytometer, 207
haemolymph, 228
hair, 245
Halsbury Statutory Instr., 90
hamuli, 248

Beekeeping Study Notes Vol. 1 – BBN&O and the Authors
offer their sincere apologies for the following misprints:

Page	Line	
4	22	delete 425mm insert 368mm
4	24	delete 243mm insert 240mm
6	12	delete 28 insert 38
6	16	delete 38 insert 35
6	25	delete 35 insert 38
10	18	insert comma after wood
14	33	delete doubling insert double
19	3	delete taught insert taut
19	4	delete taught insert taut
27	9	delete ie, insert ie.
27	18	delete eg insert eg.
27	25	delete the. insert the
31	11	delete peoples insert peoples'
34	28	delete protugu insert progeny
37	11	delete beekeepers insert beekeeper's
44	4	delete bodily insert body
45	35	delete its insert the
54	11	delete about in insert about ½in
57	10	delete ones insert one's
58	33	delete authors insert authors'
59	8	delete 216mm insert 203mm
60	40	delete protégé insert progeny
63	17	delete 1.19.2 insert 1.21.2
75	17	delete 1.24 insert 1.25
79	2	delete 1 in insert 1in
80	22	delete 1 in insert 1in
84	20	delete 000 15, insert 000÷15,
85	35	delete 13.6 insert 16
86	24	delete 6°C insert 5.5°C
90	11	delete EC insert EU
91	9	delete 1992.Amendment insert 1992. Amendment
91	24	delete the complete line
97	32	delete 8mg/kg insert 80mg/kg
98	11	delete processing insert processing,
104	18	delete 2.4.3 insert 2.4.4
104	19	delete temporally insert temporarily
106	17	delete keep insert kept
107	6	delete eg insert eg.
108	22	insert a between have and fan
110	13	delete Bottled insert bottled
110	29	delete whilst insert while

Page	Line	
112	38	delete the honey insert honey
113	25	delete 10°C insert −10°C
114	12	delete cartoon insert carton
115	40	delete on' Honey' insert on 'Honey'
122	26	delete with out insert without
122	33	delete + 52.7° insert +52.7°
122	34	delete + 88.2° insert +88.2°
122	34	delete + 121.8° insert +121.8°
126	36	delete out insert off
127	26	delete 1.25.3.2 insert 1.26.3.2
128	14	delete 1.17.3 insert 2.17.3
129	11	delete asthma. insert asthma
131	3	delete 1⅝in insert 1⅛in
131	4	delete 40mm insert 28mm
131	37	delete exhibitors insert exhibitor's
132	22	delete 44mm insert 25.4mm
132	24	delete wax insert waxed
132	38	delete 728ml insert 738ml
133	6	delete eg insert eg.
134	27	delete Currents insert Currants
134	28	tick nectar tick pollen
134	30	delete *augustifolium* insert *angustifolium*
134	33	delete *Crataegu* insert *Cratagaegus*
134	33	delete *smonogyna* insert *monogyna*
136	22	font size too large
137	44	delete *family* insert family
137	44	delete *Springwood white* insert *'Springwood white'*
139	7	delete *apomixsis* insert *apomixis*
141	2	delete colour insert colour,
144	36	delete *apomixsis* insert *apomixis*
145	8	delete ie insert ie.
145	24	delete etc insert etc.
145	32	delete etc insert etc.
146	15	delete 2.23.3 insert 2.23.4
146	22	delete 2.23.4 insert 2.23.5
146	24	delete underside insert upperside

Page	Line	Correction
146	30	delete 2.23.5 insert 2.23.6
146	41	delete 2.23.6 insert 2.23.7
147	5	delete sugar- insert sugar
147	29	delete granulate insert granulates
148	3	add a right facing arrow between energy & carbohydrate
149	9	delete honeybees bees insert honeybees
149	36	delete *and* insert and
150	22	delete Zealand insert Zealand,
150	22	delete crops insert crops,
154	8	delete (0.26%-0.17%) insert c.0.17% - 0.26%
154	24	delete eg insert eg.
159	15	delete eg.Chalk insert eg. Chalk
162	16	delete *Paentbacilus* insert *Paenibacillus*
165	11	delete rigorously insert vigorously
166	14	delete interset insert interest
169	10	delete 'OSIS insert 'OSIS'
170	40	delete complete line
170	41	delete complete line
174	19	delete days 21 insert days + 21
177	9	delete 3.15.1 insert 3.16.1
196	4	delete appendix 10 insert appendix 9
208	3	delete spores insert bacteria
210	9	delete it starting insert it is starting
221	12	delete Luddington, Warwickshire insert CSL, National Bee Unit, Sand Hutton, York YO41 1LZ
235	16	delete sensillum insert sensilla
243	28	delete a insert A
247	38	delete CO2 insert CO_2
253	31	delete F) , insert F),
256	36	delete mg. insert mg
256	38	delete 150g. insert 150g
262	26	delete ie insert ie.
262	34	delete ie insert ie.
263	8	delete ie insert ie.
266	23	delete litre insert litres
269	3	delete sensillae insert sensilla
269	28	delete remaining static insert while remaining static,
277	33	delete CO2 insert CO_2
283	27	delete bees insert bees'
285	21	delete /50.F... insert /50. F...
285	25	delete CO2 insert CO_2
287	15	delete h_{12} insert H_{12}
290	15	delete 2 Hunger insert 2. Hunger
292	4	delete certain the insert certain of the
296	4	delete ones insert one's
299	16	delete protégé insert progeny
301	2	delete 1.19 insert 1.21
303	28	delete 1.22 insert 1.23
308	14	delete 10 inspections insert 10 day inspections
308	29	delete with out insert without
311	diag 4.5	delete sensillae insert sensilla
311	diag 4.6	read ONE OF TWO POST CEREBRAL GLANDS
315	diag 4.17	delete TRACHIOLES insert TRACHEOLES
319	diag 1	delete AIRES insert ARIES
320	1	delete Airie insert Aries
327	10	delete 21 cu.in. insert 21/cu.in.
330	diag.	delete ADANSONI insert ADANSONII
332	23	delete i.e. insert ie.
337	31	delete 32°F insert 32}°F
338	19	delete eg.21 insert eg. 21
342	23	delete Stonger insert Stronger

Updated: November 1999.

File: errataVI.wpd